D1615664

THE MODERN SHOTGUN

PLATE I

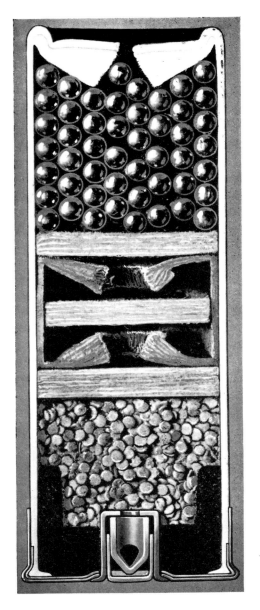

A SECTION OF A LOADED 12-BORE 2½-INCH CARTRIDGE

The case is a standard paper-tube case and the cap has a tubular anvil, while the powder is No. 60. The central wad is an air-cushion wad and the turnover is a crimp.

Frontispiece

THE MODERN SHOTGUN

VOLUME II
THE CARTRIDGE

by
Major Sir Gerald Burrard
BT, D.S.O., R.F.A. *(Retired)*

SOUTHAMPTON
ASHFORD PRESS PUBLISHING
1985

Published by ASHFORD PRESS PUBLISHING 1985
1 Church Road, Shedfield, Hants SO3 2HW

First Published	1931
Reprinted	1941
Second Edition	1950
Reprinted	1950
Third Edition	1955
Reprinted	1985

British Library Cataloguing in Publication Data

Burrard, *Sir* Gerald
   The modern shotgun. —— 3rd ed.
   Vol. 2 : The cartridge
   1. Shotguns
   I. Title
   683.4'26   TS536.8

ISBN 0—907069—13—4

Printed and bound in Great Britain by
Biddles Ltd, Guildford and King's Lynn

PREFACE TO THE THIRD EDITION

IT is now twenty-four years since the First Edition of this Volume was published, and six years since the Second Edition appeared. The eleven years preceding the appearance of the Second Edition were occupied by the Second World War and the period of general rehabilitation which followed, with all the inevitable results of shortage and restrictions of materials. It was not altogether surprising, therefore, that the promises of rapid improvements, which seemed so obvious in 1939, were delayed. But the last five years have seen big advances. The chief of these are the extension of the use of the crimp closure instead of the ordinary rolled turnover and the introduction of the " Number Sixty " range of powders.

The discovery that the over-shot card wad as the real cause of cartwheel patterns was among the most outstanding which have been made since the change of black to smokeless powder, and I have tried to deal with its more technical aspects in this Volume, leaving the practical advantages to Volume III.

Yet even if the cartridge has changed but little in its outward appearance of form there are several most important and valuable improvements which deserve to be recorded and remembered. The evolution of an efficient non-chlorate and non-fulminate cap has reduced greatly the risks of corrosion, although it cannot be emphasised too strongly that it has not removed the need for cleaning ; the introduction of the " Number Sixty " range of powders may not be so obvious and spectacular as the change from the rolled to the crimp turnover or make so strong a propaganda appeal as that of the " Non-Rusting " cap, but they provide far greater latitude in the weights of shot charges which can be used with complete safety, while the Air-Cushion wad has continued to help triumphantly to solve the problem of a suitable substitute for felt ; and improved methods of rendering cartridges more waterproof must not be forgotten.

Owing largely to the increased price of metals the hopes of a cartridge with an all-metal case have been deferred, although I am still inclined to the view that this will be the cartridge of the future.

The generally accepted " standard " observed velocity of British cartridges remains at 1070 f.s.

Many years of constant testing of shotgun cartridges for Pressure, Velocity and Recoil have continued to confirm my belief that the usual instrumental results have little real significance for the average sportsman, or even for the majority of gunmakers. I have, therefore, retained the Appendix which I first included in the Second Edition and hope that this attempt to translate seemingly theoretical figures into practical meanings may prove of some value to the less technically minded reader.

It gives me immense pleasure to express my so very sincere thanks to *Poudreries Réunies de Belgique S.A.* for their spontaneous help in supplying me with full details of different Belgian Powders. This authoritative information cannot fail to be of real value.

I am especially grateful to my friend Mr. A. Watson of the Proof Department of I.C.I., Ltd., Metals Divn., for his ungrudging help in supplying me with details of the Piezoelectric Pressure Gauge and its application to the measurement of pressures in shotguns, as well as those of an Electronic method for the measurement of shot velocities near the muzzle, which I have included as Appendices III and IV.

And finally I would thank once again my so many friends in both the Ammunition and Gun Trades for their never failing help and patient criticism. If the shooting public extend the same sympathetic welcome to this new Edition which they have given so generously and kindly to the former Editions and other Volumes of this work they will be merely embodying my personal thanks to my so many collaborators.

GERALD BURRARD.

Willow Lodge,
Hungerford,
Berks.
June, 1955.

CONTENTS

LIST OF TABLES

LIST OF ILLUSTRATIONS
PLATES

13

LINE DRAWINGS

WORKS CONSULTED

Explosives, by E. de Barry Barnett (1919).

After-Rusting in Firearms, by Dr. Wilbert J. Huff (1920).

Tir des Fusils de Chasse, by General Journée.   2nd Edition (1902) and 3rd Edition (1920).

INTRODUCTION

IN this second Volume I have confined myself to the problems relating to the Cartridge rather than to the Gun. Such problems include questions of the explosives used in both powders and caps ; and I have done my best to deal with them from the point of view of the practical sportsman who is interested in the why and wherefore of his cartridges. I have kept the description of the manufacture of the cartridge and its components as brief as possible, dealing chiefly with those details which have a practical bearing on shooting.

The chapters on Pressure, Velocity and Recoil are devoted to the ballistic side of shooting which is common to all guns and cartridges. During the course of these chapters I fear I have repeated myself unduly. But certain points, such as the turnover and the wadding, have such far-reaching effects that I have tried to emphasise their importance even at the risk of wearying the reader by repetition.

I have much help and many kindnesses to acknowledge.

The drawings illustrating the various stages in the manufacture of a cartridge-case were originally prepared by Imperial Chemical Industries, Ltd., for *Game and Gun* and appeared in that paper. Then it so happened that the Pendulum Gun which I use myself was placed in a very awkward position for a photographer. When I explained my difficulty to Imperial Chemical Industries they gave me a most excellent photograph of a similar gun which I have gratefully used in Plate XI.

The Interceptor method of measuring muzzle velocities has only recently been applied to shotguns, and the

Staff of the Research Department of Imperial Chemical Industries helped me in the most ungrudging way in my drafting of the description of the method given in Appendix II, placed all their results at my disposal and gave me the actual photographic records which are reproduced in Plates XIV and XV.

I received similar help in connection with the experiments carried out by Mr. W. D. Borland for Imperial Chemical Industries to investigate the influence of barrel length on velocity. It is entirely owing to their and Mr. Borland's kindness that I have been able to give full details of the latter's researches in Appendix IV, including the photographs of the apparatus specially designed for the work. These figure in Plates XVI, XVII and XVIII.

Parts of the chapters on Caps, Pressure, Velocity and Recoil as well as Appendix I have appeared in articles in the *Field* and *Game and Gun* during the past eight years. These have been re-arranged and partly rewritten : but this does not diminish my sense of gratitude to the Proprietors of these papers for their permission to republish what had already appeared in their columns.

My friend, Lieutenant-Colonel Philip Neame, V.C., D.S.O., R.E., has again had the patience to read through this Volume, and I owe much to his kindly and constructive criticism.

Above all I am most indebted to my friend, Mr. F. W. Jones, O.B.E. Not only has he read the various drafts of these chapters and helped me throughout with kindly, tolerating patience ; but he has also provided me with Appendix VIII which, to my mind, constitutes an analysis of the Internal Ballistics of a shotgun which is a mine of information for those who are interested in the technical problems connected with shooting.

And once again I would like to express my grateful thanks to Mr. H. R. Marchant, of the firm of Monger and Marchant, who was responsible for the great majority of the photographs which illustrate this Volume, and for whom no trouble was too great nor any detail too small. I think my readers will agree with me that the results speak for themselves.

I will but add that criticism will always be welcome.

G. BURRARD.

WILLOW LODGE,
    HUNGERFORD,
        BERKS.
            March, 1931.

THE MODERN SHOTGUN

THE MODERN SHOTGUN

CHAPTER I

POWDERS

IN the preceding volume the general principles of the construction and design of the modern shotgun have been described in some detail ; so I now propose to try to deal with the cartridge which is loaded in the gun and which contains the powder and shot charges. In any such attempt the powder needs consideration first in order that the relative importance of questions which may arise subsequently will be appreciated.

A gun is really a machine for controlling the application of force which propels the shot charge through the air. The force necessary for this propulsion is generated by the very rapid production of gases resulting from the combustion of the powder charge ; and on this account all powders which are used in cannon, rifles, shotguns and other small arms are termed Propellants.

Propellants require different properties from other kinds of explosives such as those used for blasting purposes, or for high-explosive bombs, shells and torpedoes which are detonated. Consequently it will be advisable to consider first what these properties should be, and how they should differ in the case of those propellants which are used for special types of arms. When we have done this we shall be able better to survey briefly the various shotgun powders which are commonly used, and to form an opinion as to their respective merits.

The properties which should be possessed by an ideal propellant for use in small arms, are as follows :

(1) It should produce regular ballistics and the pressures generated on combustion should be such as to result

in a maximum effect as far as the imparting of velocity to the projectile is concerned, together with a minimum strain being thrown on the barrel and action.

(2) There should be no smoke.

(3) The powder should not cause erosion. Now erosion is really due to two causes. The first of these is the actual abrasive, or scouring, action of solid particles, which are the products of combustion on the heated surface of the bore.

The second is the actual washing away of the surface of the metal by the flow of the intensely hot gases generated on combustion.

(4) There should be a minimum of fouling, and whatever fouling there is should be easily removable and of such a nature as not to cause corrosion.

(5) There should be no " blowback " due to solid particles being ejected from the muzzle.

This is especially important in shotgun work where many cartridges are fired in rapid succession, often in a high wind.

(6) The powder should be insensitive to shock ; that is it should not be liable to explode when struck. This is of extreme importance in a military propellant where there is danger of cartridges being struck by a bullet or splinter of shell. And in sporting use insensitiveness to shock adds greatly to the safety of cartridges, whether in the actual shooting field, when travelling or when kept in storage.

(7) The powder must readily ignite and without any tendency to hang fire when used in conjunction with a suitable cap.

(8) The powder must be of such a nature that it is easily handled for purposes of loading.

(9) It should remain stable when kept in storage for long periods under various climatic conditions.

In his most admirable and instructive work on Explosives Mr. E. de Barry Barnett gives certain further attributes as being necessary in the ideal propellant such as absence of Back-flash and Fume. But these are really

only applicable to artillery work where the excess of
carbon monoxide in the products of combustion may
result in this gas firing when the breech is opened. Many
accidents have been caused by this firing of the carbon
monoxide in the breech igniting other charges lying in a
turret. Further, carbon monoxide is poisonous and
causes headache when it is liberated in a turret.

But in the case of shotguns the amounts of powder
involved are so small and the conditions under which the
charges are fired are so different, that these properties
need not be considered.

There is, however, one other property which is most
advantageous in military work and also in the case of
rifles, either sporting or military. This is a combination
of high power and density. A high density means that
less space is occupied by an amount of powder which can
produce a certain amount of power, and this is obviously
an advantage in any type of arm where the reduction in
the size of each individual cartridge-case, as well as in the
amount of space required for storing ammunition in bulk,
is an important consideration.

In the case of shotguns, however, a very dense powder
can become a disadvantage because it requires a special
form of case and special loading. The weight and volume
of a shotgun cartridge are really dependent on the shot
charge and wadding, and a dense powder can make little
appreciable difference in the case. Consequently the
advantages of being able to use one type of cartridge-case
and one system of loading altogether outweigh other
considerations.

Some of these properties are obvious and need no
further explanation, but others are dependent on questions of composition and manufacture. And since some
factor which may help one property may hinder another,
I feel that a more detailed consideration may be an
advantage in some cases.

REGULAR BALLISTICS

In order to obtain regular ballistics, that is a similar force of propulsion from round to round, it is essential that the combustion of the powder must be under control. For powder definitely *burns* and during this process of burning the solid components of the powder combine chemically so as to produce gas. This formation of gas takes place very rapidly, and as all gases tend to expand, especially when heated, the resulting expansion generates the pressure which propels the projectile along the bore.

Now if all the powder is converted into gas before the projectile has moved more than a very short distance down the bore it will be quite clear that the pressure will be very great, simply because of the very large amount of gas which is formed so suddenly, all of which expands simultaneously. This high pressure gives the projectile a very big and sudden impulse which starts it on its journey ; but once this impulse is ended the projectile receives less and less assistance during its passage along the bore.

But the projectile is not the only recipient of this sudden impulse, for when gas expands its act of expansion generates pressure *equally in every direction.* Consequently the walls of the chamber of the barrel have to withstand an exactly similar pressure to that which is exerted on the base of the projectile. The higher this pressure the greater the strain on the barrel and action, and so it will be realised that a powder which is totally consumed before the projectile has moved more than a short distance down the bore results in a very severe strain on the gun, while the projectile only receives a big initial impulse, but very little further in the way of help on its journey.

If, however, the combustion of the powder takes place more slowly, gas will be given off all the time the projectile is moving down the bore, and it will consequently receive a prolonged and sustained pressure until it leaves the muzzle. An impulse which is sustained throughout the passage of the projectile down the bore not only produces a somewhat higher initial velocity, but is also much more likely to give the same velocity round after round than a more violent and sudden blow. Further, since the formation of gas is more gradual the resulting initial pressure is much less, and this means less strain on the gun.

So, from every point of view it will be seen that a very rapid combustion of the powder should be avoided.

An expanding gas does not begin to exert pressure until it has filled completely the space in which it is generated, and if a certain amount of gas is formed the resulting pressure will be less in a large space than if it is liberated in a confined space. In the free air, where the powder is not confined, the gas has ample room for expansion, so the combustion of powders in the open takes place without the production of any violence. But in a confined space the violence, or the pressure, can be very considerable ; and the smaller the space the greater this pressure.

When a projectile lies at the breech end of the bore and combustion begins, the space left for the expanding gases is small. But when the projectile has moved some way along the bore, the space for the gases is obviously larger. It will be clear, therefore, that this space is smallest at first and becomes increasingly larger as the projectile moves towards the muzzle.

Accordingly, if the rate at which gas is generated is constant, the resulting pressure will become less and less as the projectile moves towards the muzzle owing to the increasing space available for the expansion of the gases. So, if anything like a constant *pressure* is to be maintained on the base of the projectile, it will be realised that combustion of the powder must begin very slowly, and gradually increase in rate until it attains its maximum just before the projectile reaches the muzzle.

When this occurs the projectile is started on its movement by a comparatively small amount of gas, in which case the initial pressure is kept low. Further movement is continued by the steadily increasing amount of gas evolved, and a sustained and comparatively constant pressure is thus produced for as long as the projectile is in the bore. Powders cannot be made to burn in such a manner as to cause this constant pressure, but those which approach to this result are said to burn " progressively " and are called " Progressive " powders.

In artillery work progressive burning powders are invaluable, especially in big guns, but the smaller the gun the less the practical good derived from markedly progressive powders. In rifles, both sporting and military, a powder in which combustion is comparatively slow has proved in actual practice to give results as good as, if not better than, a real progressive powder.

In shotguns a very slow-burning powder, which would necessitate a large charge, is a mistake. This is because it is very important to avoid anything approaching a high pressure near the muzzle, as such pressures tend to scatter the shot charge and cause irregular patterns. This aspect of the matter does not come into rifle work, where a well-sustained pressure nearer the muzzle is advantageous.

Another reason for the avoidance of high muzzle pressures in shotguns is because such pressures increase the "muzzle blast" of the gun.

When the shot charge leaves the muzzle the pent up gas suddenly rushes out into the air, and the sudden impact of the gas on the air causes the report. If the pressure is too high the resulting gas blast immediately outside the muzzle is increased, and the report becomes more pronounced and unpleasant. This is a disadvantage where many shots are fired in rapid succession and may even result in headache.

In sporting rifles too few shots are fired to matter ; and when military rifles are used in modern war there is so much other noise that individual muzzle blasts are immaterial. Sometimes muzzle blast is confused with muzzle flash, the absence of which is most important in war as a pronounced muzzle flash renders detection far more easy. But contrary to general belief muzzle flash has comparatively little to do with the powder and is really dependent on the cap composition.

In shotguns, however, the point is not unimportant.

So it will be realised that shotgun powders should burn rather more rapidly than rifle powders, but at the same time this combustion should not be too rapid or the initial pressures will be too great.

It may now be of interest to consider the principles which govern the control of the burning of powders.

NON-POROUS POWDERS. Powders are generally of three kinds : those in which the finished substance of which the powder is composed cannot be penetrated by the hot gases generated ; those which are penetrable by these gases ; and those which are only partly penetrable.

It will be quite evident that the first kind can burn only on the surface ; that the second kind will begin to burn inside as well as on the surface owing to the penetration of the gases formed by the initial burning of the surface ; and that the last kind will burn in a manner which is intermediate between the two others.

The control of the burning of " non-porous " powders, that is of those powders which belong to the first type and cannot be penetrated by hot gases, is effected by limiting the total superficial area during combustion. This is done by making the powder up into sticks or grains, both of certain shapes and sizes.

Cordite provides an excellent example of a non-porous powder. It is almost always made up into sticks, the lengths of which depend on the length of the charge. The rate of burning is controlled entirely by the shape and size of the cross sections of these sticks, and the diagrams in Fig. 1 give four typical cross sections suitable for cordite sticks.

Fig. 1A shows a solid circular section. Combustion begins on the circumference, and as it continues the circumference gets smaller and smaller. The effect is that gas is given off most rapidly at first and that the amount of gas generated becomes smaller and smaller as combustion continues. From this it will be quite obvious that such sticks must result in a markedly non-progressive powder.

Fig. 1B shows a flat strip. Here again combustion begins only on the outside, but as the strip is consumed

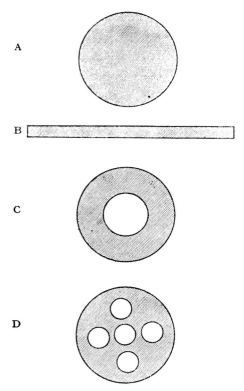

FIG. 1.—Diagrams of different types of sections used for sticks of cordite in order to regulate the rate of burning.

the sectional shape remains practically the same, because the width is so very much greater than the depth that the decrease in depth is but a small proportion of the remaining width. Sticks of this shape result in the burning surfaces being very nearly constant during combustion.

In Fig. 1C the section is tubular, and in this case both the inside and the outside surfaces begin to burn simultaneously. The area of the outside surface decreases as burning advances, but the internal area *increases* at the same time. The net result is that the total area burning at any period of the combustion is the same.

Fig. 1D shows a cylindrical stick which is perforated from end to end by a number of holes instead of by one single one. The inside surfaces of each of these holes begins to burn simultaneously with outside circumference, and as this last decreases in area, the inside surfaces increase, the result being that the total superficial area of the stick *increases as combustion advances,* with the result that the powder burns progressively because the burning surfaces become larger and larger as the powder is consumed.

It is thus possible to control the rate of burning of each individual stick, but the rate of burning of the whole charge is dependent on the *sizes* of the sticks. The length is immaterial and is dependent on the length of the charge ; but the diameter is most important, for on this depends the circumference.

Let us assume that the sticks are each 12 inches long. If the charge consisted of but one single solid stick the superficial area would be very much less than if it were made up of a large number of sticks of very small diameter, even though the total weight was the same in each case. In the latter case the total area capable of being burned would be the sum of the superficial areas of all the thin sticks, which would obviously be much greater than the superficial area of one thick one.

This applies to all the types of sticks of which the sectional areas are given in Fig. 1, and so it will be seen how the rate of burning of cordite can be controlled by the size and sectional shape of the sticks of which the charge is composed.

There is yet another, and entirely different, method by which progressive burning is obtained. This is combining two different kinds of powder in one stick. Different varieties of powders or even of the same powder, vary in their rate of burning according to their composition. Fig. 2 show the cross-section of a stick in which there is an inner core composed of a rapid-burning powder and an outer skin of a slow-burning powder. On ignition this outer skin burns away slowly before the inner core is reached, and when the skin has been completely burnt up the inner core burns rapidly. The result is that gas is generated slowly at first and more rapidly afterwards and a progressive burning effect is produced, the degree of progressiveness depending on the relative sizes of the core and skin.

As a matter of fact, strictly speaking, the term " Progressive " should only be applied to this type of powder

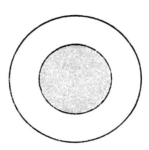

FIG. 2.—Diagram of a section of a stick of powder composed of two different types of explosive, the outer layer being composed of a slow-burning powder and the inner core of a rapid-burning powder. The result is a progressive burning powder.

as the word was coined by Nobel in his patent of 1869, when he stated that " the progressive quality is obtained by introducing substances in the outer layers of the compound capable of modifying its explosive character."

The effect, however, of the multiperforated sticks is similar to that obtained by the use of a coating of slow-burning material, and so in general practice the expression Progressive has come to be applied to all powders in which the volume of gas generated *increases* during combustion at a given pressure.

The rate of combustion of a charge, or the evolution of the gases, depends both on the extent of the burning surfaces and the pressure. The rate of evolution of the gases is directly proportional to the pressure ; this means that for any given extent of burning surface, the evolution of the gases is halved when the pressure drops from, say, 10 tons to 5 tons.

It will not be difficult to understand that the sticks of cordite used in small-arm cartridges must be so thin that multiperforation is practical impossibility ; although tubes, that is single perforation, are not only possible, but are actually adopted in the Service ·303. Consequently the multiperforation method of obtaining progressive burning is confined entirely to ordnance, and in small-arm powders the progressive character is given by coating the grains of powder with moderating substances which are allowed to penetrate to varying degrees below the surface of the grains. And when this is done the grains are said to be " surface moderated."

Because a progressive powder is one which gives comparatively low initial pressures and sustained barrel-pressures, powders which show these characteristics on combustion are frequently called progressive, even when the grains are not surface moderated.

It will be noticed that I have suddenly jumped from " sticks " of powder to " grains." This is because all small-arms powders with the exception of cordite are granular, and in cordite the " sticks," or " cords," are very thin. A granular powder is more easily handled in loading, and on this account granular powders are almost universal in small arms.

The rate of combustion of non-porous granular powders is controlled in the same general way as that described for cordite. First of all there is the size of grain which can be varied. A certain definite charge of powder which is composed of large grains will obviously, for reasons which I have already given, burn more slowly than an identical charge of the same powder which is composed of many more and much smaller grains of similar shape. So, other things being equal, it will be seen that a large-grain powder will burn more slowly than a fine-grain sample of the same powder.

Then there is the shape of grain which can be varied, just as can that of the sections of the sticks of cordite.

Cubical or spherical grains will result in less rapid combustion than flat grains. While in the case of a powder in which the grains are small cylinders with holes down the centres there is a constant rate of burning at the same pressure.

And finally there is the method of " surface moderating " the grains which has just been explained.

This method, however, is little used in the manufacture of shotgun powders, as in actual practice it has not yielded sufficiently good results when applied to the small porous grains of shotgun powders. However, at least two non-porous American shotgun powders have been made on this principle.

The fact is that too progressive a shotgun powder is not useful, and better results are obtained by other means than surface moderating a non-porous powder.

All non-porous powders are made from jelly-like mixtures which are formed into different shapes or grains, and it is owing to this jelly-like formation that they cannot be penetrated by the hot gases of combustion. On account of their formation they are known as " gelatinised " powders. Further details of such powders, however, will be given in the next chapter when we come to the brief descriptions of the different methods of manufacture.

FIBROUS POWDERS. We now come to the second class of powders, namely those which are easily penetrated by the hot gases which arise during burning.

Such powders are quite different in appearance to the previous type, and are all composed of finely divided fibres of an explosive called Nitrocellulose, of which guncotton is a type, which are rolled up into grains. Instead of having the solid appearance of a non-porous powder they look more like little balls of cotton-wool, and when the grains are examined under a pocket-lens they will be seen to consist of large numbers of fine fibres sticking together.

It is not difficult to understand that such a powder is easily penetrated by hot gases, and consequently its rate of burning is entirely independent of the shape and size of the grains. Combustion is consequently controlled in quite a different way from any which has been described, namely by incorporating in the powder a certain amount of non-explosive organic and inorganic substances which prevent the burning from spreading as rapidly as it would otherwise.

A good example of the effect of mixing a non-explosive substance with an explosive can be obtained by mixing iron filings with ordinary black powder. When the mixture consists of about equal parts it will be found that it is impossible to ignite the powder with a match. If the proportion of iron filings is reduced the powder will eventually burn, but much more slowly than it would were there no filings present.

This is the principle underlying the control of the burning of fibrous powders. At first sight the introduction of a non-explosive substance may seem a mistake in that it necessitates a larger bulk of powder for the production of a given amount of gas. In shotgun work, however, this increased bulk can be a considerable advantage in manufacture of what are termed " bulk " powders, and moreover gives a method of control, as will be explained shortly.

Fibrous powders are made into grains simply and solely for convenience in loading and handling, and the size of the grains has very little influence on their rate of burning, which is controlled entirely by the incorporation of non-explosive substances.

Owing to their nature fibrous powders do not lend themselves to surface moderation.

On account of their bulk they are never used in small-bore sporting or military rifles, although they may occasionally be used in reduced loads in rifles belonging to the " rook and rabbit rifle " class which were originally designed for use with black powder.

POROUS POWDERS. The third class of powders comprises those which are partly penetrable by the hot gases of combustion. This result can be achieved by perforating the grains of a non-porous gelatinised powder with a number of minute holes on the same general principle as the big stick of cordite was perforated by a number of holes longitudinally, as shown in Fig. 1D.

The method of perforation, however, is quite different as it would be utterly impossible to make the tiny holes in each grain of powder by any process of machinery, and so chemistry is called in to assist.

During manufacture the dough out of which the powder grains are made is mixed with some substances consisting of very fine particles, and these particles become completely incorporated with the grains of powder when they are formed. These grains are then treated with a special solvent which dissolves the fine particles, but which has no effect on the powder proper, and the final result is that minute holes are left in the grains wherever a particle of the soluble substance existed. These holes make the powder porous and so it becomes penetrable by the hot gases and the rate of burning is quickened.

This system of making porous powders is confined to shotgun and small rifle powders, but it provides a useful additional method for the exercise of control over combustion, as the degree of porosity depends on the amount of soluble substance added and subsequently dissolved.

It should be noted that ordinary black powder can really be placed in this class, although it is not made porous by artificial means. It is, however, partially penetrable by the hot gases, and so the rate of burning is not solely dependent on the extent of the surface exposed. But being only partially penetrable by the gases the rate of burning does vary with the extent of exposed surface, and therefore with the size of grain.

SMOKE

The absence of smoke is an advantage so obvious that emphasis is unnecessary. This effect can only be obtained by using powders which on combustion generate products which are gaseous at normal temperatures and non-volatile solid products at the temperature of combustion. All powders produce a certain amount of water on combustion, and in cold weather this is turned into visible mist just as it is possible to see one's breath in cold but not in warm weather. Such mist, however, is a very different thing from the smoke, which is an inevitable associate of black powder, which on combustion gives only about 44 per cent. of gaseous and 56 per cent. of volatile solid products. It is this large percentage of volatile products of combustion which cause the heavy smoke.

It should be noted that any powder which contains potassium nitrate produces more or less smoke owing to the presence of the volatile solid matter on combustion, but barium nitrate gives no smoke because its products are non-volatile. Ammonium nitrate is the only nitrate which results in the formation of entirely gaseous products, but this cannot be used in powders owing to its extraordinary attraction for moisture.

In the manufacture of smokeless shotgun powders barium nitrate is used, although a little potassium nitrate is generally added for a special reason to be mentioned later.

EROSION AND CORROSION

These two actions are very generally confused, although they are quite different and arise from different causes.

Erosion, as the word signifies, means eating out or washing away. In firearms, as was stated at the beginning of this chapter, erosion is due to two causes : the abrasive action of solid particles which are the products of combustion ; and the direct result of the very rapid motion of the very hot gases on the surface of the steel.

The first of these causes is not now an important factor because in modern smokeless powders the percentage of solid products of combustion is too small to cause any serious erosive effect. At the same time it must be admitted that it is a mistake to incorporate too much of any ingredient in a powder which results in the ultimate formation on combustion of a very hard product. For this reason barium nitrate should not be used *in excess* in any powder, as on combustion it causes the production of barium carbonate which is a very hard substance, and particles of which might have a distinct erosive effect if present in sufficient quantity and when a bullet is used.

In shotgun powders, however, the percentage of barium nitrate present is so small that there is not enough resulting barium carbonate to have any practical effect with shot.

Incidentally, it may be mentioned that the particles of barium carbonate make an extremely unpleasant blowback from the muzzle, and on this account also the percentage of barium nitrate in the powder should be kept low.

The question will naturally be asked, Why use barium nitrate at all ?

The reason was that its presence, as did that of potassium nitrate, helped the formation of an *alkaline* residue in the barrels after combustion which could be an important advantage in checking corrosion.

This fact merely shows how difficult it is to obtain perfection, and how many factors must be considered. The manufacturer who claims some special merit for his powder usually ignores some disadvantage which accompanies that particular merit, and which may completely outweigh any supposed improvement.

But let us return to the question of erosion.

With modern smokeless powders in guns and rifles erosion is the direct result of the very rapid motion of very hot gases on the surface of the steel. With some types of powder these gases are so hot that they wash away the steel of the barrel in front of the chamber. Generally speaking, powders which contain the explosive nitroglycerine belong to this type ; and cordite, which is a nitroglycerine powder, causes very severe erosive action. To reduce the effects of erosion a large jute wad is invariably inserted in a rifle cartridge-case just over the powder charge. This wad has the effect of lessening the escape of gas past the bullet, and therefore of the washing away of the bore by the stream of hot-powder gases. This washing away would otherwise be especially marked at the breech end of the bore where the bullet does not seal the bore so tightly, and the pressures are high—both of which conditions affect the gas flow, because the escape of gas is greater the higher the pressure.

Without a wad the erosive effects of cordite can be so severe as to wash away completely in a thousand shots or so that part of the bore known as the " lead "—or " leed," as I always prefer to see it spelt—which is the tapered portion which connects the front end of the chamber with the rear end of the bore, and which is of course larger than the bullet. The " leed " in a rifle corresponds to the chamber cone in a shotgun.

The gases generated by nitrocellulose powders are materially lower in temperature, and consequently they do not erode the bore to the same extent. The result is that the life of a rifle-barrel is several times as long when a nitrocellulose powder is used as when cordite is the propellant.

In shotguns there is little or no escape of gas past the wadding and so there is not the same tendency to erosion as in the rifles. For it is the movement of gases past the projectile (shot charge or bullet) which mainly causes erosion in the bore.

Since erosion is the immediate effect of the flow of hot gases on the surface of the steel, an action which takes place immediately on firing, it is entirely beyond the control of the sportsman.

Corrosion, on the other hand, is slow and deliberate. It is a chemical action pure and simple. In firearms, corrosion is really the same thing as rusting, which is the formation of iron oxide from the steel, or rather from the iron in the steel, of the barrels or action.

Iron oxide, or rust, is caused by the oxygen in the air combining with the iron in the steel. The presence of moisture helps this combination to take place, as does potassium chloride. Now potassium chloride is one of the chief products resulting from the explosion of what was for many years the standard cap, and it is deposited on the surface of the bore together with the products of the combustion of the powder. I will deal with this formation of potassium chloride by the cap more fully in the next chapter, but it is impossible to avoid reference to the subject when considering the properties of powders.

The process of corrosion, or rusting, is slow and gradual, requiring several hours at the very least in which to get started.

In a firearm corrosion is always a sign of neglect in cleaning, either through carelessness or ignorance of the best means to employ in varying circumstances. Once corrosion has set in, the surface of the metal is no longer smooth, but becomes slightly rough, and this roughened surface is fruitful ground for more corrosion to set up. One of the best protections against corrosion is a perfectly smooth surface on the metal, as a chemical action always likes some little rough point from which to begin work.

For this reason a gun which has once become even slightly corroded is more difficult to protect, and so special care should be taken in cleaning, and it might be as well to use powders which give an alkaline residue in such a gun irrespective of the type of cap used.

CHAPTER II

POWDERS (*continued*)

W E have now seen what qualities should be possessed by shotgun propellants and how some of these qualities are obtained. And so the next point at which we arrive is the manufacture of the various classes of powder. I have no intention of making any attempt to enter into details of the numerous processes adopted in the manufacture of shotgun powders, and my only purpose is to indicate briefly how the powders are made ; as until this has been done it is not possible to classify the different powders in a manner which would be readily understood by anyone who was entirely ignorant of the principles of manufacture to which reference must inevitably be made in the classification. Certain references to various classes of explosives have already been made, but such have been unavoidable. I will try now to explain any points which were omitted in the consideration of the general properties of propellants which was a necessary preliminary to that of manufacture.

BLACK POWDER. Black Powder, as Gunpowder is generally called in order to distinguish it from other propellants, all of which are in reality " Gunpowders," was until quite recent times the only propellant available or even known. It has now been in use for something like six centuries, and although improved methods of manufacture have naturally led to greater efficiency in action, its composition has remained practically the same in all countries.

The composition of sporting black powder as made in Great Britain is :

Potassium Nitrate (Saltpetre) . 75 per cent.
Charcoal . . . . 15 ,, ,,
Sulphur . . . . 10 ,, ,,

These ingredients are mixed together, and when a

uniform mixture has been obtained it is " incorporated " under heavy " edge runners " or rollers. The powder is then pressed under hydraulic pressure and broken up into grains of different sizes, which are finally glazed in order to render them easier to lead and also to add to their appearance.

In small arms the rate of burning is controlled by varying the size of grain and the time of incorporation under edge runners. As has already been explained, black powder is not impervious to the gases formed on combustion and consequently it does not burn only on the surface. But it is not very easily penetrated by the hot gases, and so the rate of burning does vary as the area of the surface exposed. On this account the size of grain is a convenient and effective method for controlling combustion in the case of small arms. But in ordnance, where much slower burning powders are necessary, variations in the size of grain are not enough, and the powder is moulded into different shapes such as cubes, pyramids and prisms with different numbers of sides and which may have perforations as well.

The size of grain is denoted by a number, and for ordinary shotgun work the size classified as No. 4 is the most suitable.

As can be imagined the efficiency of black powder depends largely on the quality of the ingredients, and only the most pure ingredients are used in the highest grade of British powder which is known as T.S. (Triple Strength).

Since sodium and potassium result in very similar general types of chemical reactions, the potassium nitrate can be replaced by sodium nitrate, which is much cheaper, and which also results in a rather more powerful powder. The great drawback to this change, however, lies in the very hygroscopic nature of the sodium nitrate ; that is in its extraordinary attraction for water. For this reason sodium nitrate powders are very liable to become damp ; when this happens they are completely destroyed from the point of view of efficiency. And so potassium nitrate powder is better.

The great disadvantage of black powder is the smoke which is formed on combustion. The reason for the smoke will be readily appreciated when it is seen that 75 per cent. of the powder is a nitrate which must form non-gaseous products on combustion which are volatile at the temperature of combustion. And it is this very large proportion of nitrate in its composition which explains the small percentage of gas (44 per cent.) resulting from combustion.

The first smokeless propellant was made by using barium nitrate instead of potassium nitrate. But this resulted in a rather unsensitive powder, and also in the formation of a large amount of residue, or fouling. This barium nitrate black powder did not live, but this use of barium nitrate was the first step in the production of a smokeless powder.

Apart from the smoke black powder is a very excellent and safe propellant. It is very regular in its effect, is very easily loaded, and will keep for an indefinite number of years if protected from damp. I myself have known of cartridges for an old black powder ·577 rifle which had been stored for 40 years and which gave just as good results as if they had been freshly loaded. Water, however, completely ruins black powder, and once powder has become damp it never regains its full strength on drying, owing to the water dissolving some of the nitrate which crystallises out on drying and thus spoils the perfect mixture of the ingredients.

Another disadvantage of black powder is that it causes a more severe recoil for the same effect than do smokeless powders. But this point will be explained in the chapter on Recoil.

For home loading, especially in the Tropics, black powder is more likely to give good results than any other propellant. Smoke, however, is the great drawback to its use ; and cartridges are so easily obtained now all over the world that few men are tempted to load their own.

NITROGLYCERINE POWDERS. The explosive compound universally known as nitroglycerine was first discovered in 1846. This compound is formed by treating glycerine with nitric acid, but in actual practice a mixture of nitric and sulphuric acids are used, as if nitric acid is used alone it becomes too weak owing to the water produced. Sulphuric acid checks the effects of the formation of this water.

Nitroglycerine is a colourless oil and is extremely sensitive to shock, and it was not until 1862 that any serious attempt was made to employ it as an explosive, when Nobel began its manufacture in Sweden. But the numerous accidents that occurred resulted in its use being prohibited in all countries. Later Nobel rendered it more safe by absorbing the liquid in porous materials such as kieselguhr (a powdery earth), which would take up considerable quantities of nitroglycerine and still remain dry.

In 1875, however, Nobel made a great discovery which really revolutionised the whole manufacture of explosives. This discovery is said to have been quite accidental and was due to his having painted a cut in his hand with collodion solution in order to protect it. Later in the day, when experimenting with some nitroglycerine he noticed that the collodion on his hand formed a jelly when brought into contact with the nitroglycerine. This was really the origin of blasting gelatine.

The use of collodion cotton, which is a kind of nitro-cellulose, was the next step, and the first gelatinised explosive was made by combining about 92 per cent. of nitroglycerine and 8 per cent. of collodion cotton. This was called Blasting Gelatine, and it is still widely known under this name.

But blasting gelatine was altogether too violent and uncontrollable for use as a propellant, and it was not until 1887 that Nobel discovered a method of control.

BALLISTITE. This was Nobel's first nitroglycerine propellant and was made by agitating nitroglycerine with collodion cotton in the presence of water, agitation being effected by compressed air. The wet mixture was passed through hot rolls which drove out the water and caused the ingredients to form into a rubber-like mass which was rolled out into a very fine sheet. This sheet was then cut up into little flat grains, or flakes, which were flat and square and of a slightly shiny, dark grey colour.

Combustion was controlled by the size and thickness of the flakes.

Owing to the gelatinising effect of the nitroglycerine on collodion cotton, ballistite was clearly a gelatinised powder. And since collodion cotton is a special form of nitrocellulose it will be seen that ballistite consisted entirely of nitroglycerine and nitrocellulose. There were no nitrates of any sort to help the formation of smoke, and the powder was very dense, containing no non-explosive ingredients.

Ballistite had the reputation amongst both sportsmen and gunmakers of being a very violent and powerful powder, but it was not really so, and the probability is that this reputation was a legacy from accidents which occurred in the past, the cause of which were not generally understood.

For example, ballistite, in common with all gelatinised powders, was not too easy to ignite and in its early days this difficulty of ignition was very much greater than later, because caps improved. So it sometimes happened that the cap exploded in the cartridge without igniting the powder charge, or only igniting a very small part of this charge. When this occurred there was sometimes sufficient force to drive the shot charge a little way up the bore, where it would remain. On opening the gun an empty case would be ejected, so the shooter might never suspect that the shot charge was left in the bore. If he then reloaded the same barrel and fired a normal round, a burst would be the almost inevitable result. Such a burst would really be due to the presence of an obstruction in the bore which had been left there by too *weak* a round. The shooter, however, might infer that the burst was due to the actual round which caused the burst being too strong.

That such accidents happened is beyond doubt, and

there is also little doubt that their occurrence led to a widespread belief in the violence of ballistite, whereas the real cause of the accidents was the difficulty of ignition.

This reputation for violence was helped by the irregular burning of the powder which sometimes occurred, some rounds being noticeably much stronger than others. But this irregularity was also due chiefly to the question of ignition.

These difficulties were later overcome and the ballistite of 1920 to 1939 certainly did not give any higher ballistics, that is pressures and velocities, than other powders. Actually the pressures and velocities developed by ballistite were rather on the low side, if anything.

Early ballistite used to leave a very objectionable residue in the barrels which had a marked corrosive effect. This was due to the fact that when the powder burned under a rather low pressure, unburnt grains were left in the bore which smouldered and gave rise to nitrous acid. If the gun was left uncleaned, this nitrous acid combined with the oxygen in the air to form nitric acid, which acted chemically on the steel.

But this difficulty was also overcome, and the residue left by ballistite rendered harmless.

Ballistite was a very dense powder and the proper charge did not occupy the same space as that required by ordinary powders. On this account special cartridge-cases had to be used in which the space available for the powder is reduced by the addition of a conical base at the bottom of the case. Such cases are consequently called " cone based " cases, and their necessity is a disadvantage, as it means a departure from the normal. For this reason ballistite is now no longer made.

CORDITE. This is the British Service propellant, and as I made use of it as an example in our consideration of the methods of controlling combustion, it deserves a brief notice even though it is never used as a powder in ordinary shotguns.

PLATE II

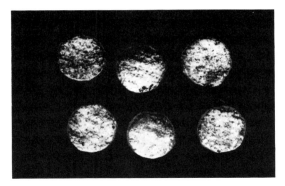

(*A*) A Photo-micrograph of No. 62 powder

(*B*) A Photo-micrograph of Cooppal Perfecta powder

(*C*) A Photo-micrograph of Olin Western Ball Powder showing
the different degrees of compression of the balls

Cordite consists of nitroglycerine, guncotton and mineral jelly ; this last ingredient being included primarily to help to cool the gases of combustion and so reduce erosion.

There is a story, which I believe to be perfectly true, that cordite was discovered by chance. A chemist was experimenting in the manufacture of ballistite at the Government Factory at Waltham Abbey, and as he did not happen to have any collodion cotton handy he used instead guncotton for adding to the nitroglycerine. The result was an entirely different powder which is now known as cordite.

Owing to the very severe erosive action of cordite the original proportion of nitroglycerine was reduced and the proportions now are :

Nitroglycerine . . .	30 per cent.
Guncotton	65 ,, ,,
Mineral Jelly . . .	5 ,, ,,

This is known as Cordite M.D. (that is " modified ") to distinguish it from the original Cordite Mark I, which contained 58 per cent. of nitroglycerine.

NITROCELLULOSE POWDERS. A number of references have been made to the explosive " nitrocellulose " and guncotton has just been mentioned in connection with cordite. So it is time that these names were explained.

Guncotton is really a form of nitrocellulose and is made by treating ordinary cotton, or cellulose, with nitric acid. In actual practice a mixture of nitric and sulphuric acids is used just as it is in the manufacture of nitroglycerine and for the same reason, namely to prevent the diluting effect of the water formed by the chemical reaction.

Nitrocellulose is a solid and is composed of numbers of minute fibres, which are the fibres of the original cellulose.

The first practical nitrocellulose smokeless powder was introduced by Schultze in 1865, and consisted of small pellets of wood which were treated with nitric acid and then impregnated with barium nitrate. Wood is a form of cellulose, and so this original Schultze powder comprised chiefly nitrocellulose and barium nitrate.

In 1870 Volkmann found that he could bring about the partial gelatinisation of nitrocellulose by treating it with a mixture of alcohol and ether, and this discovery can be regarded as originating the manufacture of the modern types of gelatinised nitrocellulose powders.

DOUBLE BASED POWDERS. Some powders contain distinct proportions of both nitroglycerine and nitro-cellulose. Such are known as " Double Based Powders."

GELATINISED POWDERS. Reference has already been made to gelatinised powders, and we can now have a brief glimpse of their manufacture.

The first step is to make a dough by treating nitrocellulose with some solvent such as acetone. When this dough is submitted to pressure in presses it can be forced out in cords, tubes, or tapes ; or when placed in rolling machines it can be rolled into a sheet from which solid grains are cut. In this way solid grains are formed which are not penetrable by the hot-powder gases, and so the powder burns only on the surface and the powder is non-porous.

If a porous powder is required the dough is mixed with fine particles of some substance which is ultimately removed by treating the grains with a solvent which does not affect the powder, but which dissolves the particles which were mixed in, and so leaves little holes in the grains. This process has already been mentioned in the section dealing with porous powders.

While the powder is still in the dough stage other ingredients are incorporated, such as metallic nitrates and mineral jelly (*i.e.* vaseline). Their purpose is to restrain the rate of combustion, ensure an alkaline residue, and increase the bulk of the powder.

Further, all gelatinised nitrocellulose powders contain a small percentage of moisture, which in Smokeless Diamond, for instance, was 1·7 per cent.

FIBROUS POWDERS. These powders are not gelatinised at all. A mixture of finely divided nitrocellulose, soluble and insoluble, is rolled into small grains, and in order to prevent these grains from breaking up during handling and loading they are " hardened." This consists of treating the grains with some solvent—in E.C. powder, for example, a solution of camphor in alcohol was used—which makes the nitrocellulose fibres cohere, more or less, without destroying their fibrous appearance. In order to restrain combustion the nitrocellulose mixture is made containing other substances such as metallic nitrates, mineral jelly and starch. These ingredients also help to produce an alkaline residue and to increase the bulk of the powder.

Fibrous powders, like gelatinised powders, contain a small percentage of moisture, which as a rule varies from 1·4 to 2 per cent.

FIBROUS AND GELATINISED POWDERS COMPARED. It may be well asked why these two distinct types of powders are both used. The reason is that the attainment of perfection of action under every possible condition is not easy in one single powder.

The chief difference between fibrous and gelatinised powders lies in the matter of the penetration of the hot gases. As has already been seen fibrous powders are very easily penetrated by these gases while non-porous gelatinised powders may be impervious to them, even porous powders only being penetrable at the pores.

The effect of this difference in capacity for being penetrated is reflected in the ease with which the powders are burnt up. Fibrous powders are much more readily consumed than gelatinised, as the grains are very easily burnt up, because the thickness of powder to be burned is only that of the diameter of a single nitrocellulose fibre.

In ordinary circumstances non-porous gelatinised powders can be ignited sufficiently readily as to be perfectly satisfactory and reliable. But in very exceptional circumstances they may fail when a fibrous powder or a porous gelatinised powder functions effectively. Such circumstances arise in extreme cold such as prevails during the winter months in countries like Russia, Siberia, East Prussia or Canada.

In very severe weather the oil in the locks is partially frozen, and this semi-frozen oil clogs the locks and prevents the tumblers from falling with their full force, thus reducing the strength of the striker blow. Further, the metal of the walls of the chamber and the face of the action, as well as the metal of the cap chamber and anvil are all intensely cold. This all tends to reduce the temperature of the cap flame, which is probably already less violent than usual on account of the weakened striker blow. The resulting enfeebled flame fails to ignite non-porous gelatinised powders, but is sufficient to ignite the more readily combustible fibrous or porous gelatinised powder.

But when there are comparatively rapid climatic variations of temperature and humidity and dryness of the atmosphere the percentage of moisture content of a fibrous powder is more inclined to vary than that of a gelatinised powder. Variations in the moisture content of a powder cause a variation in the ballistics, and although the resulting changes in pressure and velocity may not really be very great they are frequently enough to cause irregular patterns.

So in this respect gelatinised powders are an advantage and the trend in most countries now is to concentrate on gelatinised powders, many of which are double based.

BULK POWDERS

I have made several references to the question of the bulk of a powder and have pointed out that in rifles a powder which occupied a small space was an advantage, but that in shotguns the space occupied by the shot charge and wads must necessarily be so large that a slight saving of space in the accommodation for the powder could have but little practical advantage.

As a matter of fact a fairly bulky shotgun powder is of the greatest advantage in loading, which is always done by machines. The loading machines are fitted with little cups, or "hoppers," each of which holds an exact charge for one cartridge when perfectly full. Now if the powder was very dense the hoppers would be small, and any variation in the filling of the hopper would mean a bigger percentage difference in the total weight of the charge than would be the case if the powder was bulky and needed a large hopper. For the variation in filling only amounts to a comparatively few granules in any case, and if the charge is fairly bulky such variations have no practical effect.

Practical experience has shown that the ordinary size of cartridge is convenient, and guns have been standardised to take it. This size of cartridge was developed in the days of black powder, and so the space available for the powder in the cartridge-case is that space which was formerly occupied by the charge of black powder. This charge was 3 drams in the case of the ordinary $2\frac{1}{2}$-inch 12-bore case, and so it came about that the volume occupied by 3 drams of black powder became the standard measurement for the bulk of a powder charge. This may seem a somewhat archaic unit to have adopted. But it was universally recognised and understood by all.

Consequently since powders are in actual practice loaded by means of hoppers in the loading machines, that is by volume, all shotgun powders which are intended to be loaded in this way should be standardised for bulk. This standarisation was *always* most scrupulously carried out with all British bulk shotgun powders. The result is that a "bulk" powder is a powder in which the *volume* of the charge is the same as the volume of the corresponding charge of black powder.

Bulk powders are classified according to the actual weights of their standard bulks. That is a 33-grain powder is one of which the amount required to fill a

3-dram black-powder measure weighs exactly 33 grains, and a 42-grain powder is one of which the same amount weighs 42 grains.

It will be appreciated that if a powder is classified as a 33-grain bulk powder and proper standardisation for bulk has not been carried out in the process of manufacture, the results may be most dangerous.

For example, if a powder is a nominal 33-grain bulk powder the correct charge for an ordinary 12-bore is 33 grains by weight, the volume supposedly being that occupied by 3 drams of black powder. But if the bulk has not been properly standardised and this volume weighs, say, 40 grains, the result would be that the cartridge would be loaded with 40 grains instead of 33 grains if the loading were carried out by hoppers, as it always is, instead of by weighing out each individual charge.

The effect of such a charge might easily be sufficiently violent to burst a gun, and I have, in fact, investigated two bursts which were due only to the violent pressure generated by an excessive weight of powder in the charge. In each case this excessive weight was due to the fact that the powder was nominally a bulk powder, but that standardisation for bulk had not been properly effected in the manufacture. Both of these were cheap Continental powders. In one case I took samples of the same powder obtained from three different sources, and weighed the bulk which exactly filled a 3-dram black-powder measure, and found that each sample gave a different result, the actual weights being 43·5, 44·5 and 45 grains. Yet this powder was supposed to be a 33-grain bulk powder. The effect of this incorrect standardisation for bulk was that the cartridge loader who used an ordinary hopper would load his cartridges with 43·5, 44·5 or 45 grains of powder instead of the proper 33 grains. The danger arising from such an overcharge needs no emphasis.

The same principle, however, can be used for dense powders. Even though a smaller volume of powder needs a smaller measure and so any variation in the weight of the charge thrown means a bigger percentage variation in the weight of the charge, the accuracy and delicacy of modern machines are sufficient to ensure regular loading with smaller powder charges—after all, the volumes of the bulk powder charges for 28-bore and ·410 bore cartridges were not very large—and now dense powders are gradually replacing bulk.

A SUMMARY

It now only remains to give a list of the different shotgun powders which are commonly used in Great Britain, together with their characteristics. But before doing so I will give a summary of this and the preceding chapter, partly to refresh the reader's memory, and partly as a convenience for those who would like to understand the classifications of the powders, but who do not wish to go to the trouble of reading longer explanations.

NITROGLYCERINE POWDER. A nitroglycerine powder is one which contains nitroglycerine.

NITROCELLULOSE POWDER. A nitrocellulose powder is one which contains nitrocellulose but no nitroglycerine.

DOUBLE BASED POWDER. A powder which contains both nitroglycerine and nitrocellulose.

GELATINISED POWDER. A gelatinised powder is one which has been made by forming a dough or gelatinised mass which is made into grains. The dough is made by treating a nitrocellulose mixture with solvents in a mixing machine. This resulting dough-like mixture is pressed into tubes or rods or rolled into sheets from which solid grains are cut.

NON-POROUS GELATINISED POWDER. A powder made of grains which cannot be penetrated by the hot gases formed on combustion, and consequently such powders only burn on the surface. (See Plate IIA.)

POROUS GELATINISED POWDER. A gelatinised powder

which has been made porous by adding to the nitro-cellulose mixture which is formed into a dough a substance which is subsequently removed, and so leaves pores in the grains. These pores are very small and are not readily seen with a pocket lens, but they are large enough for the hot powder gases to penetrate under the pressure which is generated in a gun-barrel, and, therefore, the grains are more easily burnt up. (See Plate IIB.)

FIBROUS POWDER. A powder is called Fibrous when it is made from nitrocellulose and has a fibrous appearance when examined under a pocket lens. Actually fibrous powders are made by rolling a mixture of finely divided nitrocellulose up into grains, which are hardened so as to prevent them breaking up on handling and loading. These fibrous hardened grains can be broken down by rubbing in the palm of the hand. (See Plate III.)

Fibrous powder grains are easily penetrated by hot powder gases, and so the grains are easily ignited and burnt up.

BULK POWDER. The term " bulk " was applied to shotgun powders when black powder was replaced by smokeless powders. The standard charge for a 2½-inch 12-bore cartridge was 3 drams of black powder ; but for convenience in loading, " hoppers," or measures, were invariably used, each of which would contain a volume of black powder which weighed exactly 3 drams. Smokeless powders are much lighter in density than black powder, yet for purposes of general convenience in loading many powders are so standardised in manufacture that the same measure can be used for them as for black powder. In other words, the charge of many smokeless powders is the same as that of black powder when measured by *volume* or *bulk*, but not when measured by weight. The term " bulk " is applied to all smokeless powders which can be loaded correctly with a black-powder measure, as *volume for volume*, and give similar ballistics to the best grades of black powder.

A 33-grain bulk powder is a powder of which the amount required to fill a 3-dram black-powder measure

PLATE III

(A) A Photo-micrograph of E.C., a typical fibrous powder

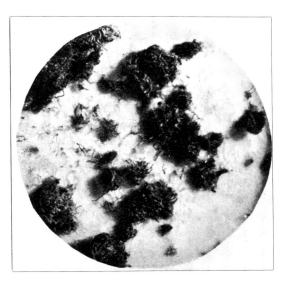

(B) A Photo-micrograph of E.C. after the grains have been powdered in the palm of the hand

The fibrous nature of the powder is most distinct

weighs exactly 33 grains, and a 36-grain or a 42-grain powder one of which the same amount weighs 36 or 42 grains.

DENSE POWDER. A dense powder is one which *cannot be loaded correctly with an ordinary black-powder measure*, as the volume of the correct charge is appreciably less than the corresponding volume of either a bulk powder or black powder. Dense powders are more concentrated, or dense, than ordinary bulk powders.

BRITISH POWDERS SINCE 1945

The end of the Second World War found the whole of British economy in a very difficult condition. Everything had been concentrated on war material : and the manufacture of practically all purely peace-time products had either been stopped completely or reduced to a trickle. A limited supply of shotgun powders was still available but it was obvious that the luxury of utilising different plants and varying methods for making a variety of powders which all really functioned in a similar manner was one which could no longer be afforded.

The reason for the change from the pre-war powders such as the 33-grain bulk Smokeless Diamond and E.C., the 42-grain bulk Schultze and the dense Neoflaks was simply and solely to keep down costs of production so as to give the shooting man a cartridge at the lowest price that was economically possible : and the most effective way of doing this was to concentrate on what may be termed one basic powder which could be moderated so as to produce varying rates of combustion. But while the evolution of this new range of powders was being prepared something had to be done at once : and this something was the introduction of Nobel No. 52.

It has already been seen that nitrocellulose is a basic ingredient of many shotgun powders and it will be obvious that cotton is essential for the manufacture of this explosive. But cotton was imported from the dollar areas and the devaluation of the pound sterling introduced a new complication and an increase in the cost of raw materials.

Accordingly certain accumulated war time stocks were used up in making a fibrous powder which was designated No. 52, while preparations were made for the manufacture of a completely new range of powders to supersede the old familiar friends of the pre-1939 era.

The old tradition of using " bulk " shotgun powders which could be loaded with the same measures as those used for black powder, and which " bulked " volume for volume with black powder, has been abandoned as had already been done by most other powder manufacturers. It necessitated extra steps in manufacture which rendered the cost appreciably higher than that of dense powders which are not " bulked."

No. 52 was never anything more than a temporary expedient and has now been replaced by the range of Nobel powders to which numbers in the sixties have been given. These are all basicly similar but are moderated to give different rates of burning. Thus the necessity for operating and maintaining different plants, each making different named powders, the functions of which are really all the same, no longer exists. This has naturally helped to keep down costs, and although the prices of shotgun powders are much higher than before 1939 they are not nearly so high as they would be were the old named and bulked powders still made, while the actual percentage increase in their price is quite appreciably less than that of many other manufactured commodities.

In general terms No. 60 can be regarded as the replacement for Smokeless Diamond or E.C. ; No. 62 for Modified Smokeless Diamond ; and No. 64 for Neoflak.

It should, however, be understood that although these powders are not true bulk powders in that the correct weight of charge for any given cartridge does not occupy exactly the same volume as that filled by the corresponding charge of black powder, they can be loaded by volume as has already been explained.

The powder measures, however, as has been stated before, are not the same sizes as those needed for the corresponding charges of black powder, but provided measures are used which will hold exactly the correct charge by weight, the procedure of loading is exactly the same as it always was in the days of true bulk powders.

SHOTGUN POWDERS IN COMMON USE

We now come to a list of the shotgun powders in general use. The list is complete in the case of British powders, but not nearly complete for either Continental or American powders. Many Continental powders have not been imported into Great Britain since 1939 and have probably not been made since 1945. However, all powders have been included which are commonly loaded in Great Britain as well as those which may be encountered in cartridges which have been loaded and purchased abroad.

In each case a brief description of the powder is given which will explain the class to which it belongs and its general characteristics.

BRITISH POWDERS

NOBEL SMOKELESS POWDERS

No. 60. A dense, porous, gelatinised, double-based powder. The flakes, or grains, are circular discs and the colour is grey.

No. 62. A dense, porous, gelatinised, double-based powder. In appearance it is similar to No. 60, but it contains a proportion of yellow granules for purposes of identification.

A slightly slower burning powder than No. 60.

No. 64. A dense, porous, gelatinised, double-based powder. In appearance it is also similar to No. 60, except that it contains a proportion of red granules for purposes of identification.

A slightly slower burning powder than No. 62.

No. 66. A dense, porous, gelatinised, double-based powder. In appearance it is also similar to No. 60, but it contains a proportion of brown granules for purposes of identification.

A slightly slower burning powder than No. 64.

No. 67. A dense, porous, gelatinised, double-based powder. In appearance it is also similar to No. 60, except that it contains a proportion of blue granules for purposes of identification.

This is a slightly slower burning powder than No. 66.

Continental Powders

(1) Belgian

Clermonite. A 33-grain fibrous bulk nitrocellulose powder. The colour is a reddish orange.

Cooppal Excelsior. A dense gelatinised non-porous nitrocellulose powder. The grains are flat and square or diagonal in shape, making it a typical " leaflet " powder. The colour is grey. This powder is made in various grades, one of which is known as *Caulille* which is specially made for use with heavy shot charges. Another grade is intended only for ·410 cartridges.

Cooppal Perfecta. A dense gelatinised non-porous nitrocellulose powder of the leaflet type. It is very similar to *Excelsior* but the grains are slightly smaller and the colour is dark pink. It is intended for use with the Continental large (6·45 mm.) cap.

Corona. A dense gelatinised and true porous nitrocellulose powder. The grains are small cylinders and the pores can be seen plainly with a pocket lens. The colour is dark greenish grey.

Mullerite. A dense gelatinised non-porous nitrocellulose powder. The grains, or flakes, are flat, square and shiny, and the colour is a dark grey.

Victoria. A dense gelatinised non-porous nitrocellulose powder. The grains, or flakes, are flat and square and the colour is magenta. It is not difficult to confuse this powder with Cooppal Perfecta, but the grains are slightly smaller and the colour not quite so dark as that of the Cooppal powder.

(2) DANISH

Only one variety of shotgun powder is manufactured in Denmark at the Government Factory at Frederiksvaark. This is a dense non-porous flake powder, the flakes being rectangular and diamond shaped. It is a darkish grey colour.

(3) FRENCH (PRE-1939)

Poudre T. A dense non-porous gelatinised nitrocellulose powder. The grains are square and flat, and the colour a slightly shiny dark grey.

Poudre S. A 42-grain fibrous bulk nitrocellulose powder, very similar in appearance to Schultze.

(4) GERMAN (PRE-1939)

Record. A 33-grain porous gelatinised bulk nitrocellulose powder. It was clearly an imitation of Smokeless Diamond but the grains were somewhat thicker and the colour was a dead black.

Rottweil. A dense slightly porous gelatinised nitrocellulose powder. The grains were flat and square and of a greenish grey.

Walsrode. A slightly porous gelatinised nitrocellulose dense powder. The grains were round and slightly cupped and of a dark greenish colour.

(5) NORWEGIAN

Ballistite. A dense gelatinised nitroglycerene powder, the flakes being rectangular and diamond shaped. It is a light grey colour and is apparently not graphited. Although stocks of this powder may still be in existence it has not been made since 1952.

Raufoss. A dense gelatinised nitrocellulose powder, the flakes being rectangular and diamond shaped. It is a very pale grey colour and is made at the Government factory at Raufoss. It is largely replacing the Ballistite as it does not need cone-based cases.

(6) SWEDISH

J.K. 1. A dense gelatinised nitrocellulose non-porous flake powder. The flakes are rectangular and diamond shaped and very small. The colour is almost black.
J.K. 5. A dense gelatinised nitrocellulose non-porous powder. The grains consist of circular and slightly cupped discs of a greenish grey colour. This is a slower burning powder than *J.K.* 1.
J.K. 6. A dense gelatinised nitro-cellulose non-porous flake powder of a greenish grey colour.

· The following American Powders are all double based dense non-porous gelatinised powders.
Du Pont MX. Grains small, flat and irregular both in size and shape. The colour is greyish black.
Hercules Red Dot. Grains are flat circular discs, each with a hole in the centre. The colour is greenish black but an occasional grain is pink.
Hercules Herco. Grains are flat circular discs very similar to Red Dot but there are no pink grains at all.
Olin Western Ball Powder. Grains vary in shape from almost perfect spheres to thin flat discs according to the degree of compression they have received during manufacture. They also vary in size according to that of the original spheres from which all were made. The colour is black.

There is one American single based powder, *Du Pont PB* 6, which is a dense non-porous nitrocellulose powder, the grains being small circular discs, each with a hole in the centre, and a dark greenish grey in colour.

CHAPTER III

CAPS

THE cap in a cartridge-case provides the means for igniting the powder charge and is consequently a component of great importance, greater in fact than is generally realised. In the early days of firearms the powder charge was ignited by a slow match; and later by a spark which was originally produced by revolving a roughened steel wheel against a piece of iron pyrites; and still later by the impact of flint on steel. The flint was held in a hammer, which fell on the trigger being pressed and caused the flint to strike against a piece of specially shaped and tempered steel. This resulted in the sparks caused by the impact being directed down on to a small charge of powder which was, in its turn, connected with the powder charge proper by a priming, or trail of powder. Flint locks, as firearms with this system of ignition were called, were in general use for about 200 years, and by the end of that period they had become extremely efficient weapons. But the method of igniting the powder charge resulted in a delay between the pressing of the trigger and the firing of the powder charge, and this delay was of uncertain and varying duration, being dependent partly on the manner in which the priming powder was placed. The result was that there was always a " fizzle " between the fall of the hammer and the ignition of the charge, and this delay added considerably to the difficulty of shooting.

Early in the nineteenth century a Highland minister, the Rev. Alexander Forsyth, successfully developed the first " detonating " gun. In this gun the powder was ignited by a flame produced by a small amount of " detonating powder " which exploded on being struck by the hammer. This was a great advance as the delay in ignition was reduced and the flash of the powder priming was eliminated. Forsyth, who was minister in the parish of Belhelvie, near Aberdeen, was a keen sportsman and was encouraged in his experiments by a desire to prevent birds and game swerving at the flash of the flint-lock priming and so escaping the most accurately aimed shots. He used to conduct his experiments in a shed at the bottom of the Manse garden and eventually evolved a " detonating powder " which was comparatively safe, but which exploded on being struck by a smart blow. At last Forsyth produced a gun-lock to fire his powder and so ignite the charge in the barrel direct, and he took out a patent on July 4th, 1807.

There is a persistent tradition in Forsyth's family that Napoleon, who immediately realised the value of this invention from the military point of view, offered him £20,000 for the patent. But Forsyth was a patriot above all things and refused. Lord Moira, the then Master-General of Ordnance, invited Forsyth to conduct his experiments in the Tower of London, and this Forsyth did for some time, although the report is on record that they were of such a dangerous nature that it was difficult to find any workman to assist him.

On the appointment of a new Master-General of Ordnance Forsyth was sent back to his Manse, but by degrees his invention found favour with sportsmen and was the origin of the term so frequently used by Colonel Hawker, " detonating gun."

Forsyth's " detonating " compound was a powder composed chiefly of potassium chlorate, and about 1840 the invention of the percussion cap, which contained mercury fulminate and was altogether more convenient than Forsyth's special lock, superseded his invention. But the credit for the invention of the percussion system is Forsyth's, although he never received any recognition during his lifetime. The British Government, however, with characteristic generosity, voted a sum of £1,000 to be distributed among his surviving relatives after his death.

And eighty-six years later, in January, 1930, a memorial tablet was unveiled to his memory in the precincts of the Tower of London.

The whole principle underlying the percussion system of ignition is dependent on the employment of a small amount of explosive mixture which is sufficiently sensitive to result in a chemical reaction being set up by the heat caused by a sudden blow. This chemical reaction changes the solid mixture into gases so rapidly that the change is, for all practical purposes, instantaneous; and consequently the gases form a very hot flame. It is this flame which ignites the powder charge just as a match lights a cigarette.

The explosive mixture in the cap, however, is not completely transformed into gas and certain solid residues are formed as well, which get carried into the cartridge-case and the bore along with the gases resulting from the combustion of the powder charge. And since this cap residue, although of small amount, can have a marked effect on corrosion, especially where many shots are fired in succession when the residue accumulates in the bore, it may be as well to study the chemical reactions which occur when a cap is exploded. The reader will then be able to appreciate fully the effects produced by the residue from ordinary caps, as well as the methods for overcoming whatever evils there may be.

When certain amounts of potassium chlorate and antimony sulphide are mixed together they have a tendency to combine chemically under the influence of heat, such as that supplied by a blow or friction. The result of this chemical reaction is as follows:

POTASSIUM CHLORATE and ANTIMONY SULPHIDE
change into
POTASSIUM CHLORIDE, ANTIMONY OXIDE and SULPHUR DIOXIDE (a gas).

This is an explosive mixture; that is, a gas is generated at high temperature in an extremely small space of

time. For the best mixture the temperature resulting
from this reaction is about 3500° Centigrade.
Technically this reaction is given by the equation

$$3\ KClO_3\ +\ Sb_2\ S_3\ =\ 3\ KCl\ +\ Sb_2\ O_3 + 3\ SO_2$$

(Potassium   (Antimony   (Potassium   (Antimony   (Sulphur
Chlorate)   Sulphide)   Chloride)   Oxide)   Dioxide)

Similarly,

FULMINATE OF MERCURY and POTASSIUM CHLORATE
change into
MERCURY, NITROGEN (a gas), POTASSIUM CHLORIDE and
CARBON DIOXIDE (a gas).

This last is also clearly an explosive mixture because
fulminate of mercury is present. However, the addition
of potassium chlorate in correct amount increases the
temperature resulting from the reaction, making it about
4500° Centigrade.
Technically this reaction is given by the equation

$$3\ HgC_2N_2O_2 + 2\ KClO_3 = 3\ Hg + 3\ N_2 +\ 2\ KCl + 6\ CO_2$$

(Mercury   (Potassium   (Mercury)   (Nitro-   (Potassium (Carbon
Fulminate)   Chlorate)   gen)   Chloride) Dioxide)

THE THREE ELEMENT CAP

The second of these two reactions does not give as
good an igniting flame alone as it does when combined
with the first, while the first mixture by itself lacks
sensitiveness. Accordingly a combination is made of the
two original mixtures, and this combination has for years
been used as the basis of the great majority of cartridge
caps. These mixtures are not made up in the exact
proportions necessary to give the absolute maximum
temperature possible, and generally an excess of antimony
sulphide is used which is, therefore, present in the flame
in the form of fused particles.
Pure antimony sulphide is not used on account of its
cost, but the mineral stibnite is used instead. Stibnite
contains about 80 per cent. of antimony sulphide, the
remainder being antimony oxide.

The actual combination of the cap composition will, therefore, be seen to comprise :

    (1) MERCURY FULMINATE.
    (2) STIBNITE.
    (3) POTASSIUM CHLORATE.

It will also be seen that if this mixture is made up in suitable proportions both the chemical reactions given will take place simultaneously under the incentive of a blow. This mixture, then, has become the basis of modern caps, and on account of the three different substances required, such caps are known as " Three Element Caps."

The varieties of the Three Element Cap are numerous. For example, the British Service ·303 cap has small additions of sulphur and black powder, while many manufacturers have added powdered glass in order to increase the friction in the mixture resulting from the blow of the striker.

But the most radical alterations which have been suggested in connection with the Three Element Cap have all been directed towards making the cap either :

(1) Non-fulminate, that is doing away with the mercury fulminate ; *or*

(2) Non-chlorate, that is doing away with the potassium chlorate ; *or*

(3) Both non-fulminate and non-chlorate.

NON-FULMINATE CAPS

The object of doing away with fulminate in a cap was primarily more to do with rifles than shotguns, for it was to eliminate the deleterious effect of mercury on the brass of the fired case. When mercury vapour attacks brass it tends to produce an intercrystalline weakening of the metal, which sometimes results in fractures or splits. Accordingly it will be realised that if cases are required for reloading and firing several times the presence of mercury in the cap reduces the possible number of times which the case can be used. And this point might easily be of some importance to wildfowlers who use guns chambered for brass cases and who like to reload these cases several times.

Unfortunately, however, the effect of antimony on brass is possibly worse than that of mercury, and it is very difficult to clean the antimony products of the cap from the fired cases, and so the presence of antimony renders these cases almost useless for melting up for cartridge brass. It is, therefore, really waste of time and effort to try to eliminate mercury while antimony remains.

But quite apart from any action on the brass, and although it is so generally used, mercury fulminate has another drawback as a cap component. For it is not a very stable substance chemically and tends to decompose into inert materials, particularly when stored for a long time in a hot, damp climate. This is obviously a disadvantage in military cartridges and consequently caps have been made in which the fulminate was replaced by sulphur, lead or copper sulphocyanide, with small additions of such substances as T.N.T. and tetryl. Unfortunately, although such caps were very stable they lacked sensitiveness, and so frequently some gritty substance such as powdered glass or calcium silicide was added to increase the friction. But the addition of these " dead " substances has two disadvantages.

The first of these lies in the fact that their presence materially reduces the temperature of the cap flame and consequently fresh difficulties arise in connection with ignition.

The second drawback to the presence of finely powdered hard substances is that the tendency to erosion is increased. In the case of shotguns the danger is admittedly small because the total weight of these hard substances is such a small percentage of the whole of the cap composition and the powder charge. But in ·22 rim-fire rifles the weight of priming in the rim is an appreciable fraction of the whole charge, and so the addition of hard substances can, and does, cause serious damage. And even in shotguns it is a pity to introduce anything which may tend to favour erosion, especially when no real benefit is conferred by the change.

In recent years chemists in Europe and America have studied hundreds of substances in the hope of finding a really efficient substitute for mercury fulminate. While a number of these can be used successfully, there is really only one which has found general acceptance. This is lead styphnate, the lead salt of trinitroresorcinol. Styphnate is very stable chemically and almost as sensitive to percussion as fulminate. Its main disadvantage is that it needs very careful handling during manufacture owing to its liability to explode from self-electrification. But in the finished cap it is as safe as fulminate. While it would be quite possible to make Three Element Caps by replacing the fulminate by styphnate and thus obtain a more stable composition, in actual practice this is not done and all styphnate caps manufactured at the present time are of the non-chlorate type which will be discussed shortly.

"AFTER RUSTING" IN FIREARMS

Before we come to the other suggested change in the composition of the Three Element Cap, that is making it non-chlorate, it may be as well to see what the purpose underlying such a change can be.

Now potassium chlorate increases sensitiveness in almost any explosive compound as it gives up its large proportion of oxygen very readily, and *without abstracting heat*. The oxygen thus liberated without any deduction of heat adds greatly to the temperature of the cap flame. No other oxydant possesses this property of parting with its oxygen without abstracting heat, and consequently any substitute for potassium chlorate must result in a lowering of the temperature of the cap flame.

When potassium chlorate has been deprived of its

oxygen it becomes potassium chloride, and after each shot this potassium chloride is deposited in the bore of the shotgun or rifle, where it adheres with great tenacity.

There is a type of corrosion in firearms which is known as " After Rusting " as it is the rusting which takes place in the bore after the weapon has been cleaned in the ordinary manner. It sometimes happens that a gun or rifle is cleaned after use and put away, but that when it is examined a few days later rusting is seen to have set in.

This " after rusting " was never known in the days of black powder or when the old shotgun powders such as Schultze were used, and it first came into evidence with the introduction of smokeless rifle powders, such as cordite.

Accordingly it was not surprising that cordite, and other smokeless powders, got the blame, at any rate at first.

It was later discovered that the cause of this " after rusting " had nothing to do with the powder fouling, but was entirely connected with the deposit of potassium chloride resulting from the cap. In 1920 Dr. Wilbert J. Huff, of the United States Bureau of Mines, explained and discussed this at great length in a publication of the American Chemical Society. Dr. Huff did not discover this fact, but he deserves every credit for investigating the subject most thoroughly and reporting the results of some of his own experiments in detail.

Potassium chloride is not an acid body, as I have seen stated. Chemically it is similar to sodium chloride, or common salt, and this would act in exactly the same way as potassium chloride were it in the barrel of a gun or rifle, just as common salt does act upon iron or steel at the seaside where it is present in the air. Potassium chloride corrodes the barrel because it is an electrolyte, and in order to effect this corrosion *both moisture and oxygen must be present.* This is an important point to realise, as if there is no moisture available " after rusting " cannot occur. Oxygen, of course, is always present in the atmosphere. As a matter of fact moisture is also almost always present in the air, except in altogether exceptionally dry desert countries, but it is not always present in sufficient quantity to help " after rusting."

When the atmosphere is completely saturated with moisture, that is when the humidity is 100 per cent., dew is deposited. But potassium chloride is slightly deliquescent, that is, it is inclined to turn into a liquid by absorbing moisture, and therefore it attracts to itself from the atmosphere before dewpoint saturation is reached the moisture necessary for corrosion.

However, a fairly high degree of humidity is necessary ; according to Dr. Huff at least 50 per cent. From this fact it will be seen that the corrosion, or " after rusting," resulting from the cap products is not that very violent action which sportsmen might imagine after reading various advertisements of the manufacturers of non-chlorate caps. Violence is comparative : and if the corrosive effect of potassium chloride on steel is described as violent, how should the action of some acid, such as nitric acid, on steel be described ?

Although the potassium chloride deposit is not removed from the bore by ordinary, and somewhat cursory, methods of cleaning, it can be completely removed with ease by making use of its natural affinity for water. If a little water is poured through a barrel after use it will entirely dissolve all the potassium chloride present, and when the barrel is dried out no " after corrosion " will occur. The water need not even be hot ; although the barrel is more easily dried after being treated with hot water on account of the greater evaporation. In fact, a couple of damp flannel patches rubbed up and down the bore, one after the other, are sufficient to remove the potassium chloride because of its extreme solubility in water.

This method of cleaning is so simple that there is really no excuse for its being omitted when there is any risk of " after corrosion."

Dr. Huff has done his utmost to prove that any

method of cleaning which does not include some form of water treatment cannot remove the potassium chloride. Now the number of British sportsmen who use water for cleaning their guns is very small, so if Dr. Huff is correct the barrels of all the shotguns in Great Britain which are cleaned without water must have the fissures of the steel filled with potassium chloride. Why is it, then, that these barrels do not all corrode ?

The reason is the same as that which explains why " after corrosion " was not known in black powder days, and is due to the fact that British shotgun powders were made to give an alkaline residue. The residue left by black powder was alkaline, as was that of the early forms of smokeless shotgun powders such as Schultze.

This fact not only explains why British shooters were not seriously troubled by " after rusting " in spite of the naturally humid atmosphere of the British Isles, but also why it was that " after rusting " at once became evident when powders such as cordite, which do not give alkaline residues first came into use. And it further explains why the smokeless powders were blamed, since the only change was the powder.

NON-CHLORATE CAPS

Before this truth was generally realised various manufacturers developed non-chlorate, or non-rusting, caps of various types ; and such caps were used largely on the Continent a number of years ago, where they were advantageous as Continental powders, such as the German Rottweil and the French T, did not give alkaline residues on combustion.

The basic principle in these caps was really the substitution of barium nitrate for potassium chlorate which resulted in the cap residue containing barium carbonate, which is mildly alkaline and has no tendency to cause rusting, instead of the corrosive potassium chloride.

It should not be forgotten, however, that steel will rust in a damp atmosphere without there being any potassium chlorate present at all, a fact which is sometimes forgotten when the merits of non-rusting caps are being discussed.

The worst of these early non-rusting caps was that they lacked the sensitiveness provided by the presence of potassium chlorate, as well as the high temperature which this ingredient gives, and so the temperature of the flame was low. The efficiency of a cap from the point of view of igniting the powder charge depends on the temperature and pressure under which the jet of burning gas is forced against the powder charge ; and pressure, as well as temperature, tends to be reduced when potassium chlorate is not an ingredient.

It will accordingly be realised that while the omission of potassium chlorate from the cap overcame the difficulty of " after rusting " this very omission brought other disadvantages in its train. As has already been pointed out, of all oxidising agents which can be used in caps, potassium chlorate is unique in that in giving up its oxygen energy is released at the same time, while other substances must have energy supplied to them before they give up their oxygen. Hence when barium nitrate is used instead of potassium chlorate some of the energy released by the explosion of the fulminate or lead styphnate is used up in decomposing the nitrate and is not available for igniting the powder. The result is that a cap containing barium nitrate and fulminate or barium nitrate and styphnate is less sensitive and less efficient than the corresponding caps containing chlorate.

More recently, however, both in Europe and America, the development of a far more complex compound has done much to solve this difficulty. The full name of this compound is 1-Guanyl-4-nitrosoaminoguanyltetrazene, but it is commonly known as " Tetrazene."

The addition of tetrazene to barium nitrate and styphnate gives a cap composition which is adequately sensitive (owing to the tetrazene), fully stable (owing to the styphnate) and non-rusting (owing to the barium nitrate). Hence we have a cap which is fully efficient as well as being both non-fulminate and non-chlorate.

This type of cap has been used in America for a number of years as well as in Great Britain for all ·22 rim-fire rifle and pistol cartridges and many types of central-fire rifle cartridges. It has also been used in almost all American and in some British shotgun cartridges, and there is little doubt that had it not been for the war its use would have been almost ubiquitous except in military cartridges, for in a very hot barrel the flash tends to become too pronounced.

But although a non-fulminate and non-chlorate cap of this type is almost certainly the cap of the future, it must not be imagined that its employment will do away with the need for cleaning, as many sportsmen seem to think. It has already been pointed out that steel will rust in a damp atmosphere without any potassium chloride being present. All that the central fire styphnate-cum-tetrazene cap can do is to reduce the danger of " after rusting " : it offers no protection against ordinary atmospheric rusting. The ·22 rim-fire pistol and rifle cartridges are frequently quoted as a contradiction of this statement since it is unnecessary to clean ·22 weapons after using non-rusting ammunition. But in the ·22 rim-fire cartridge the cap composition comprises just about one-third of the total explosive charge, while in a central-fire cartridge the cap composition is but one-hundredth of the total explosive charge. It is true that the total explosive charge of a large central-fire cartridge is much greater than that of a ·22 rim-fire cartridge, which means that the actual weights of the two cap compositions may not differ so greatly after all. But the area of the bore to be protected by the cap residue is much greater in the case of the central-fire weapon and the amount of cap residue generated is not nearly sufficient to provide the adequate protection which can be offered by the ·22 rim-fire cartridge. If there is any doubt on this point, vendors of central-fire cartridges with non-rusting caps should be asked if they will guarantee that these cartridges can be used without any necessity for cleaning and without causing any risks of rusting if cleaning is omitted. In the absence of any such guarantee it would be folly to neglect proper precautions.

THE CONSTRUCTION OF THE CAP

We have now examined the principles which govern the selection of different ingredients for the actual cap composition, and the next point to consider is how this sensitive and explosive composition is actually embodied in the cap itself. The best method to adopt in such a consideration is to take a typical example of a modern central fire cap, that is a cap which is placed in the centre of the base of the cartridge, and for this purpose we cannot do better than take a type of cap which used to be commonly employed.

This cap, as in fact do all others, consists of three main components in addition to the explosive composition. These components are : the Cap ; the Anvil ; and the Cap Chamber.

The Cap merely consists of a small cylindrical copper cup, or capsule, which is closed at one end and is about one-fifth of an inch in external diameter. An enlarged view of such a cup is shown in the upper diagram in Fig. 3.

The cap composition is placed in a thin layer on the inside of the bottom surface of this capsule.

(*N.B.*—In the actual diagram the capsule has been shown with its open end downwards for purposes of convenience in explanation. There is really no true " top " or " bottom " as the capsule can be examined equally from any point of view. But for purposes of this explanation I have called the closed end the bottom.)

The Anvil is a thin piece of brass not unlike a barbed arrow head in shape, but without the socket for the shaft. An enlarged view of the anvil is shown in the middle diagram of Fig. 3. The actual width of the anvil should be such that it will just fit inside the capsule and stay in position, that is, the width of the anvil is practically the same as the internal diameter of the capsule. The anvil is inserted into the capsule point first until the point rests on the composition, and the whole is then placed in the Cup Chamber. This is a brass cup with a dome-shaped end and flanged rim. Its internal diameter is just about the same as the external diameter of the capsule, and consequently when the latter is pushed into the cap chamber it is held in position. The bottom diagram of Fig. 3 gives a

FIG. 3.—The basic component parts of a cap.

sectional view of the cap, anvil and cap chamber. The cap chamber is shaded with cross lines, and the cap composition is coloured black. It will be seen that the two lower " barbs " of the anvil rest against the cap chamber, and consequently any pressure on the end of the cap will indent the soft copper of which it is made and compress the composition against the point of the anvil, for when the cap chamber is fixed the anvil is fixed also.

The cap chamber is fixed in a hole in the base of the cartridge as can be seen in the Frontispiece and Plate VI. The result is that when the cartridge is held in position in the gun the blow of the striker, which impinges on the

PLATE IV

(A) Flash-photographs of the Flames given by firing consecutively five
Standard British caps

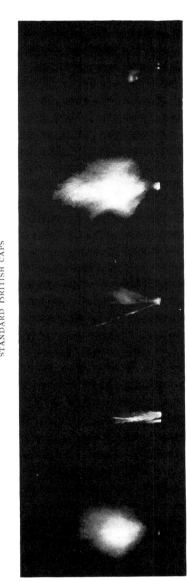

(B) Flash-photographs of the Flames given by firing consecutively five
" Large " Continental caps

centre of the cap, suddenly compresses the composition between the cap and the anvil. This sudden compression causes friction which produces heat sufficient to explode the composition, when the hot gases shoot out of the hole shown in the lower end of the cap chamber in Fig. 3 and ignite the powder charge which is resting against the outside of the cap chamber in the bottom of the cartridge.

All central-fire percussion caps are made on this principle, and the only real variations are matters of detail such as the shape and size of the anvil. These details can, however, become important : but in order to understand why, it is necessary to realise what the factors are which can affect the cap as an efficient igniter.

I have made several references in this chapter to the question of the temperature of the burning gas-jet which is really the flame produced by the cap, and which ignites the powder charge. It will readily be understood that the ease with which the powder is ignited depends partly on the temperature of the gas-jet and partly on the force with which it is driven against the powder grains ; as the greater this force is the more readily are the grains penetrated by the hot gas and ignited. Now the force with which the cap flame is driven against the powder is dependent entirely on the actual gas pressure in the cap chamber, and the higher this pressure is, the greater the force of the flame.

The gas pressure in the cap chamber depends on :

(1) The relative volume of the cap chamber and the amount of gas evolved ; and

(2) The ease with which the gas can escape.

These two points are of great importance.

If the chamber is large the amount of gas evolved by any given quantity of composition will not fill the chamber so rapidly and will not want to escape so eagerly. Consequently the pressure in the chamber will be reduced.

Similarly if the exit hole in the end of the cap chamber is very small the pressure under which the gas will escape will be very high, just as it is possible to increase the pressure on a jet of water by covering an ordinary tap with a finger and leaving only a tiny exit, when the pressure will force a jet of water right across a room. But when the finger is removed the water will merely flow from the tap.

So we come down to the important fact that the pressure under which the cap flame from a given composition is forced against the powder depends on the size of the cap chamber and that of the exit hole, or " Flash Hole."

Other things being equal, a big cap chamber, or a big flash hole, reduces the efficiency of the cap as an igniter ; while a small cap chamber and flash hole increase this efficiency.

The temperature of the gas-jet is also of great importance because the higher the temperature the more easily can the flame ignite the powder, and the more it tends to expand the gas, and so the greater the pressure developed. But this is a factor which is dependent on the ingredients used in the cap composition.

Now the size of the cap chamber is really dependent on the size and shape of the anvil, and the type of anvil used by any manufacturer is governed largely by the machinery used. The anvils are stamped out and fed into the caps by automatic machines, and if reliable caps are to result the machines must be reliable. For example, a glance at Fig. 3 will show that if the anvil were inserted into the cap the wrong way round, a miss-fire would result on the cap being struck by the striker because there would be nothing to prevent the cap from being driven forwards into the cap chamber, and so there would be nothing against which the cap could be compressed. If the automatic machines are not sufficiently delicate anvils may very easily be inverted on their way to the caps with results which have been explained. This risk of inverted anvils was one of the chief problems of the manufacturer from very early days. At one time anvils were used of such a shape that they would function whether put in either end first. But these did not produce very sensitive caps because the only resistance

CAPS

to the striker blow was offered at the edges of the cap instead of at the middle.

The type of anvil shown in Fig. 3 is unquestionably extremely efficient, but it needs up-to-date and delicate plant in manufacture. It was, however, adopted by British as well as by most American and many German and other Continental manufacturers.

There are, however, two types of Continental cap which are very commonly seen in which different types of anvil are used. In one of these the anvil is made out of the cap chamber itself by raising its base into a sort of pointed stirrup ; and in the other a very long " legged " anvil is used, the leg of which protrudes through the flash hole. Both these types of anvil are used simply and solely to avoid the risk of having anvils inverted in the assembling machines, and both of them need large cap chambers. This means that the cap itself must be made large to fill up the other end of the cap chamber, which again means a large charge of cap composition to cover the bottom of the cap.

This larger amount of composition has to be relatively weak and is not so easily exploded by a blow as a smaller amount, and so in order to increase the friction " dead " substances, such as powdered glass or silicide, are added to the composition. Such additions result in comparatively weak and low temperature flames, with lower pressures in the cap chamber.

As is often the case when manufacturers are compelled to deviate from general practice, merit is made of necessity, and all sorts of advantages are claimed for these large caps. Both the gunmaker and shooter are generally ignorant of the real causes and effects of such caps and they both assume that a large cap means more " ginger " in the cartridge. As a matter of fact, the result is exactly the opposite. Powders which have been manufactured and regulated for ignition by the high-pressure and high-temperature flame produced by the apparently smaller cap of the type used in this country, do not give such good or regular results when used in conjunction with these large caps which produce weak flames of lower temperature.

The extreme importance of matching powder and cap is not realised nearly go generally as it should be, and there can be no greater mistake than to combine British double based powders with these large Continental caps.

The flash photographs in Plate IV give a most interesting and striking example of the relative efficiency of some of these large Continental caps when compared with the British smaller, but more " high-powered," caps.

Sometimes these large caps are given the most eulogistic and extravagant names by retailers. Terms such as " triple ignition," or even " quadruple ignition," are absolutely meaningless when applied to caps used in shotguns, as will be appreciated from a study of the principles of cap construction which have been given in this chapter. These principles are the same for all the varieties of caps used in shotgun cartridges, and no system of multiple ignition is in existence.

GAS ESCAPES

On the powder charge being ignited a considerable pressure is developed. This pressure acts equally in all directions, but is controlled by the walls of the barrel and the breech of the action, with the result that the shot charge is driven forwards. Some of the expanding gases which produce this pressure naturally try to escape backwards through the flash hole and cap chamber. These gases rush into the cap with such violence that its open end is expanded against the walls of the cap chamber, and the greater the pressure the closer the contact between the front end of the cap and the surrounding walls of the cap chamber. This close contact effectually seals the only possible exit, and this sealing is called " Obturation." It will be seen that obturation is actually produced by the gas itself which thus closes its own chance of exit.

It sometimes happened, however, that the anvil was very slightly on the large size and so its insertion into the cap distorted the cap from being perfectly circular. The cross section of the cap chamber is a perfect circle, and it is clearly impossible to fill up a circular hole with an elliptical cap. The result was that a jet of gas then escaped past the cap and impinged on the face of the action. This gas was very hot and if the escapes were sufficiently frequent it caused erosion of the face of the action which became visible as pitting round the striker holes.

Nothing that the shooter could do would prevent this pitting, as the harm was done immediately on firing the cartridge.

The remedy lay with the manufacturer, who had to reduce the maximum permissible size for the anvil, or else to use anvils of a different sectional shape.

There is a common belief that such gas escapes are due to high pressures. The truth is that exactly the opposite is frequently the case. A high pressure will effect obturation even if the anvil has distorted the cap a little, as it will be sufficient to expand the copper cap completely. Low pressures, however, can only cause perfect obturation when the fit between cap and cap chamber is exact.

Gas escapes can usually be detected by noting a blackening round one portion of the rim of the cap when the base of the fired case is examined.

It must be remembered, however, that pitting round the striker holes can also be caused by corrosion if the action face of a gun is not properly cleaned ; also that if pitting has once been started by erosion it can easily be intensified by corrosion. So pitting round the striker holes of a gun cannot by itself be regarded as definite proof that gas escapes have been occurring, and in this respect it must be considered in conjunction with the general appearance of the rest of the gun. If the barrels show marked signs of rusting or corrosion, and the gun general indications of neglect and lack of care, it is probable that the pitting round the striker holes is also due, at any rate partly, to corrosion. But if the gun has obviously been treated with real and proper care and the condition is perfect in all other respects, the chances certainly are that the fault is in the cartridges and that gas escapes have been occurring with too great frequency.

Typical pitting round the striker holes caused by gas escapes is shown in the photograph of the action face of a best-grade gun in Plate Va.

THE TUBULAR ANVIL

Gas escapes do not occur when a tubular anvil is adopted instead of the ordinary flat type which has been described.

The construction and principle of the tubular anvil is shown in the different diagrams in Fig. 4. The first step is the stamping out from a sheet of brass about ·025 of an inch in thickness small flat pieces of the shape shown in Fig. 4A. Each of these is formed into a tubular anvil by being bent over into an angle somewhat less than a right angle along the line a, a, and again into obtuse angles along the lines b, b, and c, c. The edges at d, e, f and g are turned inwards until the d meets f and e meets g, as can be seen in Fig. 4B. The bottom of the anvil which is thus formed is circular, and the anvil is of such a size that it just fits into the capsule of the cap.

Fig. 4C shows a tubular anvil immediately below the capsule into which it is to be inserted.

The ridge at the top (a in Fig. 4B) touches the priming composition as can be seen in Figs. 4D and E, which give two different views of the anvil in place in the capsule, which is shown in section, the cap composition being seen covering the inside of the top of the capsule and lying between the capsule and the anvil ridge.

When the cap is indented by the striker the composition is compressed against this anvil ridge and exploded, the resulting cap flame passing downwards

PLATE V

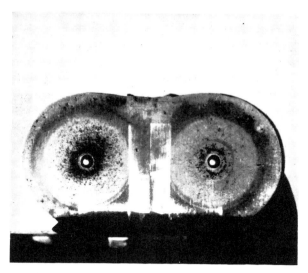

(A) An Action Face eroded by Gas-escapes

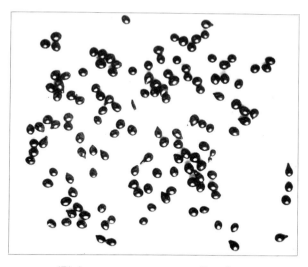

(B) An example of really Bad Shot

These pellets were obtained from a loaded cartridge which was one of a batch which proved most unsatisfactory

through the two large holes in the top of the anvil into the cap chamber.

The capsule and anvil are seated in the cap chamber in exactly the same manner as has already been described,

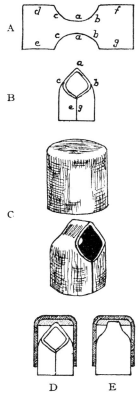

FIG. 4.—The construction of a Tubular Anvil.

A, The flat copper strip from which the anvil is made. B, This strip bent and formed into the anvil. C, The anvil immediately below the capsule. D, The anvil seated in the capsule which is shown in section. E, Another view of the anvil seated in the capsule (shown in section) from a point at right angles to the position given in D.

and Plate VI gives a sectional view of a cartridge-case in which a cap with a tubular anvil is used.

The tubular anvil was finally adopted by Imperial Chemical Industries, Ltd., in 1932, and gas escapes have been completely eliminated in shotgun cartridges made by this Company.

SENSITIVENESS

Provided suitable cap composition is used the sensitiveness of a cap depends on the thickness of the copper capsule, as a thick capsule is more difficult to indent than a thin one. In British shotgun caps the thickness of this capsule is 0·018 inch.

Sensitiveness is tested by dropping a 2-oz. weight on the cap. The weight drops on to a striker of similar shape to that on a gun, and the cap should explode when the weight is dropped from a height of 14 inches. As a matter of fact most caps will explode when the weight is dropped from a height of 12 inches, and some even when the height is but 10 inches.

Miss-fires are usually attributed to the cap, but as often as not the fault will be found to lie in the gun. On this account I propose to leave the question of miss-fires to a chapter in Volume III, as I am devoting this present volume to the cartridge proper as far as is possible.

CHAPTER IV

CARTRIDGE-CASES

IN the last chapter the cap itself was dealt with in considerable detail, and it was explained that the cap was held firmly in the base of the cartridge-case, so that it might almost be regarded as an integral part of the case. The cap chamber, as a matter of fact, really does become an integral part of the case; but it is possible to push out a fired cap and replace it with an unfired one, and then to reload the case and use it over again. The process of changing an old cap for a new one is called recapping, and there must have been many of us who have spent numerous happy hours in boyhood —and manhood too—recapping and reloading old cases in order to reduce the total of the cartridge bill. But the reloading of ordinary cases does not in practice give very good results for reasons which will be explained later.

So it is time that we considered the actual cartridge-case which can be of two entirely distinct types : Paper Tube and All Metal. Let us take these two types in turn.

To do so entails a very brief survey of the method of manufacture, as without such a survey the parts played by the various components which go to make up the case will not be appreciated ; and without such appreciation it will not be possible to understand the causes of certain defects which sometimes appear and how they can be remedied, nor to place at their true valuation the advantages or disadvantages of different kinds of cases.

THE PAPER TUBE CARTRIDGE-CASE

In general terms the cartridge-case can be described as comprising two main parts : the paper tube, and the brass head. Let us take the paper tube first.

The quality of the cartridge depends very largely on the paper tube. This should expand on firing and fit the chamber tightly : it should on no account split : it must also contract on the pressure being removed so as to facilitate extraction. So the paper used should be capable of being expanded, strong, and yet resilient. I cannot say what tests are made abroad, but frequent visits to the British factories have made me familiar with the tests adopted in this country ; and I presume that similar tests are made abroad for all the better class of cartridge-cases, although they are doubtless omitted in some of the cheapest foreign brands.

The paper is received in reels at the factory and samples from each roll are tested for weight and thickness and stretched for breaking strain. If the samples fall short of the specifications laid down that reel of paper is rejected.

These reels of paper are placed on automatic machines which cut off certain lengths, and these lengths are fed to other machines in which they are rolled up into tubes, paste being spread between every layer of the rolled tube. The tubes are packed in cages and taken to the drying-room, where they remain for twelve hours in a temperature of 100 degrees Fahrenheit. At the end of this period they are completely dry and contain no moisture at all. The next step is to place the tubes in the " conditioning " room, where they absorb from 8 to 10 per cent. of moisture, which reduces the degree of hardness assumed in the drying-room.

The purpose of these two apparently contradictory processes is to ensure all the tubes containing exactly the same degree of moisture. This is essential in the operation of polishing when the tube is given its exact size, as a definite amount of moisture is necessary so as to ensure the correct size for the gun and wadding. For a tube varies in size according to its moisture content, and so it has to be made the correct size for the moisture it normally takes up on storage.

In order to give an idea of the scale on which cartridges are made in England, I may say that the " conditioning " room of the Imperial Chemical Industries factory generally carries a stock of 6,000,000 tubes, which is continually replenished to replace usage. It should also be realised that each of these tubes is of such a length that it is afterwards cut up into three or five tubes of the correct length for a cartridge-case.

On removal from the " conditioning " room the tubes are polished and sized by machinery so that the internal and external diameters lie within certain limits. This same machine also cuts them into three or five, as has just been explained, and the tube is now ready for the reception of the brass head.

THE BRASS HEAD. This consists really of three or

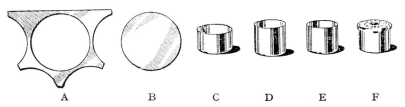

A   B   C   D   E   F

FIG. 5.—The various stages in the manufacture of the brass head of a cartridge.

four components in addition to the cap and cap chamber, namely, the actual brass head itself ; a circular iron disc with slightly cupped edges which is used for reinforcing the brass head ; an iron lining for " gas-tight " cases ; and a paper caulk or " base wad " which forms the actual bottom of the inside of the cartridge-case.

The diagrams in Fig. 5 show the different stages in manufacture of a brass head. A circular " blank " is first of all cut from a strip of sheet brass. This blank is shown in Fig. 5B, Fig. 5A being the remains of the brass sheet after the blank has been cut out.

The blank is then cupped into the shape shown in Fig. 5C, when this cup is annealed, or " tempered " by heat, and cleaned. It is then drawn out into the shape shown in Fig. 5D, after which it is trimmed into the size shown in Fig. 5E and again annealed and cleaned.

The final step is to shape it into the brass head shown in Fig. 5F and the machine which effects this shaping also prints the base at the same time.

The iron head for reinforcing is made in a similar manner, but there are not so many stages in the process,

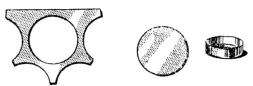

FIG. 6.—The stages in the manufacture of the iron head used for reinforcing the brass head of a cartridge-case.

and the diagrams in Fig. 6 show how a blank is cut from an iron sheet and cupped.

The base wad is made of paper which is rolled into a tight circular cylinder with a hole in the middle to

FIG. 7.—The paper base wad of a cartridge-case, before and after rolling and sizing.

receive the cap chamber. The paper before and after this rolling is shown in Fig. 7.

THE CAP CHAMBER. This is made in a similar way to the brass head and the diagrams in Fig. 8 show the different stages in the process. A brass blank is first of

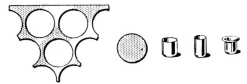

FIG. 8.—The different stages in the manufacture of the cap chamber.

all cut from a sheet, but it is naturally much smaller in size than that cut for the brass head. This blank is then cupped, annealed, cleaned, trimmed to its proper length, again annealed and cleaned, and finally flanged and pierced for the flash hole.

THE IRON LINING. The list of components of an ordinary case are now complete, but in the better grade of cases yet another component is added. This is the iron lining to the inside of the lower end of the cartridge-case. This iron lining forms a metal protection to the powder and reinforces the paper tube around the powder chamber. It further adds to the strength of the whole case. Cartridge-cases which are fitted with this iron

FIG. 9.—The iron lining for a " Gas-Tight " case : plain, varnished and rolled and shaped.

lining are termed " Gas-Tight " cases, or sometimes— quite erroneously—" Steel-Lined " cases.

The iron lining consists of a metal strip which is varnished and coiled into a hollow cylinder, one end being slightly turned in, as shown in Fig. 9, which gives diagrams of the metal strip before and after varnishing and when coiled into its final shape.

ASSEMBLING. The final processes in the manufacture of the case include assembling, capping, gauging and

FIG. 10.—The components of a " Gas-Tight " case before assembling. From left to the right these components are : the cap chamber, the brass head, the iron head, the iron lining, the base wad and the paper tube.

inspection. The diagrams in Fig. 10 show the components which I have described prior to assembling. From left to right these components are : the cap chamber ; brass head ; iron head ; iron lining (for gas-tight cases only) ; base wad ; and paper tube. These are all assembled by machinery which compresses them together so tightly that the case becomes one solid whole (Fig. 11).

The cap is then inserted, and after gauging and inspection the case is ready either for issue to gunmakers or others who load their own cartridges, or for the loading shops.

There are in all no less than 65 different operations in the manufacture of a cartridge-case before it is loaded,

FIG. 11.—The assembled case before it has been capped—that is, before the cap has been inserted.

and these do not include the processes in the manufacture of the various materials from which it is made.

WATERPROOFING. There are slight variations in the size or quality of the components, such as the depth of the brass head and the capacity for wet-resisting possessed by the paper tube. Within reasonable limits the more waterproof a cartridge-case is, the better. Quite apart from the fact that a cartridge-case which is easily penetrated by moisture does not provide efficient protection for the powder, it must be remembered that a damp case swells when the diameter may be increased to such an extent that the cartridge cannot be inserted into the chamber of the gun.

Then paper which is heavily impregnated with moisture becomes soft, and this affects the turnover, as will be explained later.

So from every point of view a waterproof cartridge-case is an advantage, and the best method of achieving this result is to use a special waterproof paper. This was done in the well-known " Pegamoid " case, and the old Pegamoid paper had very pronounced water-resisting qualities. This type of case, however, possessed some disadvantages in its original form which I will consider in Chapter VI, and before 1939 it was replaced in this country by other types of cases which were rendered waterproof by coating the paper with celluloid varnish. Such cases are called " Water Resisting."

Sometimes cartridge-cases obtain a reputation for being waterproof which is quite unjustified. For example,

PLATE VI

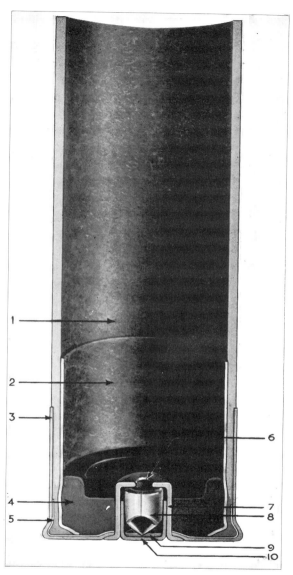

A Section of a standard British Gas-tight Cartridge-Case

1, Paper tube; 2, Iron lining; 3, Brass head; 4, Base wad; 5, Iron head; 6, Flash hole;
7, Cap chamber; 8, Tubular anvil; 9, Cap composition; 10, Capsule

one well-known and very excellent brand of Continental case used to be regarded as being waterproof, although, in reality it was no such thing. The reputation was gained because the case did not, apparently, swell sufficiently to prevent the possibility of loading. But the real explanation was that this case is made considerably smaller in the first place, and consequently the case had to absorb more moisture to make it swell to such an extent that it became too big for insertion into the chamber than it would had it been of normal size to start with.

In all cartridges in which the case alone is waterproof there is a risk of water being absorbed under the turnover. The moisture is then drawn down inside the walls of the case itself and eventually causes swelling. This swelling usually starts at the top of the cartridge near the turnover and gives the cartridge a mushroom-headed appearance. Not only does this swelling at the top frequently prevent loading, but it also loosens the turnover.

In order to overcome this possible source of weakness cartridges are sometimes dipped in some waterproofing solution, such as celluloid varnish or melted wax, after they have been loaded. This renders them more waterproof and permits total immersion in water without any harm being done, provided the immersion is of not too long duration.

There are practical disadvantages, however, which can accompany this sealing of the tops of the loaded cartridges, as the ballistics of the cartridge can very easily be affected, as will be seen later.

In 1939 Imperial Chemical Industries, Ltd., produced a new type of cartridge in which the paper tube was made of a specially waxed paper and which was sealed with a crimp turnover instead of the usual rolled turnover and over-shot wad. This crimp turnover will be considered later, but one of its effects, combined with that of the special waxed paper, was its remarkable capacity for water resistance. I tested some of these cartridges by soaking them, completely immersed, for three hours. They could then be loaded just as freely as before, while there was no change in the ballistics. The outbreak of war a few months later prevented further development, but there was no doubt that these cartridges could be regarded as completely waterproof in all normal circumstances and for all practical purposes of sport.

TYPES OF PAPER TUBE CARTRIDGE-CASES. The various types of cartridge-cases have names of their own with which shooters should be familiar in order to know exactly how they are spending their money when buying cartridges. These types are as follows :

Gas-tight. As has already been explained, a gas-tight case is one which is fitted with an iron lining to the powder chamber. This is an advantage both in the matter of ballistics and the actual strength of the case.

Ejector. In this type of case the outside of the paper tube was covered by an additional tube of thin brass which reaches to within about $\frac{1}{8}$ of an inch of the mouth of the loaded case. The object was to provide an absolutely waterproof case, but in actual practice it was found that the top of the tube which was turned over swelled quite usually. Consequently such cartridge-cases looked excellent, but they were not really so efficient as the Water-Resisting type.

Ejector cases are no longer made in England.

Water-Resisting. A case the tube of which has been made of a special paper which has been specially treated and which is almost completely waterproof. This quality of tube is usually only used in gas-tight cases, and so a water-resisting case is the highest grade of paper tube British case which it is possible to obtain.

Unlined Case. An unlined case is one which has no iron lining to the lower end of the inside of the tube such as is used in a gas-tight case.

Deep Shell. This is the term usually applied to an unlined case which is fitted with a deep brass head, the depth of which is $\frac{5}{8}$ of an inch.

Narrow Head. The term applied to cases which are fitted with narrow brass heads. The depth of these heads is $\frac{5}{16}$ of an inch in the case of British cartridges, but rather less in some of the cheaper foreign cases.

Length of Case. The length of case varies in different bore, and also in the same bore when extra heavy charges are desired. The ordinary 12-bore cartridge is nominally $2\frac{1}{2}$ inches long, although to be exact the unfired case is $2\frac{9}{16}$ inches in length. If a somewhat heavier charge is required in a 12-bore a case $2\frac{3}{4}$ inches in length is used, and this is the normal length for pigeon-guns in which heavy shot charges are considered necessary. If still heavier charges are wanted, such as wildfowlers need, a case 3 inches in length is used. For this reason cartridges should always be described by their gauge, or bore, and by their length as well, *e.g.* 12-bore $2\frac{1}{2}$-inch or 12-bore 3-inch ; 10-bore $3\frac{1}{4}$-inch, etc.

The standard American case was always slightly longer than the nominal $2\frac{1}{2}$ inches and was actually $2\frac{5}{8}$ inches in length. But in 1947, when the American manufacturers adopted the crimp turnover, the standard length of case was increased to $2\frac{3}{4}$ inches because the crimp turnover needs a greater length of case for the actual turnover than the ordinary type of turnover. But this is a problem which must be left for consideration until a later chapter.

TYPES OF CASES AVAILABLE

I have purposely given details of all the different types of paper-tubed cases which were in use before 1939, partly in order to place such details on record and partly because some of them may be made in Europe or elsewhere overseas. In Great Britain, however, only the narrow head unlined and gas-tight cases have been made since 1945. The reason is that the cost of producing the other cases would inevitably be so high that the demand would be negligible. I will deal with this question of costs fully at the end of Chapter VI.

ALL-METAL CARTRIDGE-CASES

In the comparatively early days of breech-loaders wildfowlers sought a cartridge-case which would be impervious to the effects of water. For them this was most important, especially as the early paper-tube cases were very prone to swelling when kept under damp conditions. This rendered loading difficult while the powder was also liable to be affected. In those days large bore big game rifles—12-bore, 10-bore, 8-bore and even 4-bore—were popular for use in Africa and India, and such rifles fired solid drawn brass cartridges. The cases for these cartridges were known as " Solid," and although nothing could have been more waterproof they were very costly when used for shotguns as large numbers of cartridges were fired annually, compared to the numbers fired at big game. So the demand for a metal case led to the introduction of a cheaper type which consisted of a solid drawn brass tube held in any ordinary type of shotgun cartridge brass head. This case was really like an Ejector case without any internal paper tube and of full length and was named the " Perfect " or " Thin Brass." Such cases were absolutely watertight and waterproof since they were made entirely of metal, but they could only be used in guns specially chambered and bored for them because the walls of these cases were appreciably thinner than those of ordinary cases, being brass instead of paper, and so the internal diameter was bigger in proportion to the external than in paper cases. The effect of this increased internal diameter enables larger powder and shot charges to be used, while the wads must be of greater diameter. In fact, from the point of view of loading, a 12-bore gun chambered for Perfect cases is almost the same as a 10-bore which takes paper cases.

The mouth of the Perfect case is sealed by being " crimped," as shown in Plate VIIIA, instead of by a turnover, which would be difficult to make. This crimp is only partial in that the ends of the case are merely crimped in just sufficiently to hold the over-shot wad in position and no more. Frequently the over-shot wad is held in position by shellac varnish as well, which helps to render the cartridge completely waterproof even when totally immersed in water.

Perfect and Thin Brass cases have always been expensive, but they are quite impervious to wet as far as swelling is concerned and the only risk of moisture getting to the powder is past the over-shot wad unless this is well covered by varnish. None have been made, however, since 1939 owing to the terrific increases in the prices of copper and zinc which would put these brass cartridges beyond the means of almost all shooters.

In 1935, however, a new type of All-Metal cartridge was introduced by the F.N. Company of Belgium. The case of this cartridge consisted of a solid but thin tube of zinc fixed into a brass head, but apart from the change from brass to zinc for the wall of the case the most spectacular innovation was the sealing of the case, which was effected by a full crimp in an exactly similar manner to the method of sealing used in all military brass rifle and revolver blank cartridges, and the end was dipped in wax, rendering it completely airtight. The over-shot wad was entirely omitted, and since a greater length of tube is required for a full crimp than for a partial crimp the total length of the loaded cartridge was reduced. But the reduction in length was helped by the greater internal diameter of the thin metal case, which enabled ordinary standard loads of powder and shot to occupy a shorter total column.

The difficulty of using a thin metal case in an ordinary type of gun was overcome partly by the employment of a thinner felt wad but chiefly by the adoption of a special slow burning powder which gave normal chamber and barrel pressures.

The net result was a finished cartridge which was much shorter than the standard nominal $2\frac{1}{2}$ inches, the total length being slightly less than 2 inches. (See Plate IX.)

At the same time cartridges containing an extra heavy shot charge were also loaded for wildfowlers. In these the full crimp closure was abandoned and an over-shot wad was used which was held in position by a turn-in rather than a turnover, the soft zinc rendering such a sealing comparatively easy.

These fully crimped cartridges took up less space, and 130 could easily be carried in an ordinary " 100 " cartridge bag.

Zinc, however, has its drawbacks as a material for cartridge cases as it is very soft and experience proved that these short zinc cases were very prone to denting and deformation in ordinary usage. None the less there is not the slightest doubt that these F.N. cartridges marked the beginning of a new epoch in cartridge loading and manufacture, but rather because of the method of sealing than of the actual metal case, as will be seen in the next chapter.

The most obvious substitutes for zinc were brass and aluminium, for the latter, when suitably alloyed, combines comparative toughness with the ductility needed for drawing the cases.

In passing I may mention that in 1933 I tested some all-steel cartridge-cases. The ballistics were not unsatisfactory but the steel was altogether too hard to permit the expansion necessary for adequate obturation, or sealing of the breech, and there was an obvious escape of gas with every shot which was fired.

In 1938 the Rottweil Company of Germany brought out a short all-metal cartridge which was a distinct improvement on the F.N. The case was aluminium and solid drawn, that is the whole head and wall were made in one unit similarly to a brass rifle or revolver cartridge. This case was altogether tougher than the F.N. zinc case and less liable to deformation, while the cartridges were the same size and occupied the same comparatively small space in a cartridge bag. They were, of course, fully crimped and waxed.

Then came the war, which put an end to all such work. But by 1947 Imperial Chemical Industries, Ltd., had produced a short solid drawn all-brass ·410 cartridge with

PLATE VII

THE CONSTRUCTION OF AIR CUSHION WADS

From left to right. Top Row: Cut tube and card wad; mouth of tube opened; card wad inserted. Middle Row: Top crimped; bottom also crimped; flattened and rectified; greased. Bottom Row: Fired wads

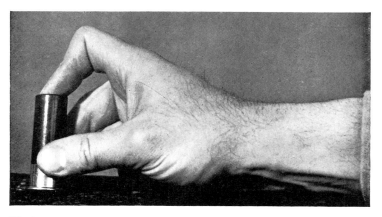

(B) A SIMPLE METHOD OF TESTING THE TURNOVER AND TIGHTNESS OF LOADING OF A CARTRIDGE

The cartridge is held as shown and tapped smartly on a table. If it has been properly loaded it should be impossible to move the over-shot wad appreciably downwards from the edge of the turnover

a fully crimped turnover and waxed end, which was issued experimentally on a considerable scale and gave great promise. (See Plate IX.) The Italians also produced a solid drawn all-brass 12-bore cartridge of normal length which was closed with a transparent celluloid over-shot wad held in position by the end of the brass case being turned in. There can be little doubt, however, that the fully crimped turnover is far more effective in every way, as not only can the cartridge be rendered absolutely and completely waterproof but the actual shooting is superior. I have kept a number of the I.C.I. all-brass ·410 cartridges completely immersed in water for 24 hours and then tested them for pressures, velocities and patterns merely to find that not one was affected to the slightest degree. These cases also, however, are no longer made because of the very high cost of brass.

THE CHOICE OF A CARTRIDGE-CASE. Let us first consider paper-tube cases. A question which is very commonly asked by shooters is whether the advantage derived from the use of a good quality case is sufficiently real to be worth the extra cost. Myself I am inclined to doubt whether in actual practice it is. From the point of view of efficiency in ballistics by far the most important part of the case is the cap ; and in all I.C.I. cases, at any rate, the cap is the same irrespective of their quality. Provided the same powder is used, and the *same quality of wadding*—a most important point as will be explained in the next chapter—I really doubt whether the practical advantages derived from a good quality case are very pronounced. In making this admittedly rash statement I am not forgetting the question of resistance to damp or water. Much must depend on the type of shooting enjoyed, but more on the care which the shooter takes of his cartridges. In fifty years I do not believe that I have lost fifty cartridges through wet. But I have always worn a cartridge belt, and when shooting in the rain have always worn a coat over the belt. There is with many people a definite psychological gain imparted by the feeling of confidence derived from the knowledge that the best possible materials are being used throughout and that the cartridges are almost, if not quite, impervious to the effects of water. Personally I am more interested in the ballistics, but I am confident and so will leave it at that.

But there is another trouble to which the cheaper cases, that is the ones with narrow brass heads and without any iron linings, may be prone, to which the better grade gas-tight case is almost, if not quite, immune. This is the risk of " Cut Offs."

A " Cut Off " or " Separation " is a separation of the paper tube from the brass head, which occurs on firing, with the result that the brass head only is ejected on the gun being opened and the paper tube is left sticking in the chamber.

This can be a nuisance, but should the paper tube, as sometimes happens, be blown a little way up the bore the nuisance becomes a danger. For in this event it is quite likely that the shooter would never notice that the brass head only had been ejected, and he would be able to load another cartridge in the chamber. And when he fired this barrel again a burst would probably result owing to the presence of the paper tube in the bore causing an obstruction.

Of all the difficulties which the cartridge manufacturer has to face the problem of the Cut Off is probably the most serious. It is experienced equally in all countries, and so far no *absolute* remedy has been discovered, but cut offs are very rare with present day cartridges. It is a fact, however, that the addition of the iron lining used in a gas-tight case to a deep brass head is very nearly an absolute remedy, and for all practical purposes can be regarded as an absolute remedy in normal circumstances.

The reason is that the iron lining on the inside and the deep brass head on the outside result in a firm grip on the tube extending farther up than is the case when the tube is held only in the brass head ; and the effect of this extended grip is to prevent cut offs in all normal circumstances.

I have, however, come across an instance of cut offs in gas-tight cases which was due to the cartridges having been stored in a heated cupboard for some considerable time. The effect of the heat was to dry the paper and reduce the moisture contents of the powder, which resulted in altogether more violent combustion than normal. The combination of the high pressures thus generated and the very dry paper tubes resulted in the tubes being cut completely off round the top of the brass heads. But circumstances such as these cannot be regarded as normal, and consequently I think that cases fitted with deep brass heads and iron linings may be considered immune to the risk of cut offs for all practical purposes.

But cut offs are rare in any kind of case provided good materials are used and proper care taken in manufacture, and the number of instances reported every season is so few as to make the percentage of cut offs so small as to be infinitesimal.

Quite apart from anything to do with cut offs a deep brass head certainly does help ejection, and on this account they were generally preferred by those who used two guns or fired numbers of cartridges in quick succession. But their cost would now be so high that the demand would never justify their manufacture.

All-metal cases are in a class by themselves. Their superiority over all other cases when a full crimp turnover is used can be so pronounced that it would seem obvious that they must become the cases and cartridges of the future. Apart from the question of cost—and again this would be too high with the present prices of metals for their manufacture to be economic—they would seem to have every advantage except one : they will never lend themselves to any loading except that of a factory. I know from long and intimate experience that nothing can surpass the deadly precision of the modern loading machines which stop automatically if any single component of the charge should fail to run smoothly into the case ; that nothing else can give the same constant turnover or crimp. But gunmakers' loading is not only a link with the past ; it is a link of comradeship between sportsman and gunmaker which is based on a friendship which has often extended through generations. It is an example of personal service which is almost bound to be forced steadily but inexorably into a mere memory by the inhuman accuracy and efficiency of machinery.

Besides, quite apart from the actual crimping, all-metal cases need special attention to wadding, which is really beyond the practical capacity of any loader other than a large factory, as will be explained in the next chapter.

STORAGE OF CARTRIDGES. Both modern powders and caps will keep for years under suitable conditions, and when cartridges are stored such conditions should be ensured as far as possible. The paper tube of the case is really the most sensitive indicator as to whether the conditions really are suitable, and few things can be worse for cartridges than successive changes from a hot dry atmosphere to a damp one and back again. The hot dry air dries the paper of the case which readily absorbs moisture when placed in damp surroundings. And even though this damp may subsequently be dried out again the changes will result in the turnover becoming loosened by repeated contraction and expansion of the paper caused by the evaporation and absorption of moisture. This loosening of the turnover can have a most serious effect on the efficiency of the cartridge as will be explained in the next chapter.

It will consequently be realised that the best conditions for storing cartridges are those in which the atmosphere is of a constant humidity, being never very dry nor markedly damp, and in which there are no great variations of temperature.

It has been suggested that the conditions which are the best for preserving old books are the best for storing cartridges, and there can be no doubt that this is a very good rule, as in both cases paper has to be preserved.

There can be no greater mistake than keeping cartridges for a long time in some hot cupboard. Not only

PLATE VIII

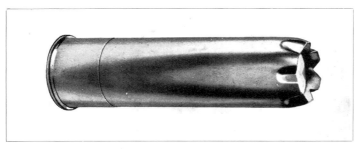

(A) A 12-BORE 3-INCH ALL-BRASS CASE SEALED WITH A PARTIAL CRIMP
AND OVER-SHOT WAD

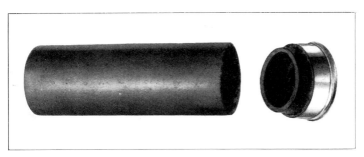

(B) A " CUT-OFF "

(C) LEAD CRUSHERS

The one on the extreme left has not been used. The others, reading from left to right,
indicate pressures which may be classed as feeble, light, normal, high, and excessive, when
occurring at one inch from the breech face in an ordinary 12-bore 2½-inch gun

are the paper tubes dried too much, but the moisture content of the powder is decreased, which tends to violent ballistics.

It must be realised that no system of waterproofing, whether the tops of the cartridges are sealed or not, nor even keeping cartridges stored in hermetically sealed tins, is any protection against the effects of temperature. Heat is not checked by soldered tins, nor the most efficient of waterproof cases. But the total amount of moisture contained in the powder charges, wadding, cartridge-cases and air inside the cartridges and the tins themselves would always remain constant, so it seems probable that such tins would help all this moisture to sort itself out again, so to say, and help the cartridges to settle down once more when cooler weather prevailed. Although the walls of the cases may prevent moisture from entering or leaving the contents of the case, that is the powder, a prolonged exposure to heat decreases the moisture content of the powder and in course of time this moisture leaves the cartridge between the wads and by the over-shot wad. It is a common experience that cartridges become violent owing to the loss of some of the moisture content of the powder during a very hot summer. But if they are kept under normal conditions this loss will gradually be made good by re-absorption of moisture from the air, and I have on many occasions tested cartridges which gave unduly high pressures in August and which developed normal pressures in November simply because the powder had recovered its correct amount of moisture during storage.

All-metal cartridges which are fully crimped and properly sealed are actually air-tight and consequently none of the moisture content of the powder, which may be evaporated out by prolonged exposure to heat, can escape from the cartridge-case. The result is that such cartridges probably recover normality more quickly once the hot and dry conditions have subsided or been changed.

The only drawback of a metal case is that it is a better conductor of heat than paper and this may result in the moisture content of the powder being reduced more rapidly. But, as has just been pointed out, none can escape from a case which has been properly sealed, and so, when the outside temperature has fallen, the superior conductivity of the metal case could help the powder to absorb with greater ease the moisture which it has lost.

When exposed for any length of time to extreme cold the metal case might help to render ignition more difficult and uncertain. But here the remedy is really in the powder, and fibrous powders should always be used when shooting in very cold climates, for such powders are more easily penetrated by the hot gases generated by the detonation of the cap composition, and so more readily ignited than non-porous gelatinised powders.

I think, therefore, that as regards immunity from the effects of heat and cold during storage there is little to chose between paper and metal cases. In theory paper may appear better because metal is a better conductor of heat, and the more the powder can be insulated from variations in temperature the better. In actual practice, however, I fancy that this somewhat theoretical advantage is counterbalanced by the tendency of the paper itself to part with some of its moisture in hot weather and so become very dry, or absorb moisture in wet weather and so become too damp.

CHAPTER V

WADDING, SHOT AND LOADING

IN a shotgun the projectile consists of a large number of small pellets ; some sort of container, therefore, is necessary in order to keep a shot charge complete until it is propelled from the muzzle when the gun is fired. The cartridge-case forms the walls of this container, and the bottom and top are formed by wads. So it will be seen that the first object of inserting wads in a shotgun cartridge is to keep the shot charge together.

But there is another, and if possible more important rôle played by the wads, namely the sealing of the bore between the expanding powder gases and the shot charge. The wads, in fact, act like a piston ; and as the powder gases expand on the combustion of the powder they drive the piston formed by the wads in front of them, and so propel the shot charge. If there were no wads between the expanding gases and the shot, the former would force their way through and in between the pellets of the latter, and the shot charge would not be propelled on its journey. And in order to ensure the maximum force of propulsion the sealing of the bore between the shot charge and powder gases must be complete.

Let us now see how these ends are obtained.

There are no less than four wads used in an ordinary shotgun cartridge and these are given the following names, starting from the powder end of the cartridge : Over-Powder Card ; Felt ; Over-Felt Card ; and Over-Shot Card.

OVER-POWDER CARD WAD. This wad is always made of cardboard, and it is usually $\frac{1}{12}$ or $\frac{1}{11}$ of an inch thick. Sometimes the underneath surface is glazed and the wad is then known as a " Field " Card wad. This glazing acts as an additional waterproofing to the powder chamber. When air-cushion wads are used the Over-Powder wad must be $\frac{1}{8}$ inch thick.

The purpose of the Over-Powder wad is to protect the powder from the felt wad, which is invariably greased.

FELT WAD. By far the most important wad of all is the Felt wad, as it is this wad which is entirely responsible for the sealing of the bore against the expanding powder gases. In order to effect this sealing some elastic material must be used which can be compressed by the resistance offered by the weight of the shot charge in front and the pressure exerted by the expanding gases in rear. This longitudinal compression results in lateral expansion, and the diameter of the wad becomes increased so that it completely fills up and seals the bore, thus producing obturation, or effective sealing against the escape of gases.

All sorts of materials have been tried for this wad, but up to the present nothing has proved better than felt, and on this account felt is almost universally used. In order to permit ample expansion a fairly thick wad is essential, as a thin wad would not expand sufficiently to give complete obturation. The actual thickness must depend on the room left in the case after the space occupied by the powder and shot has been allowed for, and so a thicker wad is used when an ounce of shot is loaded in an ordinary 12-bore cartridge with 27 grains of Number 60 powder than when $1\frac{1}{16}$ ounce is used under similar conditions. But the difference in thickness is not great and the standard thickness for the felt wad is $\frac{7}{16}$ of an inch with $1\frac{1}{16}$ ounce of shot, and $\frac{1}{2}$ inch with one ounce.

I do not think that it is possible to lay too great a stress on the extreme importance of using a good quality felt wad ; and complete obturation, which is essential for the best possible results, is dependent entirely on the quality of felt used.

Some varieties of cheap felt are almost as hard as wood and wads made of such material will never give good results.

Felt used for wads is made either from wool or from hair. The best kind is the highest grade of wool felt, which is white in colour, while the lower grades of wool felt are brown and coarser in texture.

Hair felt is coarser and more loosely put together, and is not nearly so good as high-grade wool felt, although it can be better than some of the cheapest grades of brown wool felt.

A highest grade felt wad is white in colour ; firm, but with plenty of spring in the centre.   But about 1936 a particular type of brown felt wad was introduced which gave results hardly different from those yielded by best white felt.   Such wads are costly and their employment adds considerably to the price of cartridges.   But I am convinced that money spent on best quality felt wads is well laid out, and myself I attach far more importance to the quality of the wadding than to that of the cartridge-case, provided the latter is capped with a cap which is suited to the powder used.

It is also extremely important that all the felt wads used in any lot of cartridges should be of identical consistency, as if they vary in their elasticity or hardness, irregular ballistics will be the result.   This regularity in the wadding can only be obtained with good grades of felt.

Some loaders omit the card Over-Powder wad, and use either one very thick hair-felt wad, or else two thinner wads of hair felt, on each side of which paper is stuck. This paper protects the powder from the grease in the wad, but it is not so efficient in this respect as the separate card wad.   And in any case hair felt is not so good as best wool felt.

Whatever the quality of the felt used the wad must be greased, as this grease acts as a lubricant when the shot charge travels down the bore, and helps to maintain regular ballistics.   The pink colour of the sides of white felt wads is due to the greasing.

SUBSTITUTES FOR FELT.   Owing to the high cost of good felt various substitutes have been tried, and for many years the most promising seemed to be cork.   In many ways cork is an ideal substance for the thick wad, as it is cheap, elastic and lighter than felt, which can be an advantage, as will be explained in the chapter on Recoil.

It possesses, however, the disadvantage that, owing to its very nature, it is impossible to cut the immense numbers of cork wads which are required for shotgun cartridges year after year and have every wad of the same quality and consistency. For cork is a natural substance and perfect regularity can only be obtained in some manufactured material. Wood of the same kind varies in density and hardness, and so does cork. For this reason wads cut out from whole pieces of cork can hardly be expected to give regular results, and it is really surprising that they give as regular results as they do. If, however, cork wads were used on anything like the same extensive scale as felt, irregularity would inevitably increase. The fact that the results are often as good as they are is due solely to the care in the selection of the wads.

If regularity is to be obtained on a very big scale the wads would have to be made of " manufactured " cork instead of the natural material. By " manufactured " cork I mean cork composition made up of numerous small particles of cork and held together by adhesion, for by this means alone can regularity be obtained if wads are to be used in millions. And such cork composition wads are far cheaper than those made of whole cork, which can be quite an expensive material.

But cork wads possess another characteristic which can be a disadvantage, and this is their tendency to lower the ballistics. Provided this tendency is appreciated it need not be a drawback, as it can be overcome by using a slightly heavier powder charge. I will, however, deal with this aspect of cork wadding at greater length in the next three chapters.

Another substitute for felt for the thick wad is a material known as " Feltine," which is a kind of imitation felt and is composed of compressed paper. Feltine wads can be recognised by their slate grey colour and their paper like composition when they are pulled apart. They should never be used in even moderate quality cartridges, as they tend to very weak and irregular ballistics and possess the further disadvantage of breaking up into fragments which are blown back into one's face when firing into the wind. Usually such wads are only used in the very cheapest brands of foreign cartridges. But cartridges wadded with feltine instead of felt are generally dear, no matter how low the price.

One other substitute for cork is deserving of mention if only as a warning.

Some years ago experiments were made in loading cartridges in which the felt wad was omitted altogether, but its place was taken by grains of rice. These were loaded on top of the Over-Powder wad and kept in place by another thin card wad being inserted above them. The results were most disastrous, as very high and dangerous pressures were generated, while at least one gun was burst. Consequently the idea was not followed up, and I only mention the matter in case it should be tried again.

In 1952 I tested a new French substitute for the felt wad comprising a $\frac{3}{4}$-inch card cylinder with a $\frac{1}{4}$-inch cork disc in the middle, held on either side by thin cupped card wads with the concave sides outwards. With standard loading the ballistics were very feeble and one in three left the card cylinder stuck in the bore just behind the choke. Had a subsequent shot been fired without examination of the bore a burst would have been certain.

Such experiences emphasise the importance of tests before using any new type of wadding in the field.

AIR-CUSHION WADS. For very many years experimental wads of a pneumatic type were tried as a substitute for felt, which is not surprising in view of the obvious advantages which would be conferred by a completely pneumatic wad. Until 1936 the best known wad of this type was the " Pneumatic," which has achieved both popularity and success. But in spite of its name this wad cannot be regarded as a true pneumatic wad, that is a wad which relies entirely on a cushion of air for capacity to act as an effective gas check. For the " Pneumatic " wad is made of cork and has a very small air space in the middle, and it is undoubtedly the cork which gives it by far the greater proportion of its elasticity rather than the air which is imprisoned in the small air chamber.

Experiments proved that if the air chamber in the middle of a cork wad is enlarged unduly there is a tendency for the powder gases to blow through the centre of the wad. Not only does the wad then fail completely as a gas-check, but there is also the risk of the outer annulus of the wad being left in the bore, when it will form an obstruction in the way of the next shot and a burst or bulged barrel will be the result. For cork is not strong enough to retain air under the compression which occurs unless the walls are so thick that the air chamber is a small proportion of the whole volume of the wad.

And here I would like to make it quite clear that " Pneumatic " cork wads are absolutely safe and strong because the air chamber is small and a big reserve of strength exists in the thick wall of cork.

A wad which had an air chamber which occupied practically the whole of the inside was the " Hislop " wad which was patented in 1932. Briefly, this wad consisted of two cylindrical cardboard cups, one of which was inverted into the other so as to form a cardboard cylinder with double walls and closed at both ends, containing nothing but air.

This was a most interesting idea, but long series of tests showed that it was capable of improvement and eventually led to the manufacture of the " Air-Cushion " wad by Imperial Chemical Industries, Ltd. This wad begins life as a plain but stout paper tube rather more than an inch long. A thin card wad is inserted in the middle of this tube and the two ends are then crimped so as to form a cylinder the wall of which is the central part of the tube and the two ends the crimped turnovers. The various stages in the manufacture and greasing of this wad are shown in Plate VIIA.

All risk which might possibly be caused by the very large air chamber—that is the tendency of the middle being blown out and the outer annulus, or tube, of the wad being left in the bore—is completely eliminated by (1) the use of an extra thick card wad over the powder, which is $\frac{1}{8}$ inch instead of the usual $\frac{1}{12}$ or $\frac{1}{11}$; and (2) the insertion of the thin card wad in the centre of the paper cylinder. For should any gas ever find its way into the inside of this wad it can merely force the thin card disc against the forward end of the cylinder and so seal the bore better than ever.

Air-Cushion wads which are recovered after firing invariably have a cupped appearance as can be seen in Plate VIIA.

Towards the end of 1936 I carried out a very long series of experiments with these Air-Cushion wads, which included long series of tests for pressure with Smokeless Diamond, E.C. and Empire powders as well as for patterns, and these tests were all made against similar numbers of cartridges loaded with the same powders and both white and brown felt wads. The results of these tests were published in detail in *Game and Gun* in January, 1937, and they were, I think, sufficiently complete and convincing to suggest that the Air-Cushion wad could be accepted as a really effective substitute for felt. Since then these wads have been in general use and some fifteen years of experience have fully endorsed the results of early experiments, and personally I use these Air Cushion wads with complete confidence and happiness.

With $1\frac{1}{16}$ ounce of shot these wads require one grain of No. 60 powder less than do felt, but with one ounce the charges are the same. And it is most essential that they should only be used with a $\frac{1}{8}$ inch over-powder card wad.

OVER-FELT CARD WAD. A second thin card wad is placed between the felt wad and the shot charge. As a rule this wad is $\frac{1}{12}$ inch in thickness and its purpose is to prevent the bottom layer of shot pellets sticking to the greasy felt which would spoil the pattern. This wad also protects the felt wad from being disintegrated by the shot pellets when it is forced forwards against them by the powder gases.

In America this card wad is frequently omitted, its

place being taken by a thickness of paper stuck to the felt wad in the manner which has already been mentioned. Sometimes this card wad is replaced by a thin cork wad of about $\frac{1}{8}$ inch in thickness. Such a change certainly does no harm, but after repeated tests for ballistics and pattern I have been quite unable to detect any advantage. But if any shooter thinks he does derive some benefit from this thin cork Over-Felt wad he had certainly better continue to use it.

OVER-SHOT CARD WAD. The only purpose of this wad is to hold the pellets of the shot charge in position in the cartridge-case while the cartridges are transported before and after sale and stored and carried while out shooting. The thinnest card wad which will answer this purpose would seem to be the best, and for this reason I am inclined to prefer one of $\frac{1}{20}$ inch thickness to the $\frac{1}{16}$ card which is more generally used.

This card wad very soon separates from the bulk of the shot charge on leaving the muzzle of the gun. This has been shown in the wonderful spark photographs taken of actual shot charges in flight by the American scientist Mr. Philip P. Quayle. And I once had a somewhat exceptional chance of finding this fact out in actual practice.

In 1926 and 1927 Lord Cottesloe and I tried to carry out some experiments with shotguns on his specially designed Ballistic Pendulum at Wistow. This instrument had proved a most wonderfully accurate one for recording the actual striking velocities of rifle bullets, and we were anxious to see whether it could not be adapted to shotgun work. Some of the results we obtained are given in Appendix I, and I learned one or two other facts, as one often does when working for quite a different end.

One of these facts was the rapidity with which the Over-Shot wad separates from the shot charge.

In the course of the experiments I fired just on 200 cartridges at the Pendulum at ranges from 3 to 5 yards. In order to prevent the Pendulum from being affected by the muzzle blast, Lord Cottesloe erected a very efficient screen with a hole about 6 inches in diameter through which I had to fire. This screen was set up 6 feet from the muzzle of the gun, and was examined after every shot to see whether any of the pellets had hit the actual screen instead of passing through the hole. And in every single instance we found the Over-Shot card wad the near side of the screen, although there were very few rounds in which any shot pellets failed to pass through the hole.

This proved that the Over-Shot wad was separated from the main bulk of the shot charge by the time that the latter had travelled 6 feet from the muzzle of the gun.

When a full crimp turnover is used the Over-Shot wad is naturally omitted.

SHOT

The pellets which make up the charge of shot in a cartridge are formed by dropping molten lead from a height, when the drops assume a more or less spherical shape owing to surface tension, a property common to all liquids and which is the cause of raindrops becoming round as they fall to the ground.

Pure lead will not break up sufficiently well into drops when being poured out to allow regular dropping, and on this account a small percentage of arsenic and antimony are added. The antimony is also added to produce hardness in the shot.

The liquid mixture of lead, arsenic and antimony is poured through a sieve situated at the top of a tower from 180 to 200 feet in height, the size of the holes in the sieve depending on the size of shot required.

The droppings of molten lead alloy fall down the middle of the shot tower into a large tank of water which cools them so rapidly that they retain their spherical shape.

The pellets are then shaken up, a process which dries and polishes them, and they are then rolled down a long sloping table in which there is a gap near the bottom. The perfectly round pellets roll down so fast that they gain sufficient momentum to enable them to jump the gap, but the misshapen pellets cannot get up such speed and fall through the gap and become waste.

The good pellets are then placed in a polishing barrel which shakes them up as it revolves, and they are then sized by rolling through screens which are perforated with different-sized holes. For example, the first screen is perforated with holes of such a size that they allow all pellets of the size of No. 1 shot and smaller to fall through. The holes in the next screen are slightly smaller and retain size No. 1, but let all smaller pellets pass, while the next screen holds back the pellets of size No. 2, and so on.

The different-sized pellets are again tested for roundness by rolling them down a slope and making them jump a gap, while samples are weighed and counted.

The manufacture of the shot is then complete.

In December, 1948, brief particulars were published in this country of a new Italian process for the manufacture of shot which has been devised by S. A. Continuus of Milan. Briefly, the process consists of manufacturing shot by stamping out pellets from lead wire, the different sizes being obtained by using wire of suitable gauges. I was sent a sample of this shot, plated with nickel, in September, 1954. The appearance was most attractive and the spherosity excellent. Tests for pattern, however, indicated that it tended to produce somewhat denser patterns than normal, and most surprisingly the metallic fouling was more noticeable than in the case of ordinary shot.

From the point of view of actual manufacture it would seem that the cost of producing by rolling, drawing or extruding into wire and then forming up the pellets in dies would be far higher than casting, or dropping, in the usual way. But if the capital expenditure needed for building a shot tower had to be taken into account, as would probably be the case when starting a new factory, the circumstances might be altered.

Probably the most interesting possibility about the Continuus process is the fact that it could produce shot from other materials than lead. In round figures the price of lead has risen from £9 10s. a ton between the wars to £105 in 1955.   It is impossible to foretell future prices and costs, but should the price increase still further it might become necessary to consider making shot from some other metal or alloy which might not be suitable for " dropping," and in such circumstances some different process of manufacture would also have to be considered.

MOULD SHOT.   It is impossible to obtain perfectly round shot pellets in the largest sizes by dropping, and so such pellets are actually cast in moulds, and shot which has been so made is known as " Mould Shot " as opposed to " Drop Shot."   Usually all sizes larger than AA are moulded.

CHILLED AND HARD SHOT.   Some manufacturers used to cool their shot during its fall down the shot-tower by blowing cold air across the bottom of the tower, and they consequently used to call their shot " Chilled."   In reality all drop shot is chilled, and the actual chilling process has no effect on the hardness of the pellets, as might be imagined from many statements which have been made.

The actual hardness of shot depends on the percentage of arsenic and antimony added to the lead.

Very soft shot is undoubtedly a disadvantage.   During the passage of the shot charge down the bore the pellets are jostled together with great violence while the outside pellets are pressed and rubbed against the inside of the bore.   All this tends to make the pellets irregular in shape and many lose weight on account of pieces being rubbed off, either by other pellets or against the inside of the bore. This deformation of the pellets can have a noticeable effect on their subsequent velocity, as will be explained in the chapter dealing with that subject.   Consequently the more the pellets can be saved from deformation the better ; and on this account a certain degree of hardness is an advantage.   But as long as lead is used for shot, and lead is the most suitable metal because of its weight, the pellets will never be hard enough to be able to withstand entirely the effects of their passage down the bore.   For this reason the claims put forward by some manufacturers cannot be justified in practice, and the probable truth is that there is little to choose between the degrees of hardness of British, Continental or American shot as made at the present day.

The two disadvantages with which hard shot is usually credited are the increased risk of pellets glancing off natural objects, such as stones or tree-trunks, and causing damage to other shooters or beaters ; and the risk of breaking one's teeth when biting on a very hard pellet while eating shot game. But I do not think that any lead alloy used for shot is sufficiently hard to warrant apprehension from either of these possibilities. A ricochet, or glancing pellet, is more a matter of striking velocity which depends on the range at which the hard natural object is struck ; and at very short ranges the danger of glancing pellets should never be forgotten, for the degrees of hardness of the pellets of modern shot are not sufficiently wide to make any particular make either more or less dangerous than another.

Nor will any lead alloy be as hard to bite as a steel pellet, for example. Even a comparatively soft pellet may damage a tooth, and the best safeguard is to exercise care in eating any badly shot game.

PLATED SHOT. The first patent for plating shot pellets with metals such as tin and zinc was taken out in England by Sydney Pitt in 1878, so the idea cannot be regarded as new. At first the idea was to prevent contamination of game, but the object is now to protect the pellets from becoming deformed, although the amount of plating which is put on cannot possibly have any practical effect on deformation. For example, at least one American firm of ammunition manufacturers made great claims for their " copper-plated " shot some years ago. The thickness of the copper " plating " on the pellets of this shot was just about one hundredth part of a thousandth part (0·00001) of an inch. Is it conceivable that a coating of copper, which itself is a soft metal, of this thickness could afford any useful protection to the pellets against deformation in the barrel ?

SHAPE OF SHOT. The pellets in a shot charge should be as nearly as possible perfectly round. This is most important as round pellets travel straighter through the air and overcome air resistance better. It may be wondered why I have attached any importance to the original shape of the pellets in view of the fact that I have explained how they become deformed during their passage up the bore. It must, however, be remembered that by no means all the pellets become deformed, the ones on the outside of the shot charge being the greatest sufferers owing to their contact with the walls of the barrel. Further, there are such things as more or less regular deformation and irregular deformation. A perfectly round pellet may be somewhat flattened in a number of places all over its surface, but it will still retain in the main its spherical shape. A pear-shaped pellet, however, will never fly as straight as even a deformed spherical one.

The illustration of Plate VB shows a number of pellets which were actually taken from a charge of shot in a cartridge. A good many years ago a correspondent of the *Field* found that some cartridges he had purchased gave very bad patterns and examined some out of curiosity, when he discovered that the majority of the pellets were pear-shaped instead of spherical. I was unable to trace where the shot was made, and trust that it was part of a bad batch which was made during the 1914–18 war. There can be no excuse for any manufacturer sending out shot of this shape, and I have only included the photograph as a warning of what has happened in the past and may happen in the future. In January, 1948, I examined some cartridges in which the shot was every bit as bad as that shown in this photograph, many of the pellets being " doubled," that is two pellets fused together. Many of the others were not nearly spherical. It is hardly necessary to add that shot such as this would be practically useless in the shooting-field.

SIZE OF SHOT. Regularity in the size of the pellets is of the utmost importance, and manufacturers should spare no efforts to grade the sizes of the shot so as to obtain uniformity. The weight of a pellet is directly proportional to its size and a heavy pellet travels faster over any given range than a light one, even though both started with the same velocity. For this reason any shot charge which is composed of pellets of different sizes would not give nearly such satisfactory results as one in which the pellets were all absolutely uniform.

The importance of really accurate grading for size cannot be exaggerated and uniformity of size and truly spherical shape will do far more towards the attainment of regular results than any method of plating or variations in the composition of the alloy. The shot charges which I examined in January, 1948, were marked respectively Nos. 6 and 7, but actually the count was in both cases over 600 to the ounce, while the actual pellets varied in size from a large No. 6 to a small No. 10. Such variations are bound to render the cartridges almost useless in the field.

As has been explained the sizes are obtained by a process of sifting the pellets on screens, or trays, the bottoms of which are perforated with holes of different sizes. The first tray only retains the largest pellets, the next tray those which are too big to fall through the slightly smaller holes, and so on. The pellets which are left behind in any particular tray are not all of the same size, although they have all passed through from the previous tray and are too big to pass on to the next. Some of the pellets will be of such a size that they were only just able to pass through from the previous tray, while others will be of such a size that they passed into the tray easily enough and only just failed to pass out. The remainder of the pellets will be of every size between these two limits, and although the holes in the tray are most carefully made so as to retain the pellets which give on an average a certain fixed number to the ounce, very few of these pellets will weigh just that exact fraction of an ounce which they might be supposed to weigh in theory. The theoretical weights of the pellets of Nos. $5\frac{1}{2}$, 6 and $6\frac{1}{2}$ shot in numbers of pellets to the ounce are :

No. 5½ .   .   . 240 to the ounce.
,, 6 .   .   . 270 ,,   ,,   ,,
,, 6½ .   .   . 300 ,,   ,,   ,,

It will be seen, therefore, that at the very best No. 6 shot will be made up of pellets of sizes which lie between 255 and 285 to the ounce, the figure 270 being the mean.

Further, it is generally known that in actual practice shot is not always so carefully sifted since that sold as No. 6 frequently contains pellets larger than No. 5½ and smaller than No. 6½. Variations such as these can have very marked effects on both pattern and velocity. It is perfectly true that deformation of a proportion of the pellets is inevitable, but that is no reason why we should not eliminate as many sources of error as we can ; and I am convinced that the question of the grading of shot for size is the one to which serious attention should always be paid if best possible results are desired ; and I feel that it is one of which some manufacturers as a whole do not seem to realise the importance.

All gunmakers who load their own cartridges should check the size of every batch of shot they purchase by counting the numbers of pellets in a few weighed ounces ; and interested sportsmen should do the same, taking the shot charges out of one or two cartridges selected at random.

The counting of pellets is not nearly such a laborious process as it might seem if a proper shot tray is used.

Such a tray is nothing more than a small hand shovel with a flat and solid bottom. In this bottom can be fitted a perforated false bottom in which there are a stated number of holes. When this false bottom is in position the shovel can be scooped into a bag of shot and all loose pellets shaken off. It will be found that a single pellet is retained in each hole in the false bottom, and if any hole is vacant it can be seen at a glance.

Different false bottoms can be fitted which have various numbers of holes, and the tray can thus be set to any given count desired.

In order to test any batch of shot all that need be done is to set the tray to give a count of the theoretical number of pellets to the ounce. If, for example, the shot is supposed to be No. 6, the tray is set to count 270, as this is the number of pellets of No. 6 which should go to the ounce. The tray is then dug into the bag of shot and the 270 pellets thus obtained emptied through a funnel into the pan of a balance. These pellets should weigh an ounce.

Another way is first to weigh out an exact ounce with the balance and then to pour the pellets which make up the ounce into the tray and shake it about until they are all in the holes, or until every hole is filled. If some holes are vacant the number gives the number of pellets short of the correct standard ; and if there are some pellets over after every hole is filled the excess of the standard number to the ounce is obtained.

One of these shot trays should form part of the equipment of every gunroom, and should be possessed by every shooter who takes a serious interest in his guns and cartridges. For an extensive checking of shot sizes by shooters is probably the only means of forcing manufacturers to pay more attention to this most important question.

If gunmakers would always check each lot of shot they get in and return any sizes which did not count correctly the manufacturers would take greater care in the sizing and grading of their shot.

I now give three Tables which show the standard sizes for British shot, the diameters of the pellets being the theoretical mean in each case ; the number of pellets of the different sizes which go to make up various weights commonly used as loads for shot charges ; and the relative sizes of shot as made in different countries. (See pages 117, 118 and 119.)

LOADING

Whenever cartridges are loaded on anything approaching a big scale, whether in a factory or a gunmaker's loading-room, a loading machine of some sort is used. But the principle of all loading machines is the same as that which governs hand loading. The powder is measured out in a cup, or " hopper," which is of such a size that it holds the correct charge required when exactly full.

TABLE I

SIZES OF SHOT

Size of Shot.	Number of Pellets to One Ounce.	Diameter of one Pellet in Inches.
LG	6	0·3598
MG	7	·3465
SG	8	·3314
Special SG	11	·2981
SSG	15	·2687
SSSG	20	·2443
SSSSG	25	·2267
SSSSSG or AAAA . . .	30	·2133
AAA	35	·2026
AA	40	·1937
A	50	·1799
BBB	60	·1693
BB	70	·1608
B	80	·1537
1	100	·1428
2	120	·1344
3	140	·1276
4	170	·1196
4½	200	·1133
5	220	·1098
5½	240	·1067
6	270	·1023
6½	300	·0990
7	340	·0950
8	450	·0865
9	580	·0795
10	850	·0700

Fifty years ago a set of hand-loading appliances was a common addition to the outfit included with a gun in its case. These tools usually consisted of a powder measure which was normally set to take 3 drachms of black powder by volume, but which could be adjusted to take 2¾ or 3¼

TABLE II

The Numbers of Pellets in Different Charges of Shot

OUNCES.

Size of Shot.	½	9/16	5/8	11/16	3/4	13/16	7/8	15/16	ONE	1 1/16	1 1/8	1 3/16	1 1/4	1 5/16	1 3/8	1 7/16	1 1/2
LG	3	3	4	4	4	5	5	6	6	6	7	7	7	8	8	9	9
MG	3	3	4	4	5	5	6	6	7	7	8	8	9	9	10	10	11
SG	4	4	5	5	6	6	7	7	8	9	9	10	10	11	11	12	12
Special SG	5	6	7	8	8	9	10	10	11	12	12	13	14	14	15	15	16
SSG	7	8	9	10	11	12	13	14	15	16	17	18	19	20	21	22	23
SSSG	10	11	12	14	15	16	18	19	20	21	22	24	25	26	28	29	30
SSSSG	13	14	16	17	19	20	22	23	25	27	28	30	31	33	34	36	38
SSSSSG or AAAA	15	17	19	21	22	24	26	28	30	32	34	36	38	39	41	43	45
AAA	18	20	22	24	26	28	31	33	35	37	39	42	44	46	48	50	53
AA	20	22	25	27	30	32	35	37	40	43	45	48	50	53	55	58	60
A	25	28	31	34	38	41	44	47	50	53	56	60	63	66	69	72	75
BBB	30	34	38	41	45	49	53	56	60	64	67	71	75	79	83	86	90
BB	35	39	44	48	53	57	61	65	70	74	79	83	88	92	96	100	105
B	40	45	50	55	60	65	70	75	80	85	90	95	100	105	110	115	120
1	50	56	63	69	75	81	88	94	100	106	113	119	125	131	138	144	150
2	60	67	75	83	90	98	105	113	120	127	135	143	150	157	165	173	180
3	70	79	88	96	105	114	123	131	140	149	158	166	175	184	193	201	210
4	85	96	106	117	128	138	149	159	170	181	191	202	213	223	234	244	255
4½	100	113	125	138	150	163	175	188	200	212	225	237	250	262	275	287	300
5	110	124	138	151	165	179	193	206	220	234	248	261	275	289	303	316	330
5½	120	135	150	165	180	195	210	225	240	255	270	285	300	315	330	345	360
6	135	152	169	186	202	219	236	253	270	287	304	321	338	354	371	388	405
6½	150	169	187	206	225	244	263	281	300	319	338	356	375	394	413	431	450
7	170	191	212	234	255	276	298	319	340	361	383	404	425	446	468	489	510
8	225	253	281	309	338	366	394	422	450	478	506	534	563	591	618	647	675
9	290	326	363	399	435	471	508	544	580	616	653	689	725	762	798	834	870
10	425	478	532	584	637	691	744	797	850	903	957	1,009	1,062	1,114	1,168	1,221	1,275

drachms in case of a 12-bore ; a similar measure for shot which could be adjusted to take 1, $1\frac{1}{16}$, $1\frac{1}{8}$ and sometimes $1\frac{1}{4}$ ounces ; and a wooden rammer for inserting the wads. Small re-capping and turnover machines were always extra.

TABLE III

RELATIVE SIZES OF SHOT IN DIFFERENT COUNTRIES

Size.	Pellets to One Ounce.					
	British.	American.	French.	Italian.	German.	Belgian.
1	100	72	74	79	75	104
2	120	87	85	96	91	122
3	140	107	99	120	112	140
4	170	134	113	175	140	172
5	220	170	170	220	178	218
6	270	220	221	270	231	270
7	340	295	260	340	308	340
8	450	404	402	450	422	450
9	580	577	680	580	601	580
10	850	858	963	850	897	850

The outfit thus briefly described is really all that is necessary for loading, and a machine carries out all the work more or less automatically apart from the re-capping which is not necessary when loading new cases.

The powder is first measured out by the hopper and emptied into the case. The thin card Over-Powder wad is then inserted and pressed down. This is followed by the thick felt wad which should be pressed well home, and then comes the thin card Over-Felt wad. The shot is measured out by a hopper in a similar manner to the powder, and on top of this is placed the Over-Shot wad.

The hoppers expand and contract in hot and cold weather and so vary slightly in size. Such variations may not be much, but they are frequently quite enough to cause errors of half a grain in a charge of powder. On this account the weights of powder thrown by the hoppers should be checked constantly, once a day at the very least, by all cartridge loaders.

The risk of variation in the weight of shot charge is not so great as it can seldom be more than a few pellets one way or the other, and the minimum variation possible is one pellet.

TURNOVER

The final step is the making of the turnover, and this is the most important of all in loading.

It will be clear that the amount of case left available for turning over is that which extends beyond the Over-Shot wad.   Provided standard charges and wads of the right size are used there should be about one quarter of an inch left for the turnover, but there may be more or less according to how tightly the various wads have been rammed home.

The two most compressible contents of a cartridge are the powder and felt wad, and so the amount of case left for the turnover is really dependent on the amount by which the powder and felt wad are compressed.   In hand loading there is considerable difficulty in pressing down the felt wad to exactly the same distance every time, and for this reason hand-loaded cartridges can seldom be as regular as machine-loaded, for the machine makes a stroke of compression of exactly the same length every time.

So it will be seen that the first important point towards getting a regular turnover is to leave exactly the same amount of case protruding above the top of the Over-Shot wad in every cartridge.

The turnover is actually made by a chuck of special shape being revolved against the top of the cartridge. This turns the end over and in.   Provided the amount of case available for the turnover is constant, regularity depends on how tightly the actual turnover has been made, and this depends on the degree of pressure used for pushing the case against the revolving chuck.

The turnover should be sufficiently tight to prevent any possibility of movement of the Over-Shot wad when the cartridges are shaken about during transit, or when carried out shooting. In fact, one of the functions of the turnover is to keep the cartridge properly loaded, and it cannot do this unless the part of the case which is turned over is pressed tightly down on to the Over-Shot wad.

But the turnover plays another altogether different and absolutely essential part in the making of an efficient cartridge. It holds the shot charge and wads against the initial pressure developed by the expanding gases on the first ignition of the powder charge, and so offers resistance to the expansion of the gases. This is a most important rôle, for unless there is sufficient resistance to expansion in the first instance the shot charge will move too easily and the full pressure of the powder gases will never be properly developed. If regular ballistics are to be obtained it is essential that this resistance should be the same in every cartridge, and it is for this reason that regularity of turnover is a matter of such extreme importance. The effects of variations in turnover will be considered more fully in the following chapters, so I will now only say how turnover is measured.

The base of the cartridge of which the turnover is to be tested is cut off, and the cartridge emptied of its contents. A metal wad of exactly the same size as the card wads is then dropped down from behind against the turnover, and a hook is screwed into this wad. The tube of the cartridge is then clamped in a fixed stop and the hook is fastened to a spring balance. Tension is gradually applied until the turnover pulls out when the indicator of the spring balance shows the force which was necessary to bring about this result.

It is important that the turnover should not be " supported " in any way. That is, the end of the case should protrude from the stop quite free of any support such as would be provided by the walls of the chamber.

Fig. 12 shows the principle adopted in testing turnovers by the method just outlined.

The correct pull for a normal unsupported turnover is 45 lb. If the turnover stands a pull much greater than this amount the resistance offered to the expansion of the gases is too great for the best results ; and if it pulls out at 30 lb. the resistance is too little.

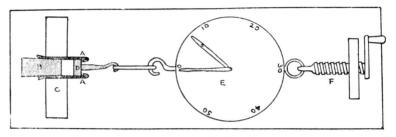

FIG. 12.—Diagram of apparatus for testing the strength of turnover.

A A, the top half of the case to be tested for the turnover (shown in section) This is held by means of the conical wedge, B, which is inserted into the rear end of the tube of the case which is placed in a hole in the stop, C. The case is thus held firmly against the metal " wad," D, which is linked to a spring balance, E, on which a pull can be applied by means of the screw, F. When a pull is applied by means of the screw, F, the turnover is eventually straightened out, and the pointer on the dial of the spring balance shows the strength of the pull in pounds necessary to produce this result.

As can be understood, there is yet one more factor which determines the strength of a turnover and that is the quality of the paper used for the tube of the cartridge-case. A very soft kind of paper may result in it being impossible to obtain a stronger turnover than 15 to 20 lb. if the normal quarter of an inch of case is left beyond the Over-Shot wad. In such circumstances the loader should use slightly thinner wads and leave more for turning over, the correct amount being ascertained by actual experiments with different lengths of case for turnover, and tests with the turnover testing machine.

Tests for turnover should constantly be carried out by all cartridge loaders as a check on the cartridges they are loading, but I fear that this is seldom done except in the factory. As a rule, gunmakers are too prone to trust to eye for getting a good turnover, and there can be no doubt that an experienced loader can judge his turnover with great nicety. Provided he always uses the same class of case he will be all right ; but if he were suddenly given cases made of some very soft paper, as some water-proof papers used for cartridge-cases are, he would probably give too weak a turnover unless he checked his results on a machine.

Turnover can really be regarded as the most important of all the factors in loading, and on this account it is impossible for any loader to give it too much attention. A turnover testing machine can be made so simply, and at such a low cost, that really there is no excuse for any gunmaker who loads his own cartridges not having one.

A somewhat rough, but by no means bad, test for the turnover and tightness of loading may be carried out as follows.

Hold the cartridge to be tested cap end downwards between the thumb and second finger of the right hand and press hard on the Over-Shot wad with the end of the first finger. Now tap the brass head of the cartridge smartly on a table, taking care not to strike with the base quite flat on the table so as to avoid any risk of exploding the cap. Plate VIIB shows how the cartridge should be held.

If the turnover is weak and the cartridge loosely loaded the whole charge can easily be settled farther down into the case when a space will be left between the top wad and the turnover. With a well loaded cartridge it is almost impossible to depress the top wad from the turnover in this way, but in a badly loaded cartridge the top wad can easily be forced downwards.

It should be appreciated that this test is really one for tightness of loading rather than turnover, and it might be possible to have loose loading combined with a strong turnover. As a general rule, however, loose loading means a weak turnover.

FULLY CRIMPED TURNOVER. Since the earliest days of breech loaders almost everyone connected with shotguns and shooting had become so accustomed to cartridges sealed with an Over-Shot card wad that any other method of closure would have seemed almost fantastic. Looking back, this apparent acceptance of finality is surprising in view of the fact that for very many years all blank rifle and revolver cartridges were sealed with a complete crimp. It is true that these were cartridges in which the cases were all solid drawn brass, but at the same time wildfowlers had for years used Perfect cases although these were sealed with the usual Over-Shot card wad which was retained in position by a partial crimp. The full crimp, like that used in blank rifle and revolver cartridges, was probably never tried because so many of these Perfect cases were loaded and reloaded by amateurs. Anyhow the ordinary Over-Shot card wad and turnover remained unchallenged as a method of closing shotgun cartridges for at least sixty years, and then a paper-tubed shotgun cartridge did appear on the Continent which was sealed with a complete crimp and without any Over-Shot wad. But this cartridge attracted little attention at the time, and the next event was the appearance in 1935 of the Belgian 2-inch all-metal 12-bore shotgun cartridge which was sealed with a full crimp similarly to a blank rifle or revolver cartridge, the end being waxed to render it air tight. (See Plate IX.)

This cartridge quickly aroused interest, but at first chiefly because it was completely waterproof and less bulk than the ordinary paper-tubed $2\frac{1}{2}$-inch 12-bore cartridge, as explained on page 93. In passing, however, I would point out that although reduction in bulk can be an undoubted advantage it is not accompanied by a reduction in weight, and it is the weight which tells when carrying a cartridge bag throughout a long day.

It was not long, however, before many gunmakers and sportsmen began to find that these F.N. cartridges gave appreciably denser patterns than ordinary cartridges, and, further, that cartwheel and scattered patterns were never recorded on the pattern plate. The whole problem of patterns is outside the scope of this present Volume

PLATE IX

(A) ALL-METAL CARTRIDGES WITH FULLY CRIMPED CLOSURES

The two larger diametered cartridges on the left are original F.N. 2-inch zinc cartridges. The others are British solid-drawn brass .410 cartridges. On the extreme right there is a fired case of one of these cartridges which shows the total length of the case

(B) BRITISH PAPER-TUBED FULLY CRIMPED CARTRIDGES

On the left there is an empty unfired case. Next is a loaded case with the top partially closed by the first stage of the crimp. The three cartridges on the right are finished and the shortened length of the case caused by the crimp closure as well as the appearance of the closure and the method of marking the shot size are clearly visible

and is considered at length and in detail in Volume
III, but it must be mentioned now because it was the
improvement in patterns which caused the whole question
of the full crimp closure to be investigated thoroughly
both in Europe and America, and it was a wonderful
series of spark photographs obtained in America which
proved conclusively that the Over-Shot wad was sometimes enveloped by the shot charge almost immediately
after its exit from the muzzle, and that when this occurred
a bad pattern was invariably recorded. It is true that
the light Over-Shot card wad was left behind by and fell
away from the shot charge very quickly, but the mere
fact that it had been caught up and surrounded by the
shot charge was sufficient to break up the cohesion of the
pellets, and it was this loss of cohesion which resulted in
a widely dispersed pattern.

The result of this discovery was that the whole
problem of sealing shotgun cartridges was considered and
investigated anew for paper-tubed cases as well as for
all-metal. It has already been pointed out that all-metal
cases need the use of special slow-burning powders, and
so it is not surprising that efforts were primarily directed
to the adaptation of the full crimp closure to the paper-
tubed case in order to eliminate the need for an Over-Shot
card wad. The results of these efforts were the introduction towards the end of 1938 in Great Britain and America
of a fully crimped paper-tubed cartridge. The stages in
the making of the actual crimp in the British cartridge
are shown in Plate IX from which it will be seen that a
longer length of tube must be left for the closure than is
needed for an ordinary turnover when an Over-Shot wad
is used.

In the first trial issue of the British cartridges the
standard nominal $2\frac{1}{2}$-inch cases—actually $2\frac{9}{16}$ inch—
were used and the resulting cartridges proved to be
somewhat on the short side. The actual results, as far
as ballistics, patterns and general " shooting " were concerned, were wonderfully good in every way, but it was
thought that there might be a risk of these nominal $2\frac{1}{2}$-

inch cartridges being used in short chambered 2-inch 12-bore guns, and so a 2¾-inch case was adopted. This gave a finished cartridge of the normal " 2½-inch " length, which was rendered waterproof by the use of a specially waxed paper as mentioned on page 90 and which gave results which were fully up to the most optimistic expectations.

And a great advantage of this new cartridge was that it could be loaded with ordinary powders by gunmakers exactly like all other paper-tubed shotgun cartridges, while the crimp closure could easily be made with a suitable machine. Further there was probably less risk of variations in the strength of this closure since it would be obvious if too much or too little of the case had been left for the crimp as the top of the cartridge would not be neatly sealed. If too much case had been left there would be an overlap, and if too little there would be a hiatus in the middle. This will be readily appreciated by examining the sealed ends of the loaded cartridges shown in Plate IX, which are both correctly crimped with an exact fit in the centre.

A crimp turnover needs a stronger force to open it than a rolled turnover and the normal pull is 60 lb.

In 1939 another most interesting cartridge was introduced. The case was paper-tubed with a full zinc lining which protruded beyond the end of the paper tube. This extra length of zinc lining was used for a fully crimped sealing, the outer paper tube ending just at the shoulder of the crimped zinc lining. These cartridges were made by Imperial Chemical Industries, Ltd., specially for Messrs. Holland and Holland, and differed from the Belgian and German all-metal cartridges in that the internal diameter of the case was the same as that of ordinary paper-tubed cartridges, since the walls of the cases were thicker than the thin metal walls of the F.N. and Rottweil cartridges. These cartridges were naturally fully waterproof and gave perfect results, but the outbreak of war in September, 1939, put an end to all such experimental work. It can, however, be stated that the cost of these cartridges, which combined a best quality deep-shell paper case with a full length metal lining, could never be anything but very high and can no longer be considered a practical or economic proposition.

" HOME LOADING " CARTRIDGES

In these days of machinery the number of shooters who load their own cartridges at home must be very small, while modern dense powders are not suitable for amateur loading. Yet some may derive pleasure and interest from experimenting. It is probable that all such understand the work so well that no further information is necessary, yet there may be some less experienced who should be warned to go very carefully. Accordingly a brief description of the procedure may not be superfluous. It must, however, be realised that this procedure is not adapted for fully crimped cartridges since the crimping machine required would probably be quite beyond the reach of the average amateur.

For loading new cases the following implements are required.

POWDER MEASURE. This is merely a small cup with a long handle attached for convenience. The cup is adjustable in capacity so as to enable the loader to measure out different charges of powder. As a rule these cups are always marked in drachms, which were the units used with black powder.

The measures are made in different sizes according to the bore of the gun. It should, however, never be forgotten that a loader takes great risks unless he checks the graduations on his measure by weighing the charges thrown on a balance. This check should be made with every sample, or batch, of powder used before beginning any loading.

CHEMICAL BALANCE. For reasons which have just been given I think that a chemical balance should be included in the list of essential implements for home loading. This balance need not be a very delicate instrument, but should be capable of weighing to $\frac{1}{10}$ of a grain.

FUNNEL. Any ordinary funnel will serve the purpose, and it does not matter whether it is made of glass, enamelled iron, or other material. This funnel is a great convenience and safeguard when loading either the powder or shot, as these can be tilted from the measure into the mouth of the funnel, the nozzle of which is inserted into the case. Any risk of spilling either the powder or shot—a most annoying occurrence—is thus prevented.

SHOT MEASURE. This usual type of shot measure is similar in appearance to the powder measure and is adjustable in the same way. It should be checked by counting the number of pellets thrown.

But an altogether better type of measure, which gives greater accuracy and regularity, is a shot-counting tray, such as has been described in the section on Shot in this chapter. The tray can be set to take the required number of pellets and filled to this capacity with ease. But if a tray is used a funnel becomes essential for ensuring that all the shot pellets enter the cartridge-case.

WOODEN RAMMER. This is a plain cylinder of wood with a handle at one end. The cylindrical part should fit the inside of the cartridge-case as closely as possible. The rammer is used for pressing down the wads, and it is a good plan to mark rings round the circumference of the rammer to indicate when the wads are home, as this will help regularity in ballistics.

One ring should be exactly one-quarter of an inch from the end, as this greatly helps the making of a regular turnover. If the Over-Shot wad is always pushed down into the case until this mark coincides exactly with the top of the case there will always be just one-quarter of an inch left above the top wad with which to make the turnover.

Special rammers are made with adjustable stops fitted so as to ensure the rammer being inserted exactly the same distance every time. Theoretically this is a great advantage as the stop can be set to any position and with its help the Over-Powder card wad can be shoved down exactly the same distance every time, which means that the degree of compression to which the powder is submitted is constant in every cartridge.

In actual practice, however, it has been found that the advantage of this stop is doubtful. With practice the powder can be compressed with extraordinary regularity without any such help, and if a mark for the depth of case to be left for turnover is used, the loading should be as constant as is possible with hand-loaded cartridges.

TURNOVER MACHINE. There are many varieties of machines for making the turnover, but the principle is the same in all, whether the machine is a small one which clamps on to a table, or a large one worked by a treadle like a lathe.

This principle, as has already been explained, is to press the end of the cartridge-case against a revolving chuck which turns the end in and over. In the smaller machines the chuck is revolved by hand, but in the larger by a foot treadle.

CRIMPING MACHINE. This takes the place of the turnover machine if Perfect or Thin Brass cartridges are to be loaded instead of cartridges with paper tubes : but, as has already been explained, it is suitable only for a partial crimp and an Over-Shot wad and not for a full crimp. There are various types of crimping machines, or tools, but the method of operation is similar in all and is quite simple. A shorter length of case is left above the Over-Shot wad than is left when making a turnover and this length should be as nearly as possible exactly ⅛-inch. This length left for the crimp has a considerable influence on the ballistics, especially on pressure.

LOADING TRAY. This is not an essential, but it is a great convenience if home loading is likely to become a habit. It is merely a box tray fitted with a rack to take 100 cartridges. The empty cases are placed mouth upwards in this tray which prevents any from being accidentally knocked over.

N.B.—In order to ensure regularity it is always advisable to load 100 cartridges at a time unless only a few are required for experimental purposes.

PROCEDURE OF LOADING

But whatever number of cartridges is to be loaded, all the powder charges should be loaded first, *and a careful inspection should then be made to see that the powder really has been put into every case.*

The Over-Powder card wad can then be inserted and pressed down evenly with the wooden rammer. *Two card wads should never be used as the lower one tends sometimes to slip sideways into the powder charge, and on firing may be left in the bore.* Then comes the felt wad, which must also be pushed home, and followed by the over-felt card wad or wads and then the shot. As has already been explained a funnel will be found to be a great convenience when inserting both the powder and shot charges.

The penultimate step is the insertion of the top wads, and these should be pressed down until exactly one-quarter of an inch of case is left clear above them—no less and no more. *But on no account should one try to push the felt wad home by pressing down the shot.*

The final step is turnover, and in making this, whatever type of machine is used, the great secret is to maintain a firm but even pressure during the whole of the time the chuck is being revolved against the end of the case.

RELOADING FIRED CASES

The reloading of fired paper cases is not to be recommended because the paper tube becomes " dead " as the result of the pressure generated by the combustion of the powder, and so it is almost impossible to make a satisfactory turnover. Further, the saving in cost is so comparatively slight as to be hardly worth the trouble involved and the risk of unsatisfactory results in the end.

However, some shooters, especially those living in out of the way places abroad, may wish to reload their fired paper cases ; and any wildfowlers who may hold a stock of all-brass cases for their specially chambered guns will naturally wish to reload them.

The only implement necessary for reloading fired cases in addition to those which have already been described as being required for the loading of new cases, is a re-capping machine, and for Perfect or Thin Brass cases a re-sizer.

As in the case of turnover or crimping machines there are various types of re-capping machines, but such types are all very similar, and consist of two parts. The first part is used for forcing out the old cap, and the second for inserting the new one.

All fired cases which are to be used for reloading must first be re-sized so as to ensure ease of loading as well as the reduction of the internal diameter to the original dimension before it was fired as far as is possible since this will help to ensure satisfactory obturation by the wadding in the actual cartridge-case.

For Perfect or Thin Brass cases special tools or presses are made in which the fired case is pushed through a steel reduction ring or die, chamfered on one side so as to ensure easy entrance of the cartridge-case. In those tools in which the fired case is inserted into the die by hand a chamfer is not necessary.

No special tool is needed for the rough re-sizing of paper-tube cases.

The wooden rammer, which should exactly fit the inside of the case, should be inserted into a case and then this should be rolled backwards and forwards between two boards with the brass rim outside the boards. This is an important step, as it renders the paper tube round and suitable for the insertion of the wads as well as more compact for turning over again.

After each case to be reloaded has been treated in

this manner the whole lot can be loaded in the way which has already been described. It is, however, always a good plan to test every reloaded cartridge in a gauge, so as to ensure that it is not too large in diameter for easy loading in a gun.

All-metal cases which have been sealed with a full crimp are not suitable for reloading because, quite apart from the difficulty of making a full crimp after the case has already been opened by firing, it is essential that special powders should be used. These powders are not sold loose owing to the uncertainty of the results when they are loaded by inexperienced loaders who have not complete appliances for testing.

CHAPTER VI

PRESSURE

WHEN an ordinary shotgun is fired at a bird and that bird is killed there are certain fundamental forces which must have been present, and without which human skill alone would have been useless. In the first place the shot must have been travelling with sufficient velocity to penetrate some vital organ of the bird ; then the pellets of the shot charge must have been properly and evenly spread out over a certain area so as to ensure the bird being struck by a sufficient number of pellets to cause a kill, and yet not by too many or the flesh would have been spoiled for food ; the gun itself " kicks " the person who fired it, and unpleasant though this may be this kick is one of the fundamental forces, or elements, which must accompany the discharge of a gun. And finally, there is the actual force developed by the combustion of the powder which really began everything ; that is, it propelled the shot charge from the muzzle of the barrel with velocity sufficient to reach the bird and kill it. So we see that there are four main elements connected with the discharge of every gun : velocity, which ensures penetration ; pattern, which ensures the bird being hit by the suitable number of pellets ; recoil, which is unpleasant but inevitable ; and pressure, which is the force generated by the combustion of the powder and which sets the shot charge in flight.

These four elements can be termed the Ballistic Elements of a shotgun. They are interdependent, and all are essential to success, but Pressure is really the most important although it is the one about which sportsmen as a rule think least. There are few shooters who do not take some sort of interest in the patterns thrown by their guns, or the penetration which their cartridges give at sporting ranges. Recoil, or " kick," is ever present ; and although some are more sensitive to it than others, all realise that some sort of recoil is unavoidable. Pressure, however, receives little attention : few sportsmen ever think about it, and if they do it is to connect it in some vague way with the questions of guns bursting or doing something equally unpleasant. But without pressure no shot could succeed : it is the most basic element of the four ; the one which can be most readily controlled ; and the control of which results largely in the control of the other three.

In Chapter I we saw that the pressure generated in any rifle or shotgun was due to the combustion of the powder which liberated gases with great rapidity and at a very high temperature. These hot gases begin to expand immediately they are generated, and this sudden and rapid expansion of the powder gases results in great force, or pressure. Something has to give way, for the pressure developed by any propellant fired and confined in its own volume is greater than any firearm can withstand : this something is the shot charge or bullet, as everything else is held too firmly in position. But the shot charge is held fairly tightly in the cartridge by the turnover, as we saw in the last chapter, and so it does not give way too easily, with the result that a considerable force is generated in the cartridge, or chamber of the gun, before anything begins to move ; and once the shot charge does begin to move the pressure which has been developed pushes it along the bore of the gun and out of the muzzle with great force, thus imparting to it what is known as Muzzle Velocity, or the velocity with which the shot charge, or any projectile, leaves the muzzle of the barrel.

But as was explained in Chapter I the pressure behind the shot charge during its passage up the bore is not constant, but becomes less and less the further the shot charge travels from the breech until it has dropped away to something like one-twentieth part of its maximum amount when the shot actually leaves the muzzle. So it will be seen that at first the pressure rises very rapidly, and then gradually decreases as the volume behind the shot charge which is filled with the powder gases is increased by the shot charge travelling farther from the breech.

It will be realised that if for some reason or other sufficient force is not accumulated behind the shot charge to push it sufficiently rapidly along the bore the resulting velocity may be too low to ensure the pellets reaching the target. In other words, the pressure developed must not be too feeble to impart sufficient velocity to the shot charge.

On the other hand, if the pressure developed is too high the movement of the shot charge may not relieve the expanding gases sufficiently, in which case they will seek relief in another direction and may break, or burst, the gun at its weakest point. Such a pressure would naturally be excessive or dangerous.

We find, therefore, that the pressure must lie between two limits, one low and one high, if the best and safest results are to be obtained. Many years of experiment and actual practice have established what these limits should be, and the makers of both guns and cartridges control their work to fit in with these limits. Similarly all manufacturers of powders which are used in shotguns should work within these same limits, and proper tests of cartridges will show whether the pressures set up are correct or not.

The measurement of pressure should be part of the routine work of every competent gunmaker and cartridge loader, as this is the only way he has of ensuring that the cartridges which he sells are loaded so as to give safe and satisfactory results. Pressure can be very easily measured ; more easily than either velocity or recoil, the two other Ballistic Elements which are really governed almost wholly by the cartridge, pattern being controlled as much by the gun as the cartridge. Yet the method employed for measuring pressure is not generally known to sportsmen, while even some who actually measure pressure do not seem to realise certain very important points, the ignoring of which can easily result in wrong records being obtained. Accordingly, a brief account of the method of measuring the pressure generated by shotgun cartridges may not be altogether out of place. First of all a special barrel is required. There is nothing very peculiar about this barrel except that it should be made much thicker and stronger than the barrel of any ordinary game gun because it may be necessary to measure pressures which are known to be excessive and which might burst a thin barrel. The only other special feature about the pressure barrel itself is that both the bore and the chamber should be bored to what is known as " minimum gauge." It was explained in Volume I that in Great Britain the Gunmakers' Association had laid down dimensions which were generally accepted for the minimum sizes of chambers. This means that the chamber of every gun must be bored larger than this minimum limit so as to ensure its ability to receive cartridges of the standard size. Some gunmakers work nearer this minimum gauge than others, but all leave a margin in their sporting weapons, for in actual practice it would be fatal to make the chambers of an ordinary game gun of the minimum size, because a cartridge slightly on the large size, or one which had become a little swollen by wet, could not be inserted except with some difficulty while the case might very easily stick after it had been fired. A certain amount of looseness is essential.

In a pressure barrel, however, a slight jam is immaterial. There is no necessity for very quick loading and a cleaning-rod can always be used for shoving out the fired cases.

A chamber of minimum size holds the cartridge more tightly than a wider one, and this closer fit between case and chamber results in the shot, wadding and turnover all offering greater resistance to movement, which means a higher pressure.

Similarly the bore of the barrel must also be bored to minimum size. In this case the dimensions for the breech end of the bore are laid down by the Rules of Proof, but as will be seen when we come to the question of the Proving of Guns a certain amount of latitude is allowed for guns intended to fire one particular size of cartridge, and it is possible for a gun to be built for ordinary 12-bore cartridges which is appreciably wider in the bore than the legal minimum.

The Rules of Proof do not lay down any dimensions for the forward part of the bore, and here again almost all gunmakers bore their barrels on the wide side for reasons which are explained in Volume III. This again tends to reduce pressure slightly, although it will not have any effect on the pressure developed near the breech. But the fact that guns are generally so bored must be remembered.

When the pressure developed by any batch of cartridges is to be measured it is absolutely essential for reasons of safety to find out the *maximum* pressure possible. Consequently it is necessary to use a barrel which is bored to minimum gauge throughout, as then one can be quite confident that no higher pressure is likely to be generated than the maximum measured if similar cartridges are used in an ordinary gun.

In order to measure the pressure at any given point in this minimum gauge barrel a hole is bored radially through the wall of the barrel, that is exactly at right angles to the longitudinal axis of the bore. In this hole is inserted a metal plug, which has an enlarged and flat head. This plug, or piston, is made of such a size that it is free to move in the hole, yet the fit is so close that when there is plenty of lubricating oil it forms an airtight plug exactly like the piston in the cylinder of any engine. The inner end of this piston is made flush with the surface of the bore.

Over the head of the piston on the outside of the barrel there is fixed a stirrup-like attachment which is made an integral part of the barrel, and through the top of this stirrup there is inserted a large screw with a flat lower end. This screw moves up and down radially to the bore in exactly the same way as the piston is free to move.

The diagram in Fig. 13 shows a longitudinal section through the middle of a pressure barrel with the piston and fixed stirrup.

Since the bore is circular it makes no difference how the hole for the piston is bored so long as it is radial.

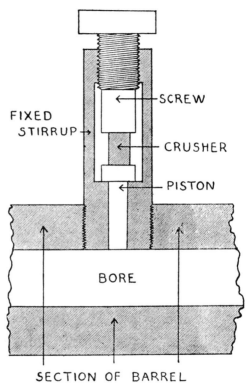

SECTION OF BARREL

FIG. 13.—A sectional diagram of the apparatus used for measuring pressure.

The attachment just described for measuring pressure can be fitted to either side of the barrel, underneath or on top—the pressure will be the same in any case—but as a matter of ordinary convenience in use it is usually placed on top of the barrel as shown in the diagram.

The only other thing required beyond the actual cartridge is a " crusher." This is a cylinder of lead containing a small amount of a hardening agent, half an inch long, and about one third of an inch in diameter. It is placed standing up on the flat head of the piston and the large screw which works in the fixed stirrup is screwed down on to the upper end of the crusher, which is thus held firmly in position as shown in Fig. 13.

When any pressure is generated inside the barrel the sides of the bore hold together, but the piston is free to move and is forced upwards by the expanding gases. As it rises the piston squeezes the lead crusher against the immovable screw, with the result that the soft lead crusher is compressed and changes its shape. The final length of the crusher is now measured with a micrometer, and the amount of reduction in length is proportional to the pressure which was generated. Tables are provided with every box of crushers which give a value for the pressure in tons per square inch for every thousandth of inch reduction in the length of the crusher, so it is a simple matter to read off the pressure from the table directly the crusher has been measured.

The photograph in Plate VIIIc shows crushers in varying degrees of compression. The one on the left has not been used, but all the others have, and in the case of an ordinary 12-bore these crushers from left to right would denote pressures which could be described as feeble, normal, lively, excessive and dangerous.

Some readers may wonder whether this system of measuring is accurate, and whether the figures obtained from the tables do really represent the actual pressure exerted in tons per square inch. This is a most difficult question to answer. The tables from which the results are obtained have been compiled from a combination of numerous actual experiments in compressing lead and series of mathematical calculations.

Recently this problem has been investigated by using a piezoelectric method of measuring pressure. In this method a quartz crystal is compressed by a piston on the same principle as that adopted for lead crushers. The crystal produces an electrostatic charge proportional to the gas pressure acting on the piston and so measurements of this charge can be translated into pressure values.

The calibration of lead crushers by means of the piezoelectric gauge suggests that the lead crusher pressures are somewhat on the low side, 2 tons per square inch being about 2·5 with the piezoelectric gauge ; 3 tons per square inch being about 4 ; and 4 tons per square inch being about 5. But these differences are really immaterial from the practical point of view.

The real point to realise is that the absolute accuracy of the figures used for denoting pressure does not matter in the least provided everyone understands what the results mean. The unit of measurement is purely arbitrary, and it would be just as useful to talk about a pressure of 3 units as one of 3 tons. So long as we all know what a pressure designated as 3 tons means it is immaterial whether the pressure is in reality an absolutely exact 3 tons. The only thing that matters is that everyone who measures pressures should adopt exactly the same system of measurement, and then the results obtained will all correspond irrespective of the unit employed. In order to obtain the same results from exactly similar cartridges, the means employed for measuring must be the same so as to eliminate as far as possible the existence of individual instrumental errors, for if apparently trifling changes are made the results may be very different.

Let us see what these trifles are.

First of all, it is fairly obvious that the actual size of the piston hole can be a source of variation. The larger this hole the greater the volume of gas available for forcing the piston upwards, and consequently it is not difficult to see that a piston of but $\frac{1}{4}$-inch diameter will not be pushed up so far, and will not therefore compress the crusher to the same extent as one with a diameter of $\frac{1}{3}$-inch. As a matter of fact, two alternative diameters have been laid down as standard, and complete tables are issued with every box of crushers for each of these diameters, which are 0·274 and 0·225 of an inch. And it is essential for every pressure taker to have his pistons made exactly to one of these measurements.

It will also be realised that the weight of the piston may affect the pressure readings. For this reason all pistons should be made of standard weight. These standards have been fixed by agreement at 300 and 150 grains respectively for the 1-inch and 6-inch pistons. But there are many individuals who take pressures who neglect this point of the weight of their pistons and consequently the results which they obtain will not bear a true relation to those obtained with properly standardised apparatus.

Another source of relative error is to be found in the crushers themselves. The lead may not be of the correct composition and will consequently vary in hardness, or the initial lengths of the crushers may vary. Any such variations from standard composition and size would produce irregular results, but this danger is remote because all crushers used in Great Britain are made in the same factory under standardised conditions of manufacture.

The commonest sources of error are incorrect weights and sizes of pistons, but if proper attention is paid to these points the results will be perfectly reliable.

There is one more source of error, namely that due to some variation in the distance of the point where the pressure is measured from the breech end of the gun.

It has already been explained that the pressure rises very rapidly and falls away gradually as the distance from the breech is increased. So if we want to ascertain the maximum stress to which a barrel is to be submitted by any lot of cartridges it is essential that we should know how far from the breech the greatest pressure occurs. The position of maximum pressure has been ascertained by calculation and by actual experimental data given by the repeated measurement of pressures at short intervals all along the barrel from breech to muzzle.

A typical curve showing the rise and fall of the pressure developed along the barrel by a 2½-inch 12-bore cartridge loaded with the standard charge of any suitable powder, dense or bulk, and $1\frac{1}{16}$ oz. of shot when fired in a barrel bored to minimum gauge is shown in Plate X.

It will be seen that the maximum pressure occurs at positions along the barrel less than about $1\frac{1}{2}$ inches from the breech and so if a position within this range is chosen as the point for measuring the pressure a maximum reading will be obtained. In actual practice, after due consideration of the internal structure of the cartridge and the design of gauge, the position of the centre of the piston was standardised at one inch from the breech.

The actual taking of the pressure is a simple matter. A hole about $\frac{1}{10}$-inch in diameter is pierced in the cartridge-case at a distance of 1 inch from the base. This is done by placing the cartridge in a special grooved holder with its base against the end. The awl for piercing the case works through a hole in a bridge which is a fixed part of the holder, and so there is no chance of error. The cartridge is then loaded in the chamber of the barrel, care being taken to insert it with the hole uppermost so as to bring it immediately underneath the end of the piston. The only object of the hole is to allow the gas to have a perfectly free and even access to the base of the piston, as otherwise irregular results might be obtained.

The breech is then closed and the cartridge fired, after which the compression of the crusher is measured with a micrometer when the pressure is read off from the table.

The pressure thus obtained is the maximum pressure, as has been seen, and if a series of rounds is fired it is possible to ascertain the highest stress in a barrel likely to be caused by any particular batch of cartridges.

It will, accordingly, be seen that the pressure at 1 inch is the most important of all as it informs us of the safety of any lot of cartridges, and if the mean pressure is found to lie between certain high and low limits we will know that at least one of the four principal ballistic elements is satisfactory. If, however, the 1-inch pressure proves to be very near the lower limit the question of the efficiency of the cartridges arises, instead of their safety. For just as pressures should not be too high, they must not be too low or there may not be sufficient force to propel the shot charge in a satisfactory manner. If the pressure at 1 inch is very low it will probably mean that there will not be an adequate sustained effort farther up the barrel, and it has already been seen the pressure should not fall away too rapidly after reaching its maximum point quite close to the breech.

The only way to find out whether pressure developed by a cartridge is sufficiently sustained is to measure the pressure farther along the barrel. A combination of experience, experiment and calculation has shown that the most suitable distance is 6 inches from the breech, as if the pressure is sufficiently maintained at this point the cartridge should be likely to prove satisfactory. So all pressure barrels are also fitted with a second piston at a point 6 inches from the breech, and as a rule when cartridges are tested readings are taken with this piston as well as with the 1-inch one. The 1-inch piston tells us whether the pressures are too high, and the 6-inch piston whether they are properly maintained ; while the two readings together give us all the information necessary as to the behaviour of any lot of cartridges as far as the pressure element is concerned.

It may now be as well to give some actual figures for the high and low limits which have been mentioned. But before doing so I would ask the reader to realise that for reasons which will be explained shortly the actual values of pressures vary in different bores, and so at first we will only consider the ordinary 12-bore $2\frac{1}{2}$-inch cartridge.

The most suitable 1-inch pressure for this cartridge is generally regarded as being from $2\frac{1}{2}$ to 3 tons. A pressure of $3\frac{1}{2}$ tons should be regarded as excessive, and one of 4 tons as dangerous. Some cartridge loaders regard a pressure of from 2 to $2\frac{1}{2}$ tons as being too low, their reason being that such values are always obtained in a pressure barrel which, as has been explained, is bored to minimum gauge and so gives higher readings than would be obtained in an ordinary game gun. They hold the view that many guns in general use are old and very worn, with the result that the ballistics of cartridges are lowered considerably when fired in them. If the pressure is over 2½ tons there is sufficient in hand to allow for the reduction resulting from the loose gun without producing feeble ballistics.

This is a perfectly sound argument, and if I were a cartridge manufacturer I would undoubtedly load my cartridges with an ample margin in the way of pressure to allow for their use in old and worn guns. For it must be remembered that nothing gives any particular brand of cartridges a bad name more effectively than a reputation for "weakness." The reason is a psychological one, as sportsmen always like to feel that their cartridges are powerful and full of "ginger." The cartridge manufacturer is a business man and cannot afford to risk losing custom by selling "soft" cartridges, and so he meets the average sportsman's demand and loads for lively ballistics.

I must admit, however, that personally I am strongly in favour of a slightly lower pressure cartridge. It will be seen in the chapters on Patterns that these are more affected adversely by high pressures than almost anything else, and I am a great believer in good patterns above all else. For this reason I would myself always prefer to use cartridges which gave 1-inch pressures ranging from 2 to 2½ tons than those which developed nearly 3 tons. In good, well-bored guns I am convinced in my own mind that the lower pressures will give better practical results and I cannot see why the test of a good cartridge should be its efficiency when fired in an old, worn, and probably worthless, gun.

I think, however, that 2 tons should be the low limit for the 1-inch pressure, and that even cartridges which developed this mean pressure should not be regarded as satisfactory unless the 6-inch pressure was well-maintained, that is over 1·5 tons.

It must never be forgotten that it is the pressure which generates the velocity of the shot charge, and consequently we cannot afford to risk lowering pressure too much. But velocity does not rise in direct proportion to pressure, and in actual practice a pressure of 2·8 tons may give just as high a velocity as one of 3·4 tons. For the 1-inch pressure can only start the shot charge on its passage down the bore : the muzzle velocity will depend on how the pressure has been sustained at 6 inches. So when cartridges are tested for efficiency these points must be taken into consideration. Nevertheless, if any batch give pressures which are just below the border line of the low limit, say 2 tons, they should be regarded with suspicion even though the 6-inch pressure seems to be maintained and the velocity is satisfactory. The reason is that such cartridges can have nothing in reserve. Even an ordinary good gun will reduce the ballistics slightly below those given in a pressure barrel, but this reduction is negligible so long as the 1-inch pressure is above 2 tons and the 6-inch pressure and the velocity are satisfactory. But if the pressure reading obtained in a pressure barrel is below 2 tons there is insufficient reserve of power, and the ballistics are liable to drop right away when the cartridges are used in a game gun.

FACTORS AFFECTING PRESSURE

There are various factors which affect the pressure developed in a shotgun cartridge, some of which are obvious, and some of which may not be, but all of which should be realised.

SHOT CHARGE. The first of these is the weight of the shot charge, and this is one of the obvious ones. A heavy shot charge is more difficult to move and offers more resistance than a light one ; consequently it results in the combustion of the powder being more advanced before it yields to the expanding gases, and this means a higher pressure. Similarly a light shot charge causes a reduction in pressure.

SIZE OF SHOT. Owing to the larger number of pellets, very small shot sets up more friction on the sides of the bore and offers more resistance to movement. This results in a higher pressure.

In the same way a few pellets of a very large shot are comparatively easy to move, and so the pressure is reduced.

In actual practice there is little difference between the 1-inch pressure when cartridges are loaded with the ordinary sizes, such as from No. 4 to No. 7. But No. 9, for example, would result in quite a noticeably higher pressure being developed than by a very large size such as BB.

POWDER CHARGE. Other things being equal the bigger the powder charge the higher the pressure, because more gas is generated on combustion.

DENSITY OF LOADING. This is a very potent factor in the determination of pressure. The actual loading density is obtained by dividing the weight of the powder charge by the weight of water necessary to fill the volume occupied by the powder charge, thus :

$$\text{Loading Density} = \frac{\text{Weight of powder charge}}{\text{Weight of water required to fill the space occupied by the powder charge}}.$$

So it will be seen that if the powder is compressed very tightly in loading the space which it occupies is reduced, and so the Loading Density is made greater. Similarly, if the cartridge is loosely loaded the Loading Density is decreased.

A high loading density results in a high pressure, and a low loading density in reduced pressure.

This brings us to a system of loading which used to be favoured by some Continental manufacturers and which is known as " Constant Volume Loading."

In this system the inside of the powder chamber of the cartridge-case is fitted with a thin lining which reaches up only as far as the front end of the powder chamber. The effect of this inner lining is to provide a

PLATE X

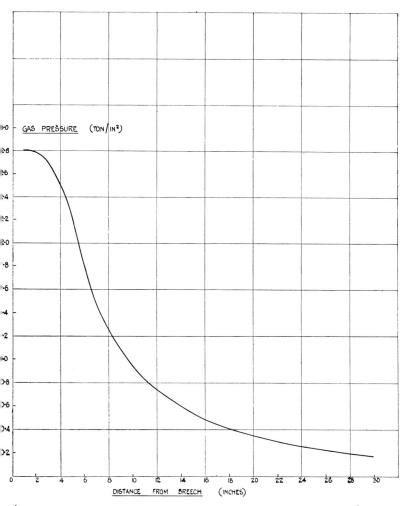

A TYPICAL CURVE SHOWING THE GAS-PRESSURE DEVELOPED BY A $2\frac{1}{2}$-INCH
12-BORE CARTRIDGE LOADED WITH NO. 60 POWDER, AN AIR-CUSHION WAD
AND $1\frac{1}{16}$ OUNCES OF NO. 6 SHOT

shoulder on to which the over-powder card wad rests. The result is that this wad cannot be pushed down too far so as to compress the powder, and yet it will always be pushed down against the step. This means that the wads are always pushed down exactly the same distance in every cartridge and the volume of the powder chamber is always constant.

In theory this system is excellent, but in practice it can result in greater variations in ballistics than the ordinary method of loading.

The reason is that no hopper of any loading machine will always throw *exactly* the same weight of powder in the charge, and there will always be slight variations in the weights of the powder charges in every batch of cartridges which have not been loaded by weighing each powder charge out separately on a balance.

In the ordinary system of loading the pressure used for forcing down the wads is constant, and so a slightly heavy charge is not so compressed as one which is rather on the light side, and thus a more or less automatic compensation occurs, the loading density being practically the same in every case, and the only variation in pressure being that resulting from the slight variation in the weights of the powder charges.

In Constant Volume Loading, however, the volume occupied by the powder charge is always exactly the same, and so variations in the weights of the powder charge also bring about variations in the loading density, with the result that there is a double source of variation in the pressure.

SIZE OF BORE. The size of bore has a great effect on the actual pressure developed, and pressures which would be dangerous in one size may be normal in another. This result is brought about in two ways : by a big increase in the weight of the shot charge used in a large bore ; or by the reduction of the effective area for the application of pressure in a small bore.

In the case of large bores the shot charge is increased very considerably, for example it is 2 oz. in an 8-bore and may be as much as 4 oz. in a 4-bore. Such heavy charges require relatively greater force to propel them with sufficient velocity than is necessary to propel a charge of but 1 oz., and this means a higher pressure per square inch. So for this reason the standard pressures in large bores are higher than those developed in an ordinary 12-bore, and long-chambered 12-bores, such as 2¾-inch and 3-inch, for the same reason give appreciably higher pressures than the 2½-inch.

The case of the small bore is not quite the same. Here the diameter of the shot charge is smaller in proportion to its weight than is the case in a 12-bore 2½-inch. This means that the effective area of the rear end of the shot charge, that is the area of the wadding, is less in proportion to the weight of the charge. Consequently a more intense pressure is necessary to bring about the same result in velocity.

WADDING. The felt wad can have a great effect on the pressure, and by the term " felt " I am including the various substitutes used for felt in wadding.

In the last chapter I emphasised the extreme importance of the felt wad. If the felt is not of the best quality it may fail to expand properly and seal the bore effectively, but the effects of such incomplete obturation will not be reflected in the 1-inch pressures, for at this distance from the breech the wad is still in the cartridge-case. The 6-inch pressures, however, may vary considerably. An example of such variation is provided by the use of dry felt wads. In tropical countries the lubricating grease with which the felt wad is usually impregnated will sometimes melt and soak through the case, when the appearance of the cartridge is affected. This may not matter to the sportsman who has a stock of cartridges in hand, but it can matter very much to the retailer who may fail to sell cartridges which do not look quite right. Consequently cartridges intended for the tropics are sometimes loaded with dry felt wads. When these are used there is a tendency for a slight reduction in the 1-inch pressure, but the falling away of the 6-inch pressure is very marked, and these dry felt wads invariably tend to reduce the velocities. So if any loader wishes to use dry felt wads he should allow for the reduced ballistics by loading a slightly heavier powder charge.

Cork wads also tend to reduce the ballistics in a similar way, but in this case the 1-inch pressure is also reduced to a great extent.

In fact, the ballistics developed when cork wads are used are so feeble that the cartridges are frequently useless.

This, however, can be very easily corrected by using a heavier powder charge, and 29 grains of No. 60 powder will generally produce standard ballistics when cork wadding is used in an ordinary 12-bore. About twenty years ago cork wads were tried by a good many gunmakers, and at first the results were not very satisfactory. But this was entirely owing to the reduction in ballistics not being realised, and now this property of cork wads is generally understood. Provided this fact is realised and a heavier powder charge is used cork wads can give excellent results ; but they call for exceptionally careful loading.

Feltine wads always cause low and irregular pressures, both at 1 inch and 6 inches and it is almost impossible to obtain really good results with this type of wadding.

Air Cushion wads tend to raise the pressure and lighter powder charges are necessary as was explained on page 107.

TURNOVER. I dealt with the question of turnover at considerable length in the last chapter, but will repeat now that it can have a greater practical effect on the ballistics of a cartridge than almost any other factor. It is perfectly possible to load cartridges with the same charges of powder and shot to give almost any desired pressure, simply by varying the turnover. It is true that such changes are not always due entirely to the turnover, although indirectly this may be so. A tight turnover needs at least $\frac{1}{4}$ inch of the end of the case left protruding above the over-shot wad, as otherwise there is not sufficient case left to make the turnover really firm. The usual length is from $\frac{1}{4}$ to $\frac{5}{16}$ inch. But if the powder and wadding are compressed to their limit it is possible to leave $\frac{3}{8}$ or more inch of case free for the turnover. This will add to the tightness of the turnover, which will raise the pressure. But the pressure will also be raised by the compression of the powder which will have increased the loading density.

But just as turnover can be a most potent factor in the raising of the ballistics, it can be even more potent in lowering them, and an insufficient or weak turnover is one of the most common causes of low ballistics.

It will be remembered that one of the purposes of the turnover is to hold the shot charge in position while the cartridges are carried about. If the turnover is not quite tight down on the over-shot wad in the first place the pellets will shake about during any transit of the cartridges and will loosen the turnover still further. So it is very important that the turnover should have a firm bearing against the over-shot wad.

Fully crimped closures are far more likely to be constant since any variation would be obvious immediately on examining the front end of the cartridge. Consequently there is less chance of any variation in pressure being caused by this method of sealing the cartridge, although there is a tendency to a slight increase of about 0·2 to 0·5 ton which is met by reducing the powder charge by from one to three grains.

LUBRICATION IN THE CARTRIDGE-CASE. The actual lubrication is effected by the grease in the felt wad, but some brands of cartridge-cases are made from greased paper in order to make them waterproof. Such cartridges frequently have a tendency to lower the ballistics. This result is actually brought about in two ways. First, the grease in the paper tube acts as a lubricator and helps the wadding to move easily in front of the expanding gases when the pressure generated is reduced. Secondly this grease actually makes the paper soft and so renders a firm turnover almost impossible.

A most noticeable example of this double effect was given by the old Eley Pegamoid case. In this case the special paper which was used was so soft that a firm turnover was very hard to make. These facts were thoroughly appreciated by the makers and formerly Eley Brothers always used to cap their Pegamoid cases with a special strong cap which had the effect of producing more lively combustion and so counteracting the effects of the lubrication and soft turnover.

This special cap, however, was not quite so sensitive as the ordinary cap and just after the first world war a few instances of miss-fires were reported. Nothing can do any make of cartridges more harm than a reputation for miss-fires, even though in all the instances reported the fault probably lay in the gun. Consequently the special cap was given up and the ordinary cap substituted, with the result that Pegamoid cases invariably gave low ballistics, until at length a change was made in the paper, when the behaviour of these cartridges became normal once more.

CAP. The example of the old type of Pegamoid case which has just been given shows how a cap can affect pressure. The most common cause of variations in pressure resulting from caps is the use of British powders in some foreign cases capped with the " large " caps, which some gunmakers and many sportsmen quite erroneously think are more powerful than the smaller type of cap preferred by British manufacturers. Frequently these large caps result in very feeble pressures, owing to their failure to ignite the powder charge properly. The importance of matching powder and cap cannot be exaggerated, and some of these large foreign caps are so ill suited to British powders that they reduce the 1-inch pressure well below the minimum limit necessary for an efficient cartridge.

GUN. All game guns develop lower ballistics than those obtained in a pressure barrel for reasons which have already been given. This reduction is allowed for, consciously or unconsciously, by the cartridge loader and is normally quite immaterial. But if rather " soft " cartridges which give 1-inch pressures bordering on the low limit are used in a very old and worn gun the pressures may be pulled down to such an extent that the cartridges cease to be effective. But in any ordinary gun, even though of the cheapest quality, such results should not be experienced.

STRENGTH OF STRIKER BLOW. Experiments in pressure barrels have shown that the pressures developed by cartridges from the same batch are affected by the strength of the blow of the striker. But if the cartridges develop normal pressures, and the variation in the strength of the striker blow is within the limits of sound gun manufacture, the resulting variations in pressure are insignificant and cannot cause any appreciable change in the ballistics.

But if the cartridges are weak, a weak striker blow accentuates this weakness ; while if the cartridges are violent, a strong striker blow increases the violence of the pressure.

If, however, the cartridges develop pressures which lie within the normal maximum and minimum limits, and the striker blow is sufficiently strong to result in the proper detonation of the cap and not cause hang-fires, there is no proof that any extra strength of blow produces more violent combustion of the powder.

LENGTH OF CARTRIDGE. Some American and Continental cartridges can be slightly longer than the corresponding British size. If such cartridges are used in guns chambered for the shorter cases higher pressures will result. Where the extra length is but $\frac{1}{16}$ of an inch the increased pressure may not be dangerous, but the possibility of danger should be realised. I have come across many instances of sportsmen abroad using $2\frac{3}{4}$-inch 12-bore cartridges in guns chambered for the ordinary $2\frac{1}{2}$-inch case as well as cartridges of other gauges longer than those for which the gun was chambered, and when this has happened the gun has usually been damaged considerably.

In England the possibility of such things happening is not great, but abroad, where there is far bigger variation in the lengths of cases and loads, the danger is real.

The fully crimped cartridge, however, raises quite a different problem. As was explained on page 125 a longer length of case is necessary with a full crimp than is needed when an ordinary turnover and over-shot wad are used in order to produce a finished cartridge of the same standard length. For this reason $2\frac{3}{4}$-inch cases are necessary with a full crimp to ensure that the loaded cartridge is of the correct normal length for a nominal $2\frac{1}{2}$-inch cartridge.

When a true $2\frac{3}{4}$-inch cartridge is fired in a $2\frac{1}{2}$-inch chamber the pressure is increased for two separate and distinct reasons : (1) the length of the loaded cartridge is exactly the same as that of the actual chamber and so, when the turnover is opened on firing the mouth of the case is prevented from opening completely by the chamber cone ; and (2) the actual powder and shot charges are heavier than those of a $2\frac{1}{2}$-inch cartridge.

The effect of the mouth of the case being held in by the chamber cone is much the same as that of giving the cartridge an exceptionally heavy turnover, and the effect on the pressure will be obvious. For it must always be kept in mind that the greatest effort of the powder gases is needed to *start the shot charge moving*. The initial resistance to movement is partly due to the inertia of the shot charge and wadding and partly to the actual resistance of the turnover, which must be pushed fully back in order to allow the shot charge to leave the case. Once this initial resistance has been overcome and the shot charge has begun to move the pressure begins to drop. If the mouth of the cartridge is compressed by being held by the chamber cone, the resistance to the initial movement of the shot charge will be greater and the pressure will be increased.

The result of the heavier powder and shot charges

must be equally obvious. The nominal charge for a 2½-inch 12-bore cartridge is 26 grains of No. 60 powder and 1 1/16 ounce of shot. That for a 2¾-inch cartridge, 29 grains of the same powder and 1¼ ounces of shot. And exactly the same principles apply to cartridges of other gauges and different lengths.

It will be realised, therefore, that the increase in pressure is the result of the longer *loaded cartridge* rather than that of the longer *unloaded case*.

But although these two factors causing an increase of pressure do certainly exist, the first is far greater than the second. In 1938 I tested some of the first lot of British fully crimped paper-tube cartridges which were issued. These, as has already been explained, were loaded in 2 9/16-inch cases. I fired a series of ten shots for pressure and obtained very even and perfectly normal results. Two months later I tested another lot which were loaded in 2¾-inch paper-tube cases. The shot charge in both lots was 1 1/16 ounce and the powder charges were similar. I fired twenty-five shots for pressure and again obtained a very even series with no higher pressures than those given by the first lot. Since 1946 I have tested many more lots and these results have proved quite definitely that for all practical purposes any increase in pressure due to the longer cartridge case really does not exist provided the correct powder and shot charges for a nominal 2½-inch cartridge are used. It is true that all American fully crimped cartridges loaded with but 1⅛ ounce of shot develop pressures which are considerably higher than those given by the corresponding British cartridges, but this is due to the relatively higher powder charge adopted by the Americans rather than to their use of a 2¾-inch case.

The dominant factor is the cause of increased pressure is the load and the 2¾-inch case has for so long been associated with a heavier load that the longer case and high pressure have become to be regarded as inseparable, which is a pity.

GAS-TIGHT CASES. On account of their greater strength

Gas-tight cases generally tend to a slight increase in pressure. The increase, however, is not sufficiently great to make any practical difference, although it might happen that the pressure was reduced in an ordinary unlined case by the use of cork wadding, or some such cause, to just below the permissible limit. In such circumstances it is possible that gas-tight cases might make enough difference to raise the pressure to just over the low limit.

ATMOSPHERIC TEMPERATURE AND HUMIDITY

Finally the conditions under which cartridges are kept and stored. Almost all shotgun powders contain a small percentage of moisture, and if this moisture content is changed appreciably the pressures developed by the powder can also be varied. An increase in the moisture content results in a low or feeble pressure, while a decrease causes high and even violent pressures.

It not infrequently happens, therefore, that cartridges which are stored for a considerable time in excessive heat get so warm that the powder which they contain gradually loses a proportion of its moisture content through the ordinary process of evaporation. When this occurs the pressures developed will become high or quite excessive. But if the cartridges are removed to a cooler storage place, or if the temperature of the original storage place is lowered, the powder gradually recovers its original moisture content and the pressures will once again be normal. This change in pressure is a very common phenomenon even in England during a hot summer, and I have frequently had cartridges sent me in August which developed pressures which were excessive. This invariably followed a long hot spell and I always suggested to the sportsmen concerned that they should keep those cartridges until November by which time they would have recovered normal behaviour. Tests made later with the same lots of cartridges invariably proved the correctness of this prophecy, which was merely based on a well-known characteristic of most nitro shotgun powders.

Similarly, long spells of very wet weather can easily cause the powder in shotgun cartridges to absorb some extra moisture while still more can be extracted from the wadding and cases. Bone-dry wadding and cases, on the other hand, will extract moisture from the powder when the pressures will be increased. This is particularly likely to occur in all-metal cartridges which are hermetically sealed by a full crimp and waxed end. The cartridges are air-tight, and just as no moisture can get in so none can get out. If the wads are bone-dry the total amount of moisture which is contained by the powder and the air within the case will soon become distributed evenly throughout the cartridge, some being absorbed by the dry wadding. If the air was dry when the cartridges were being loaded this can only mean that the wadding has attracted to itself some of the moisture content of the powder with a consequent rise in pressure.

It was this change in the moisture content of the powder which caused some quite excessive pressures in the pre-1939 all-metal cartridges. The wadding used was too dry and the cartridges were too waterproof in that they were air-tight. Even the most efficient water-resisting paper-tube case is seldom, if ever, really air-tight and so the risk of the wadding extracting moisture from the powder does not arise. But with all-metal cartridges sealed with a full crimp and waxed end this risk must be realised, and the only remedy is so to condition the wadding before it is used that it contains exactly the same proportion of moisture as the powder. There will then be no cause for the wadding to extract moisture from the powder or *vice versa*. But such conditioning of the wadding must obviously call for a special conditioning room, and such a luxury is certainly beyond the capacity for any loaders other than a large factory, which explains my suggestion that the loading of all-metal cartridges with fully crimped turnovers is likely to be beyond the capacity of any gunmaker.

This question of the moisture content of shotgun powders is most important and explains the danger of storing shotgun cartridges in some hot cupboard or close to some hot radiator as well as that of drying off paper-tube cartridges which may have got wet by placing them close to a hot fire.

TABLE IV
PRESSURES OF DIFFERENT CARTRIDGES

CARTRIDGE.		PRESSURE IN TONS PER SQUARE INCH.				
		1 Inch.			6 Inches.	
Bore.	Length of Case in Inches.	Standard.	Maximum.	Minimum.	Standard.	Minimum.
*4	4¼	3·75	4·75	2·75	1·8	1·5
4	4	3·5	4·5	3·0	1·7	1·4
*8	4¼	4·25	5·25	2·5	1·9	1·6
*8	4	4·0	5·0	3·0	1·9	1·6
*8	3¾	3·8	4·9	2·9	1·9	1·6
*8	3½	3·5	4·5	2·5	1·8	1·5
8	3¼	3·3	4·2	2·4	1·7	1·4
*10	3¼	3·3	4·2	2·4	1·8	1·5
*10	3	3·2	4·0	2·4	1·7	1·4
10	2⅞	3·1	3·9	2·3	1·6	1·3
10	2⅝	2·9	3·7	2·1	1·6	1·3
*12	3¼	3·75	4·5	2·5	1·9	1·6
12	3	3·2	4·0	2·4	1·9	1·6
12	2¾	3·1	3·9	2·3	1·8	1·5
12	2½	2·7	3·5	2·0	1·6	1·3
12	2	2·25	3·0	1·8	1·4	1·2
*14	2½	2·8	3·6	2·0	1·6	1·3
*16	3	3·2	4·0	2·4	1·8	1·5
16	2¾	3·1	3·9	2·3	1·8	1·5
16	2½	2·9	3·7	2·1	1·7	1·4
*20	3	3·4	4·3	2·5	1·8	1·5
20	2¾	3·3	4·2	2·4	1·8	1·5
20	2½	3·2	4·0	2·4	1·7	1·4
*24	2½	3·2	4·0	2·4	1·7	1·4
28	2½	3·4	4·3	2·5	1·7	1·4
*32	2½	3·0	3·8	2·2	1·5	1·2
*·410	3	3·75	4·75	2·5	1·6	1·3
·410	2½	3·5	4·5	2·5	1·4	1·2
·410	2	2·8	3·6	2·0	1·4	1·2

* No longer made.

The preceding table gives particulars for the pressures at 1 and 6 inches for all the different cartridges used in Great Britain.

It will be noticed that out of the twenty-nine different cartridges given in the Table fourteen are now no longer made. Of these three are the very rare bores, such as the 14, 24 and 32. The other eleven comprise cases of different lengths, notably the $4\frac{1}{4}$-inch 4-bore, four different lengths in the 8-bore, and the 3-inch 16 and 20-bores. The demand for all these cartridges was so small that it was felt that as a means of increasing productivity and decreasing costs, it would be better to concentrate on the $3\frac{1}{4}$-inch 8-bore, since over 60 per cent. of those sold were of this length, while the 3-inch 16- and 20-bores had very small sales.

CHAPTER VII

VELOCITY

OF the four Ballistic Elements—Pressure, Velocity, Pattern and Recoil—Velocity and Pattern undoubtedly receive most attention from both gunmakers and shooters ; and it is probable that shooters think more about velocity than they do about pattern. This is not altogether surprising, as the velocity of the shot charge controls to a great extent the effective range of a gun. For unless the pellets of the charge possess adequate velocity when they strike a bird they will fail to penetrate sufficiently to pierce some vital organ : and the greater the distance from the gun at which the velocity is sufficient for penetration the greater the possible effective range. So we see that the velocity of the shot charge must attain a certain standard if game is to be killed cleanly up to a certain distance.

But velocity plays another and very important part in the use of a shotgun.

The difficulty of shooting at any moving object consists of firing at some imaginary point exactly the right distance ahead so as to allow for the movement of the object during the time taken from the instant of pressing the trigger to the arrival of the projectile at the target. The longer this time the greater the difficulty of making a successful shot ; while if it could be eliminated altogether it would be almost, if not quite, as easy to hit a moving object as a stationary one. Ever since game shooting became a sport, shooters, gunmakers and ammunition makers have striven to reduce the time between the pressing of the trigger and the shot charge reaching the bird ; and up to a point they have achieved a certain measure of success.

But in order to appreciate what has actually been

accomplished we must analyse the time period which it is desired to reduce. Although I have just stated that this period begins with the pressing of the trigger, in actual practice this is not correct, as it begins with the shooter's decision to press the trigger, which is not necessarily the same thing, as some men's brains work quicker than those of others ; and what is more work differently from day to day. Taking this fact into account there are three different and distinct periods which together make up the whole time under consideration, namely :

(1) The time taken from the brain's decision to fire, to the actual pressing of the trigger, which may be called the " Sportsman's Time."

(2) The time taken from the pressing of the trigger to the exit of the shot charge at the muzzle, which is usually known as the " Time up the Barrel."

(3) The time taken from the exit of the shot charge at the muzzle to the arrival of the shot charge at the target, perhaps 40 yards distant, which is the " Time of Flight."

It is obvious that the first of these periods is a personal matter entirely and can be affected by no one except the actual shooter. Consequently it is of little use for others than the individual concerned to worry about it. But it can be a very potent factor in the difficulty of shooting so sportsmen should remember its existence.

The second period, or the " Time up the Barrel," has by long-accepted custom always been measured so as to include the time of ignition—that is the time from the impact of the striker on the cap to the initial movement of the shot charge, and the time taken by the shot charge to travel up the barrel. Actually measured " times up the barrel " may include the time taken by the tumbler, or hammer, to fall, or a part of this time, according to the method employed for making this measurement. So it will be appreciated that there are three elements which together make up the Time up the Barrel, and of these two have values which are practically fixed, namely :

The fall of the tumbler, or hammer (about 0·0020

second) ; and the time of movement up the barrel (about 0·0026 second).

The third, and variable, element is the time of ignition, which with modern smokeless powders and caps is about 0·0010 second.

It is the Time of Ignition of this second period which has been tackled most successfully and which has been reduced enormously by human ingenuity. A hundred years ago flint locks were at their zenith, but even the best of these guns went off with a fizzle of appreciable duration before the powder charge was ignited ; or in other words, a gun always went off with what we would now regard as a very bad hang-fire. An additional difficulty in actual shooting was added by the fact that the duration of this " hang-fire " fizzle of the flint lock varied from round to round. Consequently the shooter's only hope of success when firing at a crossing bird lay in keeping his gun moving ahead of the bird after he had pressed the trigger. This maintained movement of the gun, or " swing," had the additional merit of neutralising any error due to the first of the three periods of time already mentioned, and is the secret of all successful shooting at moving objects, either with gun or rifle, and the remarkable success achieved by many shooters a hundred years ago must be attributed to the fact that they had to cultivate a regular swing before they could hope to hit a flying bird ; intercepting snaps with a flint lock were doomed to failure.

The change from flint to percussion locks reduced this time of ignition of the powder very considerably. Colonel Peter Hawker asserted that he only needed half the forward allowance on a crossing bird with his " detonator " of that required with his flint lock. And in 1926 the late Mr. F. W. Jones and I tested this statement of Hawker's with a chronograph. My friend, Mr. Ingo Simon, kindly lent me a beautiful Joe Manton flint-lock gun from his collection, and we measured the " Time up the Barrel " in the case of this gun and that of a Purdey muzzle-loading percussion gun. When the Time of Flight of the shot charge over a range of 30 yards was added to this Time up the Barrel we found that the average total time was as nearly as possible double in the case of the flint lock as it was in that of the percussion lock. This experiment was quoted by the late Mr. Eric Parker in his Introduction to the modern Edition of Hawker's *Instructions to Young Sportsmen*.

The introduction of the Central-Fire Breech-Loader reduced the time of ignition still further, as anyone can test for himself by trying a few shots at clay targets with a percussion lock muzzle-loader, when he will notice a slight, but just perceptible, hang-fire with every shot.

But although the central-fire breech-loader did result in a shorter time of ignition the reduction was not nearly so great as that brought about by the invention of the percussion cap, which still remains the biggest single advance ever made in the problem of reducing the forward allowance on a moving target.

The reader will probably wonder what all this has to do with the velocity of a shot charge. My reason for this seeming digression is that when supposed improvements due to enhanced velocity are considered this matter of reduction in forward allowance is not infrequently quoted as an example of what has been done in the past and as an indication of what might be done in the future. The real truth, however, is that the reductions which have been brought about in forward allowance are almost entirely due to a reduction in the Time up the Barrel, and not in the Time of Flight of the shot charge, which is still practically the same now as it was in the days of Hawker. This is a point which should be thoroughly appreciated as it will save many misunderstandings.

The reason why the Time of Flight has not been reduced to any appreciable extent during the past hundred years is because it depends on the average velocity of a given size of shot over whatever range is under consideration. This average velocity is governed by the muzzle velocity with which the charge begins its flight and the capacity possessed by the individual pellets for retaining that velocity. It is in the time of flight that all the more modern experimenters have striven to make a reduction, for the time of flight is of far longer duration than all the other periods which we have considered put together, and the forward allowance on a bird is really governed by the time of flight. This fact will be appreciated better if it is remembered that the average time of flight for a charge of No. 6 shot over 40 yards is about 0·14 second, and we have already seen that the three elements which make up the time up the barrel amount to but 0·0056 second, or but one twenty-fifth part of the time of flight.

So it is not altogether surprising that the problem of the time of flight has received a great deal of attention.

As has been seen the time of flight is dependent on the average velocity of a given size of shot over whatever range is under consideration. If this average velocity could be increased to any appreciable extent the necessary forward allowance on a flying bird would be reduced in proportion, and the chief difficulty in shooting at winged game would be decreased. When we remember the wonderful improvements which have been made in guns, powders and cartridges during only the past sixty years, it seems extraordinary that the range at which birds can be killed with ordinary game guns and the time of flight of the shot charge are practically the same as those of the days of our grandfathers. It must not be imagined that no efforts have been made to bring improvements about, but the difficulties are almost insuperable, as they depend on the laws of nature rather than instrumental efficiency.

The average velocity of a charge of shot over any given range is governed by the velocity with which the charge leaves the muzzle of the gun and the capacity possessed by the individual pellets for retaining that velocity. Accordingly it is clear that the most obvious starting point for possible improvement is the muzzle velocity of the shot charge, a fact which is emphasised considerably by the great advances which have been made in rifle ballistics even in the past twenty years.

These advances in rifle ballistics have undoubtedly

influenced the problem of shotguns to an appreciable extent. This is, after all, easy to understand ; for rifles and shotguns are asked to perform very similar functions, and they possess many similar characteristics. To give an idea of the advances which have been made in rifle ballistics it is only necessary to point out that in the early 'nineties a muzzle velocity of but 1,700 feet per second was considered very high ; and now one of 3,000 feet per second is quite ordinary.

It must, however, be borne in mind that these enhanced muzzle velocities are not due solely to improvements in powders and cartridge design. In every single case of a very big increase in muzzle velocity the bullet has been lightened considerably. For example, the original German 7·9 mm. Service bullet weighed 244 grains and was fired with a muzzle velocity of just over 2,000 feet per second. When the muzzle velocity was increased to 2,800 feet per second the weight of the bullet was reduced to 155 grains. The British ·303 Service cartridge provides another case in point, although we did not go quite to the extremes which the Germans did. The Mark VI cartridge had a 215-grains bullet and developed a muzzle velocity of 2,060 feet per second, while the Mark VII cartridge has a bullet of 176 grains and a muzzle velocity of 2,450 feet per second.

In rifles the advantages obtained by these greatly increased muzzle velocities are :

(1) Flatter trajectories, especially over sporting ranges, which reduce the difficulty of judging distance.

(2) Increased striking velocity at longer ranges.

(3) Reduction in forward allowance necessary on a moving target.

The first two of these advantages together mean an increased effective range, and so it will be seen that for purposes of sport the enhanced velocities of modern rifles increased the range and reduced the difficulty of shooting at running animals ; the two very improvements which have for so long been sought for shotguns. It is not surprising, then, that experimenters have worked on similar lines to those which gave such success with rifles and have concentrated on increasing the muzzle velocity developed in shotguns.

Now velocity can, in general terms, be increased in two ways : by reducing the weight of the projectile—that is the shot charge in the case of a shotgun ; or by increasing the weight of the powder charge. The second of these two alternatives cannot be utilised alone in ordinary game guns, because it would result in excessive pressures and too severe a recoil.

Higher pressures would mean heavier guns. In the case of rifles the pressure has been increased, bore for bore, by from 30 to 50 per cent. by the change from black powder to cordite, and it is these increments in pressure which have brought about the enhanced velocities. But at the same time, for the sake of safety, the weights of the rifles themselves have been increased on an average by one-third. Would any shooter like to use even an 8-lb. gun in a grouse butt or against driven partridges or high pheasants ? We know that such a gun would not be tolerated and would, if it were used, be an overwhelming handicap against quick work which is the essence of success in shooting with a shotgun.

It must be remembered that the whole tendency in gun construction during the past thirty years has been towards lighter weapons. Formerly a gun of 7 lb. was considered ordinary ; then the usual weight became 6 lb. 12 oz. ; now it varies from 6 lb. 4 oz. to 6 lb. 10 oz., and in the case of special weapons it is as little as 6 lb. or even less. A gun of 8 lb. or more is out of the question, and such a gun would be necessary on the score of safety if shotgun pressures were increased to the same extent as rifle pressures have been.

Then recoil, too, is one of the principal factors which must ultimately govern shotgun construction and shotgun ballistics. In the final chapter this important ballistic element will be considered in detail, so I will now only say that recoil depends on (1) the velocity with which the shot, wads and powder gases leave the muzzle ; and (2) the total weight of the shot, wads and powder gases. If the recoil is to be kept more or less constant and the velocity is increased, then the total weight of the shot, wads and powder gases must be reduced. The weight of the shot charge is by far the greatest component of this total and is the only one in which it is possible to make any appreciable change.

An example of this principle of cartridge design is provided by the ·303 Mark VII cartridge. The recoil developed by this cartridge is the same as that given by the Mark VI ; but the velocity is 400 feet per second, or 20 per cent. higher, while the bullet is 39 grains, or 20 per cent. lighter.

Recoil is of greater importance in the case of shotguns than rifles because many more shots are fired in a day and because the modern shooter demands a lighter weapon. Forty years ago the standard weight of the shot charge for an ordinary 12-bore 2½-inch case was $1\frac{1}{8}$ ounce. It is now $1\frac{1}{16}$; this reduction was not made to increase the velocity but to reduce the recoil so as to render possible the use of lighter guns.

Now a shotgun differs from a rifle in that its projectile is made up of a large number of pellets which begin to separate from each other within a few feet of the muzzle of the gun, and continue to separate still farther as the range increases. Accordingly there must come a point when the pellets are so far apart that a bird can fly between them, and when this range has been reached hitting is no longer a matter of skill, but entirely one of luck. It is obvious that the fewer pellets there are in the charge in the first place the sooner will come the range when it will only be by chance that a bird is hit with even a single pellet. Further, it is not enough even for one pellet to strike a bird ; at least two or three are required if the odds are to be in favour of hitting a vital part. So, other things being equal, a light shot charge means a shorter killing range, whereas in rifles a lighter bullet makes no difference to the chances of hitting the mark.

It is true that a charge of one ounce is now very

popular in an ordinary 12-bore. This further reduction, however, has been made just as much in order to reduce recoil as to increase velocity. But in any case an ounce is a reduction of but 6 per cent., and it has been seen that in the case of the ·303 cartridge a reduction was made in bullet weight of 20 per cent., while in some instances of enhanced rifle velocities the bullet has been reduced by over 30 per cent.

So we come up against the hard fact that it is quite impossible to make anything like the corresponding increase in shotgun velocities to those which have been made in rifles for two reasons.

First, the weight of the shotgun cannot be increased and so the pressures necessary for the enhanced velocities would be dangerous.

Secondly, the weight of the shot charge cannot be decreased to nearly the same extent as can a rifle bullet and so recoil would be excessive.

Shotguns, however, suffer from another handicap which is not imposed on rifles to nearly the same degree and which prevents them from utilising to the same extent as rifles even that limited increase in velocity which is possible.

I have already pointed out that an increase in effective range is partly dependent on the striking velocity at any distance. For instance, if the striking velocity of the pellets of a charge of shot at 60 yards could be increased to what it usually is at 40 yards we would get an increase in effective range owing to the fact that the penetration at long range would be increased.

Similarly the forward allowance on a moving target depends on the time of flight, which in its turn depends on the *average* velocity of the shot charge over the range.

Now both the striking velocity at any distance, and the average velocity of the charge over that distance are dependent on two things : (1) the muzzle velocity ; and (2) the capacity of the shot charge for retaining that velocity.

It is no use increasing the muzzle velocity unless the

increase is properly maintained, and so we must now consider the factors which influence the capacity possessed by any projectile for retaining its initial velocity.

When any projectile travels through the air it loses velocity all the time during its flight on account of the resistance of the air, but some projectiles can fight against this air resistance more effectively than others, and such projectiles will possess a greater capacity for retaining their initial velocity.

The factors which govern the capacity which any projectile possesses for retaining its velocity, that is for fighting successfully against the air resistance, are :

(1) WEIGHT. A cricket ball can be thrown farther than a cork ball of exactly the same size. The strength of the thrower's arm is the same, and both balls are thrown with the same initial velocity. But the heavier cricket ball travels farther, simply because its greater weight enables it to overcome the air resistance more effectively.

(2) SHAPE. A sharp-pointed bullet cuts through the air much better than one with a blunt head, just as the bows of a racing yacht cut through the water more easily than those of a barge.

(3) AREA OF SURFACE EXPOSED TO AIR RESISTANCE. The smaller this area is the less the power which can be exerted by the resistance of the air. In all projectiles this area is circular, since all shells and bullets are circular in section in order to fit the bore of the cannon or rifle, while the pellets of a shot charge are also theoretically circular in section. So the area exposed to air resistance is really dependent on the diameter of the projectile. It is for this reason that a long thin bullet has a longer range than a shorter one of larger diameter although of the same weight, in exactly the same way that a narrow racing yacht moves through the water more easily than a boat which is much broader in the beam.

These three factors are of vital importance and entirely govern the design of all shells and bullets. They cannot all three be combined in every case, as weight must frequently be kept down for reasons which have been given. But there is ample scope for taking advantage of the benefits conferred by a pointed head and a small diameter. The influence which these two factors have had on the design of rifles and bullets can be seen in the gradual evolution of the modern small-bore rifle, both military and sporting. The first British Service breech-loading rifle was the Snider, which had a bore of ·577. This was followed by the ·450 Martini, which was replaced by the ·303.

Similarly the nose of the bullet became sharper until it reached an absolute point in the ·303 Mark VII cartridge.

These improvements in bullet design have really had almost, if not quite, as much to do with the increase in range and reduction of forward allowance which have been made in sporting rifles as have the enhanced muzzle velocities ; for the improved shape of the bullets have conferred upon them a greater capacity for overcoming air resistance which has enabled them to retain the enhanced velocities to the greatest possible extent.

In shotguns, however, there is no scope for such improvements in the design of the projectile, since the projectile can only consist of the shot charge which in its turn can only be made up of a number of pellets of shot. The shape of these pellets can, at the best, be but spherical ; and a spherical surface is not a good one for overcoming air resistance.

Again the diameter and weight are largely beyond our control, as both depend on the size of shot to be used.

So it will be seen that in shotguns we cannot adapt our projectile as we can in rifles so as to take full advantage of even that comparatively limited increase in velocity which it is possible to obtain.

But there is yet another difficulty in connection with air resistance.

Air offers very little resistance to slight movement, just as the knuckles of the clenched hand may be laid gently against a brick wall without any feeling of dis-comfort. But if the knuckles are pressed hard against the bricks the result is at first uncomfortable and, as the pressure is increased, finally painful. Similarly the more any body pushes against the air by moving through it, the more the air pushes against that body : or, in other words, any increase in the velocity of a moving object results in a much greater increase in the air resistance. In the case of a charge of shot travelling at normal speeds beyond 25 yards with standard velocity and 30 yards with high velocity this resistance varies as the square of the velocity. But at ranges less than 25 and 30 yards for standard and high velocities the air resistance becomes very much greater. That is to say, if the velocity of the shot charge is doubled the air resistance becomes four times as great ; and if the velocity could be trebled the resistance would be nine times as great.

Consequently a shot charge which is propelled from the muzzle of a gun with a very high velocity loses speed much more rapidly than does a similar shot charge which is propelled with a low initial velocity, on account of the greatly increased air resistance which the former charge has to fight against during its flight.

The further a shot charge travels from the gun the lower becomes its actual velocity at any instant and the less becomes the air resistance, as the more successful the air is in opposing the movement of the shot the more it reduces its opposition to that movement.

In the case of a charge of shot it is interesting to see how this air resistance varies at different ranges for normal velocities and those resulting from the most enhanced velocity which it is possible to obtain in an ordinary 12-bore cartridge. Since the actual resistances in pounds per square inch can be confusing I will give these resistances in percentages, taking the resistance to the standard load at a range of 10 yards as 100. Working on this principle the approximate comparative resistances to the movement of shot charges are given in the following table.

This table shows clearly how the high velocity charge has to fight a harder battle against air resistance throughout its flight, especially in the initial stages, but that at

TABLE V
COMPARATIVE AIR RESISTANCES AT DIFFERENT RANGES

Range.	Comparative Air Resistance.	
	Standard Velocity.	High Velocity.
Muzzle	291	450
10 yards	100	175
20 ,, ...	58	70
30 ,, ...	43	48
40 ,, ...	33	36
50 ,, ...	24	27

the longer ranges the resistances to the standard and high velocity charges approach one another more nearly. *This is because at these ranges the differences between the actual velocities of the two charges are becoming less and less as both are forced to slow down.* So it will be clear that however hard a charge of shot is propelled from the muzzle of a gun it is quickly brought up all standing, so to say, with the result that at long ranges the velocity becomes nearly the same even when the initial velocity of the charge is varied between wide limits, provided the same size of shot is used in each case.

Consequently it is quite wrong to assume, as many shooters and cartridge loaders do, that an increase in the velocity of the shot charge of 100 feet per second when the shot charge is 10 yards from the muzzle of the gun means a corresponding increase of 100 feet per second when it is 40 or 50 yards away from the gun. As a matter of fact, if the velocity of a charge of No. 6 shot is increased by 100 feet per second over the standard velocity at 10 yards, the increases at 40 and 50 yards are but 40 and 35 feet per second respectively, while at 60 yards the increase is even less.

So it will be seen that although the difference between the velocities of the shot charge may be considerable at very short ranges they become less and less as the range is increased, and consequently at very long ranges the original considerable difference becomes one which is negligible.

This does not happen in the case of rifle bullets because it is possible to adapt the design of a single projectile so as to enable it to fight against air resistance more effectively. But we cannot adapt the design of the pellets of a shot charge in the same way. Further, the individual pellets are so light that their capacity for overcoming air resistance is feeble in the extreme ; and it is for this reason, above all others, that they cannot derive benefit from increased velocities as the much heavier rifle bullets can.

A simile which I have frequently used is that of a child's air balloon. It is possible to send one of these balloons quite a considerable distance across a room by a gentle tap ; but once a certain distance has been reached it is almost impossible to increase it, no matter how hard one hits the balloon. The very light balloon has no power for overcoming air resistance, and when it is given a moderate velocity by a gentle tap it succeeds in travelling a certain distance because the air does not put up much fight against moderate speed. But directly the balloon is given a higher velocity by a smart blow the air objects strongly and offers a much greater resistance to the balloon's advance with the result that the balloon soon gives in, because it has such a feeble capacity for overcoming air resistance. The effect is that however hard one hits the balloon its actual velocity at the end of a very short distance is always very nearly the same.

Another example of this power possessed by air for reducing velocity may be noticed during any shower of rain. The rain drops fall from a considerable height under the influence of gravity, and if there was no air they would be gathering speed every moment of their descent until by the time they had reached the ground their velocity would be so great as to cause considerable pain, if not actual injury, to any person on whom they fell. The resistance of the air, however, counteracts gravity to a great extent and holds the rain drops back with the result that they never attain any great speed since the harder gravity pulls them down the harder the air holds them back.

The only variation which is noticeable in the force with which rain drops fall is connected with their size ; very fine rain falls more gently than does a heavy shower consisting of large drops. *This is because the air has more power to hold back the small drops than the large ones ; or in other words because the large drops can fight against the resistance offered by the air more successfully than the small ones on account of their greater weight.*

It is exactly the same with shot. The heavier the pellets the more capable they are of putting up a better fight against the resistance of the air and of retaining their velocity. For this reason larger shot loses its velocity more gradually than small shot ; or, to put it another way, large shot retains its velocity longer than small shot.

At first sight the reader may wonder why this should be so since a large pellet offers a bigger surface to the air resistance than does a small one, and it may appear that this disadvantage would cancel any advantage conferred by the increased weight. To a certain extent this does happen, and the advantage derived by the increased weight is not nearly so great as it would be if it were possible to keep the size of the pellets the same. The weight, however, varies as the *Cube* of the diameter ; while the area only as the *square*. The net result is, therefore, that —

Capacity for overcoming Air Resistance varies as $\dfrac{\text{Weight}}{\text{Surface}}$; that is as $\dfrac{D^3}{D^2}$; and that is as D, where D is the diameter.

So we come down to the very important fact that the larger the size of the shot the better the pellets of the charge retain their initial velocity, with the result that the velocity at long ranges in the case of big shot is greater than small even though the muzzle velocity was the same for both sizes. If, for example, charges of No. 4 and No. 6 are both fired with the standard velocity, the remaining velocity at 50 yards of the pellets of No. 4 is 577 feet per second, while that of the pellets of No. 6 is but 518 feet per second. *That is, the pellets of No. 4 have 60 feet per second more velocity at 50 yards than those of No. 6, although they left the muzzle of the gun at the same speed. And in the case of still larger and smaller sizes of shot the difference in the remaining velocities at 50 yards would be still greater.*

At this stage of our consideration of the subject of the Ballistic Element of Velocity it may be as well to summarise the facts which have emerged. These are as follows :

(1) Partly on account of the necessity for avoiding high pressures and partly because of the necessity for keeping recoil on the light side it is impossible to obtain the big increases of velocity in shotguns which have been made in the case of rifles.

(2) If velocity is increased the air resistance is increased very much more, with the result that a projectile loses velocity more rapidly when it is travelling at a high speed than it does when moving at a more moderate speed.

(3) On account of their shape and light weight the pellets of a charge of shot have a very feeble capacity for overcoming air resistance, and consequently they cannot maintain whatever enhanced velocity is obtained as well as a rifle bullet can.

(4) Because of their greater weight the pellets of large sizes of shot retain their initial velocity better than the pellets of smaller sizes.

Such are the general facts : but in order to enable the reader to see for himself exactly what increases in velocity can be made above the general accepted standard, and what these increases can actually mean, the velocities of different sizes of shot resulting from varying initial velocities will be set out in tabular form for purposes of comparison. Before, however, we can come to definite figures it is essential that the meaning of all these figures should be quite clear. And to make these meanings clear I will describe briefly the method employed for measuring the velocity of a shot charge.

CHAPTER VIII

VELOCITY (*continued*)

VARIOUS methods have been employed for measuring the velocities of shot charges. The actual velocity with which the charge may be travelling at any point is really immaterial. All projectiles, including shot pellets, lose their initial, or muzzle, velocity on account of the resistance offered by the air, and in doing so conform to certain known laws. As has been seen, this loss in velocity is dependent on the shape, size and density of the projectile. In the case of shot pellets the shape is, on the average, the same (some pellets are less round than others, but the average shape of different charges of shot is constant). All are made of lead, which means that the density is the same. And so it will be quite clear that the only possible source of variation is in the different shot sizes. Different charges of the same size of shot lose their velocity at exactly the same rate, and so all that it is necessary to do is to measure the comparative velocity at some fixed point when we will obtain a perfectly true comparison of the velocities of the two cartridges at all ranges.

One of the earliest methods employed for the measuring of the comparative velocities was by testing the penetration of the shot charges on special card pads, tin sheets, etc. Now it is quite reasonable, and fits in with all experience in gunnery, to take penetration as a function of velocity. This being so it will be seen that a measurement of striking velocity is also a measurement of penetration. The reverse, however, is not the case ; for a measurement of penetration is not necessarily a correct one of velocity. This is because when one body strikes another the amount of penetration varies with the relative hardness of the two bodies. If the striking body is readily deformable penetration is inclined actually to decrease as the striking velocity increases. This has been proved in many ways.

In the early days of big game hunting sportsmen found that heavier powder charges, which produced higher velocities, frequently resulted in the lead bullets then used flattening out on striking the bones of large animals ; and it was only by hardening their bullets with tin or antimony that they were enabled to use heavy powder charges with success.

When nickel envelopes were first introduced for rifle bullets the penetration of solid pointed bullets such as the ·303 took sportsmen entirely by surprise. A later development in sporting rifles gave, as we have seen, considerably increased velocities, and at first these new weapons caused many disappointments on account of their decreased penetration when used against heavy ponderous game. The fault lay in the envelopes which were of the same thickness and consistency as those which had proved so satisfactory at lower velocities. And when stouter and harder envelopes were introduced the penetration was found to be increased again.

Some years ago a gentlemen who was interested in the North Canadian fur business discussed with me his difficulties in connection with shooting narwhal. He employed Eskimos to shoot these whales with ·303 rifles and had bought up a very large consignment of ·303 Mark VII ammunition at a low price in 1919. But unfortunately he found that the bullets mushroomed out almost on impact and failed to penetrate more than a few inches into the narwhal, even though the ranges at which shots were taken were always very close—under 20 yards.

I suggested that the remedy might lie in reducing the powder charges, and so reducing the velocity of impact. As the target was large and the range close the questions of accuracy and trajectory hardly came in. The ammunition was all of Canadian manufacture and loaded with Du Pont No. 16, a granular powder. Apart from the labour there was no great practical difficulty in removing the bullets from the cases and emptying out some of the powder charge and then pushing the bullets back again.

At first my friend was rather incredulous, but I asked him to try a few shots. If the idea failed, no harm would be done. He agreed, and in due course wrote to me to say that the penetration became ideal if about one quarter of the powder was removed from each cartridge. And he set his Eskimos, whom he told me were wonderfully clever with their hands, at reducing the powder charges in all the cartridges he had bought up.

In the case of the shotgun, too, there have been similar results. Comparisons with velocity tests have shown that penetration tests may place the cartridges in the wrong order, *i.e.* cartridges having the higher velocity would give the lower penetration.

This is not difficult to understand because in the penetration of pads so much depends on the pellets retaining their spherical form, and the higher the velocity the more likely pellets are to be deformed. It is a common experience, when conducting penetration tests with pads or sheets of cardboard, to find that it is the round pellets which have carried on through the greatest number of sheets.

When a sportsman is in doubt about the efficiency of his cartridges he sometimes feels that he must use some means of testing them. Pellet pads may be used for comparative tests, but the comparisons must not be pushed too far, for reasons which I have given, and it has actually been proved by experiment that a reduced powder charge, and therefore a lower velocity, can give a higher degree of penetration than a normal charge with normal velocity.

It might be argued that since a reduction of velocity may enhance the penetration a high velocity is a disadvantage. It should, however, be remembered that the game on which shotguns are used offers various kinds of resistance to the pellets according to whether bones or different parts of the body are struck. Also the actual shock to the living creature which is imparted by a high velocity must not be forgotten. Years of practical experience have proved the limits within which the best results are obtained, and I have only indicated some of the difficulties which attend the measurement of penetration in order to warn shooters against placing too much reliance on individual results obtained when using the ordinary pads for penetration experiments.

The late Dr. J. H. Walsh devoted a great deal of attention to this subject seventy years ago and rejected penetration tests as a means for measuring velocity in favour of an instrument called a " Force Gauge." This instrument measured the whole striking energy of the entire shot charge ; and since energy is directly proportional to velocity, it gave a very fair indication of the actual striking velocity. It was, however, a somewhat clumsy affair and was very soon replaced by a later invention which was worked electrically and known as a Chronograph.

Now, in actual practice it is difficult to measure the striking velocity as a routine test, and there is always the additional doubt of the best distance to take. Some would say 30 yards, while others recommend a longer range. So it will be seen that if striking velocities are measured at one range we would still be dependent on calculation in order to ascertain the striking velocity at any other range. Since we are thus dependent on calculation, no matter what range is taken for measuring the striking velocity, the actual length of this range makes little material difference. This being so, a range was adopted by all who measure velocities in this country on account of its practical convenience, a very important point when many tests have to be carried out. As a further convenience in experimental work, the velocity is measured *over* the first 20 yards of range instead of *at* any particular point. The velocity thus obtained is the average velocity of the pellets during their passage over the first 20 yards. This velocity is for all practical purposes identical with the actual striking velocity at 10 yards, the mid point.

Further, this velocity provides excellent data from which the velocities for all other sporting ranges may be calculated and tabulated, and so it may be regarded as a true measure of striking velocity, not for one range only, but for all.

The chronograph adapted for this purpose was invented by Le Boulenge of Belgium and is known as the Boulenge chronograph. It is a most wonderfully delicate instrument with which it is possible to measure to one five-thousandth part of a second. The broad principle lies in the measuring of the time between the breaking in succession of two electrical circuits, and the actual principles and working of the instrument can best be explained by a brief description of the instrument itself and the method of working.

A piece of soft iron is turned into a powerful magnet by winding round it a coil of insulated wire through which a current of electricity is passing. There are two electrical circuits, each complete in itself, and in each circuit there is one such coil of wire, through the centres of which are fixed two soft iron cores. Then, so long as a current flows in either circuit, the soft iron core in that

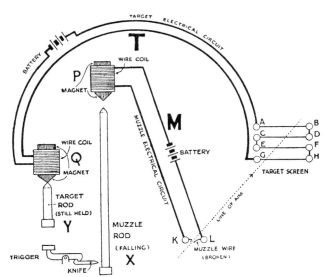

FIG. 14.—Diagram showing the essential parts of a chronograph.

circuit will be a magnet and will hold up any piece of iron which is not too heavy. Directly the current is broken the soft iron is no longer a magnet and the piece of iron which it held up will immediately drop under the influence of gravity. In the diagram given in Fig. 14, M is one of these two circuits, in this case known as the Muzzle circuit, while T is the other, or Target circuit. P is the oft iron core, surrounded by a coil of insulated wire and capable of being turned into a magnet, which is placed in circuit M. Q is a similar core and coil placed in circuit T. So long as the current is flowing in circuit M the magnet P will hold up the long iron-tipped rod X (known as the muzzle rod). Similarly the magnet Q will hold up the short (target) rod Y while there is a current in circuit T.

In the circuit T there are also eight terminals, A, B, C, D, E, F, G and H, all in one vertical plane, which are connected up as shown in the diagram with very fine copper wire (nickel-plated copper wire is preferable, being somewhat stronger to handle).

In the circuit M there are two terminals, K and L, which are connected by similar fine wire.

So long as all these wires are connected up and unbroken the circuits are complete and the magnets P and Q will hold up the rods X and Y. But directly the thin wire joining K and L is broken the current no longer flows in circuit M and consequently P is no longer a magnet, with the result that the rod X will immediately begin to fall.

Similarly the rod Y will be released directly any one of the thin wires AB, CD, EF or GH is broken.

The rod X merely falls straight down into a receptacle, but the rod Y falls upon a trigger which releases a knife which in its turn flies forwards under the influence of a spring (not shown in the diagram) and makes a small but clean mark on that part of the rod X which is immediately opposite it at the instant of release.

It will not be difficult to see, then, that if the two circuits are broken simultaneously the knife will mark the rod X very near to its lower extremity ; while if the circuit M is broken an appreciable time before T the knife mark will be some way from the lower end. In fact, the distance of the knife mark from the lower end of the rod X gives an indication of the time which passes between the breaking of the two circuits. This indication has been converted into actual fractions of a second by a process of not very intricate calculation, and the result is mechanically obtained by measuring the distance of the knife mark from the lower end with a special measurer on which the answer may be read in fractions of a second.

That is the whole principle of the electric chronograph.

In actual practice the wire connecting the terminals K and L is placed immediately across the middle of the muzzle of the gun which is to be used for firing the cartridges which are to be tested. The screen supporting the terminals A, B, C, D, E, F, G and H is placed exactly 20 yards from the muzzle. There is no mystery about this distance. It has simply been selected on account of its general convenience. When the gun is fired and the shot charge leaves the muzzle the wire KL is immediately severed and the rod X begins to drop. At least one of the wires AB, CD, EF or GH is sure to be broken by one of the pellets of the charge when it has travelled the 20 yards, and when this happens the rod Y is released which in its turn releases the trigger and the knife registers its mark on the rod X. The measurer then gives the actual time which has passed between the breaking of the two circuits, that is the time taken by the shot charge in passing over 20 yards, whence a simple calculation gives the average velocity of the shot charge over these 20 yards. For all practical purposes this average velocity may be assumed to be the actual velocity of the shot charge at mid-way, that is at 10 yards, and consequently this is the point at which velocities of shot charges are usually measured. And we have already seen that once the velocity is obtained at any one point a perfectly true and accurate comparison can be obtained for different cartridges at all sporting ranges.

The only variations ordinarily met with from the

method which has just been described are in the type of screen used for the target. When a number of cartridges have to be tested for velocity it is a nuisance to have to renew the wires on the screen after every shot, and so some observers use a swinging plate which moves away from electric terminals when struck by the shot charge. Others again use a fixed plate target on which is fixed a vibrating member. The electric current passes through this member, which is set in vibration when the target is struck, this breaking the circuit. Both these screens are undoubtedly more convenient than the wire screen, and save a considerable amount of trouble ; but I am inclined to doubt whether they are so certain. If, for example, either the swinging plate or vibrating screen is set so that it moves too easily, it is quite possible for the sound wave from the discharge at the muzzle to break the contact. This has been proved by firing a series of blank cartridges at one of these vibrating screens. The records obtained were wonderfully even, and every round gave a result of just over 1,100 feet per second. It so happens that this is quite an ordinary velocity to obtain for a charge of shot, but in this particular instance there was no shot, and the chronograph was merely recording the velocity of sound.

I cannot, therefore, help thinking that this type of screen might result in wrong deductions being made, because if the velocity of the shot charge was rather less than that of sound, as it normally is, the record obtained in every case would be the velocity of sound, and not that of the shot charge, if the screen had come out of adjustment. The advocates of this type of screen contend that the whole apparatus is checked before and after observations are made, and so chances of error are eliminated. I have no doubt that this is so, but at the same time I must confess to a preference for instruments in which the possible sources of error have been reduced to a minimum. With wire screens a record can only be obtained when a wire is actually severed by the projectile, and so the records obtained must be absolutely definite and cannot be open to doubt.

PLATE XI

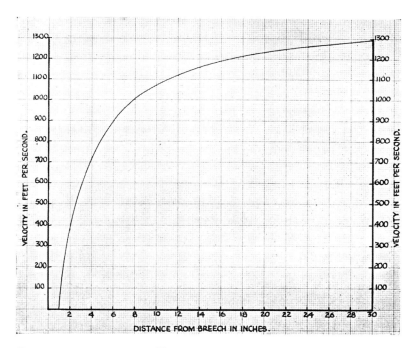

CURVE SHOWING HOW THE VELOCITY OF A SHOT CHARGE IS DEVELOPED IN
A PRESSURE BARREL

Load : 33 grains of Smokeless Diamond Powder and 1⅛ ounces of No. 6 Shot

And there is another advantage in the wire screen, namely that it simplifies the measuring of striking velocities at other ranges when one wishes to check calculations. For example, if we wish to obtain the striking velocity at 30 yards we can use two wire screen targets, one for each circuit, so as to obtain a measurement of the time interval between two points, each of which is at an equal distance from 30 yards, usually 25 yards and 35 yards.

Since 1939, however, a new type of screen has been evolved which combines almost all the advantages of the wire screen with the convenience of a vibrating screen. In this type the wires are really replaced by copper rods, the ends of which are held loosely in holes in short vertical brass or copper plates. The circuit is exactly similar to that shown in Fig. 14, the short brass or copper plates which carry the horizontal rods being shown by BD, CE and FH. Wooden side pieces prevent the rods from slipping out sideways and so preserve the contacts. These contacts are made by the weights of the rods resting in the holes in the vertical plates.

When any of the rods is struck by one or more pellets it is shaken momentarily and the contact is broken, but the weight of the rod then comes into play and the original contact and circuit are restored. The delicacy of the screen can be varied by the number of the rods as well as by their weights. The principle remains unaltered.

I have used one of these screens for some years and am quite confident that it yields nothing to the wire screen in accuracy of results. Its only disadvantage compared to the wire screen is that it cannot be adapted so easily for measuring the time interval between two points both of which are beyond the muzzle of the gun, since the pellets are deformed and deflected when striking the rods and do not continue in their original line of flight. At the same time it is probable that very good readings could be obtained by using a screen in which the rods were well separated from one another, so as to allow ample space for a sufficient number of pellets to pass between the rods of the first screen and on to the second, in which the rods could be placed closer together so as to ensure definite contact between pellets and rods. But for normal routine work of measuring series of velocities the convenience of the rod screen is so great that no one who has used it would ever wish to return to wires which have to be replaced after every shot.

There are one or two objections which may be raised to this brief explanation of the working of the electric chronograph.

First of all, it is well known that a charge of shot does not travel in one flat vertical plane at right angles to the line of fire, but strings out to an appreciable extent. How then can we be sure that one of the wires of the target screen has not been broken either by a very advanced or else by a very backward pellet ? In either case the result would be a false value.

The reply to this is that a series of rounds are always fired for velocity and the mean result taken. Also, that experience has proved that the wires are only broken or the copper rods are moved by the main bulk of the charge except on rare occasions, the front or back pellets seldom making a record. And when such a thing does occur the discrepancy of the reading from the rest of the series would indicate the firing of another confirming round. Further, in the type of gun almost invariably used for taking velocities, the recoil of each round is measured as well ; and it will be seen in the next chapter that this provides a wonderfully delicate check on the values obtained for velocity. If, for instance, one round in a series of five gave a very low velocity reading while the recoil was the same as the others, we would know that the velocity reading was that given by an exceptionally backward pellet and another confirming round would be fired.

The other objection to the chronograph method for measuring striking velocities is that, as has been emphasised already in this chapter, no projectile loses its velocity absolutely regularly. Consequently it is incorrect to assume that the striking velocity at 10 yards is the same as the average velocity over the whole 20 yards. This is true. As a matter of fact, the average velocity over the whole 20 yards is, as nearly as it is possible to determine, the same as the striking velocity at 9½ yards, and for the most accurate calculations this range is adopted ; but for purely practical convenience the difference between this distance and the actual mid-range is usually ignored, and so long as all who measure velocities with chronographs adopt the same plan the comparison remains true. And in any case the resulting error is so slight at all sporting ranges that for all practical purposes it is negligible.

The distance of 20 yards for measuring the velocity may also seem rather unsuitable, and one of 30 yards might appear more useful, as this is possibly nearer to the average range at which game is killed.

It should, however, be remembered that once the velocity has been obtained for any one distance the striking velocities, and velocities over the range, can be calculated for every other distance. It is, accordingly, immaterial what distance we take in the first place. The shorter range is more convenient in practice, as the observer, or his assistant, has not so far to walk in between shots to renew the wires on the target screen ; and it is extraordinary how the time occupied for this renewal mounts up when a large number of rounds have to be fired. There is also the fact that at 30 yards the shot charge has spread out more from front to rear, and so there is not quite such a good chance of getting the wires broken by the bulk of the shot charge every time as there is at 20 yards.

On the Continent the distance is 20 metres, and the Americans usually quote velocities over 40 yards.

ACTUAL VELOCITIES

We are now in a position to deal with the actual values for velocities which are generally obtained, when we will be able to see what increases have been made.

The time registered by the chronograph for the interval between the breaking of the muzzle and target circuits almost always lies between 0·055 and 0·06 of a second, which means that the average velocity of the shot charge during its first 20 yards of range is between 1,000 and 1,100 feet per second ; and for the standard load for an ordinary 12-bore game gun the velocity is round about 1,050 feet per second. There is nothing magical about this figure. Long experience of thousands of shooters spread over a great many years has taught us that the combination of powder and shot which results in this velocity is as good an all-round load as can be desired for ordinary game shooting. There has really been no appreciable change in this velocity for fifty years, and probably not for a hundred. Modern smokeless powders have rendered shooting far more pleasant : they produce less recoil ; no smoke ; less fouling in the barrel ; and are altogether nicer to use ; but they have made no appreciable change in the velocity of the shot charge. So it will be realised that this velocity is the same, for all practical purposes, as that developed in the guns used by our grandfathers, which explains why they could kill game just as far as we do now, although the effective sporting range of rifles has been quite doubled in the same period.

It must not be imagined, however, that no increase in velocity can be obtained. Cartridges can be specially loaded which give a velocity of about 1,150 feet per second, an increase of roughly 10 per cent. over the standard load at 10 yards. This may not seem much in comparison with the 20 and 30 per cent. increases in the cases of rifles, but it has been pointed out that these enhanced rifle velocities were only obtained by correspondingly big reductions in bullet weight, and increases of from 30 to 50 per cent. in pressure.

A shot charge of $\frac{15}{16}$ oz. is the lightest which can be used effectively in an ordinary 12-bore, and an ounce gives more certain results. These are reductions of but 12 and 6 per cent. on the standard load of $1\frac{1}{16}$, and if the velocity were increased further the resulting recoil would become excessive and the pressures would be too high.

So the fact must be faced that a velocity of about 1,150 feet per second is the biggest practical increase which can be made for a 12-bore 2½-inch cartridge ; that is, for the ordinary case. One friend of mine who devoted a great deal of time and thought to the subject used 2½-inch cartridges loaded with an abnormally heavy powder charge and $\frac{15}{16}$ oz. of shot which developed, on an average, a velocity of about 1,200 feet per second over 20 yards, and had a pair of special guns made to shoot them. But such cartridges require most careful loading if the best results are to be obtained ; and further, as will be seen when we come to consider Patterns, they need special guns.

Of course, a special type of powder could be made which would burn more slowly and which could be used in this class of cartridge with general safety ; but the slight extra velocity which it would give over that already obtainable—but 50 feet per second—is too small to make the manufacture of such a powder worth while.

Accordingly shooters must realise that a velocity of about 1,150 feet per second is the highest which can be obtained in an ordinary modern game gun firing 2½-inch cases, and so now it is time for us to see what advantages such a velocity gives over the standard in the matter of striking velocities at various ranges.

This can best be done by the help of tables which set out the actual striking velocities at all distances for different values of the ordinary velocity over 20 yards which is measured by the chronograph and which is always known as the " Observed Velocity."

I have also added tables giving the Times of Flight and average Velocities over the Range as these facts can be both interesting and instructive.

In all cases I have kept the velocities as appropriate as possible to the various sizes of shot, since the combination of high velocities and large shot is just as impracticable as that of low velocities and small shot.

STRIKING VELOCITIES IN FEET PER SECOND FOR DIF-
FERENT SIZES OF SHOT AT VARIOUS RANGES FOR
DIFFERENT OBSERVED VELOCITIES

TABLE VI
OBSERVED VELOCITY, 850 F.S.

Size of Shot.	Muzzle	RANGE IN YARDS.									
		10	20	30	40	50	60	70	80	90	100
A	904	847	772	703	637	574	516	461	411	361	319
BBB	908	846	768	693	625	559	498	442	388	341	296
BB	910	846	763	686	614	546	483	424	370	321	276

TABLE VII
OBSERVED VELOCITY, 900 F.S.

Size of Shot.	Muzzle	RANGE IN YARDS.									
		10	20	30	40	50	60	70	80	90	100
BB	968	895	808	727	653	583	517	456	399	347	300
B	972	895	803	719	641	568	502	439	381	330	281
1	977	895	796	708	625	547	477	412	352	298	250
2	982	894	790	696	610	529	457	390	329	274	226
3	988	894	785	687	596	513	437	369	307	250	204

TABLE VIII
OBSERVED VELOCITY, 950 F.S.

Size of Shot.	Muzzle	RANGE IN YARDS.									
		10	20	25	30	35	40	45	50	55	60
BB	1,026	945	849	807	766	726	688	652	616	582	548
B	1,031	944	844	800	758	717	677	639	602	564	532
1	1,037	944	837	790	745	697	660	619	580	542	506
2	1,042	944	831	782	734	688	645	606	565	526	488
3	1,048	943	826	774	724	676	630	586	544	504	466
4	1,054	943	818	764	711	660	612	566	521	481	441
4½	1,061	942	812	754	700	647	597	549	506	464	423
5	1,067	942	808	748	691	638	587	538	491	449	407
5½	1,071	942	804	743	685	630	578	528	481	436	395
6	1,077	942	798	733	674	616	565	515	465	415	376

TABLE IX

OBSERVED VELOCITY, 1,000 F.S.

Size of Shot.	Muzzle	Range in Yards.									
		10	20	25	30	35	40	45	50	55	60
BB	1,089	994	888	844	803	762	723	685	648	612	577
B	1,093	994	882	837	793	751	710	671	633	596	561
1	1,103	993	876	826	780	735	692	651	610	571	534
2	1,111	993	869	818	769	721	676	633	591	551	513
3	1,118	993	863	810	758	709	662	616	574	532	492
4	1,129	992	854	798	744	692	643	595	550	507	466
4½	1,139	992	848	789	732	679	627	578	531	487	445
5	1,145	991	844	783	725	670	617	567	519	474	432
5½	1,152	991	840	778	718	661	608	557	508	462	418
6	1,162	991	835	771	709	651	595	543	493	446	402
6½	1,170	990	830	763	693	636	576	523	473	426	382
7	1,182	990	824	755	690	628	569	515	462	414	369
8	1,217	989	811	737	666	600	537	478	425	374	327
9	1,242	988	796	715	640	569	505	443	388	336	288

TABLE X

OBSERVED VELOCITY, 1,050 F.S.

Size of Shot.	Muzzle	Range in Yards.									
		10	20	25	30	35	40	45	50	55	60
BB	1,167	1,043	927	878	835	793	753	714	677	640	605
B	1,174	1,043	923	872	827	783	742	701	662	624	588
1	1,188	1,043	914	861	813	766	723	680	639	599	561
2	1,203	1,042	907	851	801	753	706	662	619	578	538
3	1,212	1,042	900	843	791	740	692	645	601	558	517
4	1,228	1,041	891	832	778	724	673	624	577	534	491
4½	1,242	1,041	884	822	763	712	655	605	556	510	468
5	1,251	1,040	880	816	757	700	646	594	545	498	454
5½	1,259	1,040	875	811	750	691	637	584	534	486	441
6	1,271	1,040	869	802	740	680	623	569	518	469	424
6½	1,283	1,039	865	795	731	669	611	557	504	456	408
7	1,297	1,039	859	787	720	657	596	539	487	437	391
8	1,335	1,038	842	765	692	624	560	500	447	395	346
9	1,369	1,037	828	746	669	596	529	467	408	356	307

TABLE XI
OBSERVED VELOCITY, 1,100 F.S.

Size of Shot.	Muzzle	RANGE IN YARDS.								
		10	20	25	30	35	40	45	50	55	60
4	1,329	1,089	923	858	802	749	697	647	599	553	511
4½	1,345	1,088	916	849	790	733	680	628	579	532	488
5	1,354	1,088	911	842	782	724	669	616	566	518	473
5½	1,363	1,087	906	838	775	715	659	606	554	506	460
6	1,380	1,087	900	830	766	704	646	591	539	489	442
6½	1,393	1,086	894	822	756	693	636	577	524	474	426
7	1,410	1,086	888	813	745	679	619	560	505	455	407

TABLE XII
OBSERVED VELOCITY, 1,150 F.S.

Size of Shot.	Muzzle	RANGE IN YARDS.								
		10	20	25	30	35	40	45	50	55	60
4	1,420	1,135	949	882	823	769	716	665	617	570	527
4½	1,438	1,135	942	872	811	753	698	646	596	551	506
5	1,450	1,134	937	865	803	744	688	634	583	534	488
5½	1,461	1,134	932	859	796	735	677	623	571	521	475
6	1,475	1,134	925	851	786	723	664	609	555	504	457
6½	1,492	1,133	919	843	777	713	652	594	540	489	440
7	1,512	1,132	911	835	765	698	637	577	521	470	421

TABLE XIII
OBSERVED VELOCITY, 1,200 F.S.

Size of Shot.	Muzzle	RANGE IN YARDS.								
		10	20	25	30	35	40	45	50	55	60
4	1,508	1,182	972	901	840	781	728	676	627	580	537
4½	1,520	1,181	963	890	828	769	713	661	610	565	518
5	1,532	1,180	958	883	820	760	702	649	597	547	500
5½	1,544	1,180	953	877	812	751	692	638	585	534	487
6	1,562	1,179	946	870	803	739	679	622	569	517	469
6½	1,577	1,178	940	861	792	728	666	608	552	501	452
7	1,596	1,177	932	852	781	714	651	591	534	482	432

TIMES OF FLIGHT IN SECONDS FOR DIFFERENT SIZES OF SHOT OVER VARIOUS RANGES FOR DIFFERENT OBSERVED VELOCITIES

TABLE XIV

OBSERVED VELOCITY, 850 F.S.

Size of Shot.	RANGE IN YARDS.									
	10	20	30	40	50	60	70	80	90	100
A	·0340	·0707	·1118	·1564	·2076	·2629	·3240	·3915	·4699	·5580
BBB	·0339	·0707	·1121	·1574	·2090	·2659	·3299	·4012	·4839	·5780
BB	·0338	·0707	·1124	·1584	·2104	·2689	·3359	·4109	·4979	·5980

TABLE XV

OBSERVED VELOCITY, 900 F.S.

Size of Shot.	RANGE IN YARDS.									
	10	20	30	40	50	60	70	80	90	100
BB	·0320	·0668	·1071	·1505	·1993	·2528	·3143	·3860	·4630	·5520
B	·0319	·0668	·1074	·1515	·2018	·2573	·3218	·3970	·4800	·5800
1	·0318	·0668	·1077	·1525	·2043	·2618	·3293	·4090	·5000	·6100
2	·0317	·0668	·1080	·1535	·2068	·2663	·3368	·4220	·5230	·6420
3	·0316	·0668	··1083	·1545	·2093	·2708	·3443	·4360	·5500	·6760

TABLE XVI

OBSERVED VELOCITY, 950 F.S.

Size of Shot.	RANGE IN YARDS.									
	10	20	25	30	35	40	45	50	55	60
BB	·0303	·0632	·0818	·1010	·1212	·1425	·1644	·1890	·2130	·2400
B	·0301	·0632	·0820	·1014	·1220	·1437	·1662	·1915	·2165	·2450
1	·0299	·0632	·0822	·1018	·1228	·1449	·1680	·1940	·2200	·2500
2	·0297	·0632	·0824	·1022	·1236	·1461	·1698	·1965	·2235	·2550
3	·0295	·0632	·0826	·1026	·1244	·1473	·1716	·1990	·2270	·2600
4	·0293	·0632	·0828	·1030	·1252	·1485	·1735	·2015	·2305	·2650
1½	·0291	·0632	·0830	·1034	·1260	·1497	·1752	·2040	·2340	·2700
5	·0289	·0632	·0832	·1038	·1268	·1509	·1770	·2065	·2375	·2750
5½	·0287	·0632	·0834	·1042	·1276	·1521	·1788	·2090	·2410	·2800
6	·0285	·0632	·0836	·1046	·1284	·1533	·1806	·2115	·2445	·2850

TABLE XVII

OBSERVED VELOCITY, 1,000 F.S.

Size of Shot.	RANGE IN YARDS.									
	10	20	25	30	35	40	45	50	55	60
BB	·0284	·0600	·0778	·0958	·1154	·1359	·1565	·1790	·2029	·2273
B	·0283	·0600	·0780	·0962	·1161	·1370	·1582	·1815	·2064	·2320
1	·0282	·0600	·0782	·0966	·1168	·1381	·1599	·1840	·2099	·2367
2	·0281	·0600	·0784	·0970	·1175	·1392	·1616	·1865	·2134	·2414
3	·0280	·0600	·0786	·0974	·1182	·1403	·1633	·1890	·2169	·2461
4	·0279	·0600	·0788	·0978	·1189	·1414	·1650	·1915	·2204	·2508
4½	·0278	·0600	·0790	·0982	·1196	·1425	·1667	·1940	·2239	·2555
5	·0277	·0600	·0792	·0986	·1203	·1436	·1684	·1965	·2274	·2602
5½	·0276	·0600	·0794	·0990	·1210	·1447	·1701	·1990	·2309	·2649
6	·0275	·0600	·0796	·0994	·1217	·1458	·1718	·2015	·2344	·2696
6½	·0274	·0600	·0798	·0998	·1224	·1469	·1735	·2040	·2379	·2743
7	·0273	·0600	·0800	·1002	·1231	·1480	·1752	·2065	·2414	·2790
8	·0272	·0600	·0803	·1012	·1247	·1508	·1802	·2135	·2524	·2950
9	·0271	·0600	·0806	·1024	·1265	·1550	·1862	·2225	·2654	·3150

TABLE XVIII

OBSERVED VELOCITY, 1,050 F.S.

Size of Shot.	RANGE IN YARDS.									
	10	20	25	30	35	40	45	50	55	60
BB	·0266	·0571	·0743	·0913	·1101	·1299	·1497	·1718	·1939	·2177
B	·0265	·0571	·0744	·0916	·1107	·1309	·1513	·1740	·1970	·2220
1	·0264	·0571	·0745	·0919	·1113	·1319	·1529	·1762	·2001	·2263
2	·0263	·0571	·0746	·0922	·1119	·1329	·1545	·1784	·2032	·2306
3	·0262	·0571	·0747	·0925	·1125	·1339	·1561	·1806	·2063	·2349
4	·0261	·0571	·0748	·0928	·1131	·1349	·1577	·1828	·2094	·2392
4½	·0260	·0571	·0749	·0931	·1137	·1359	·1593	·1850	·2125	·2435
5	·0259	·0571	·0750	·0934	·1143	·1369	·1609	·1872	·2156	·2478
5½	·0258	·0571	·0751	·0937	·1149	·1379	·1625	·1894	·2187	·2521
6	·0257	·0571	·0752	·0940	·1155	·1389	·1641	·1916	·2218	·2564
6½	·0256	·0571	·0753	·0943	·1161	·1399	·1657	·1938	·2249	·2607
7	·0255	·0571	·0754	·0946	·1167	·1409	·1673	·1960	·2280	·2650
8	·0253	·0571	·0756	·0952	·1179	·1437	·1723	·2030	·2390	·2810
9	·0251	·0571	·0760	·0962	·1199	·1478	·1783	·2120	·2520	·3010

VELOCITY

TABLE XIX

OBSERVED VELOCITY, 1,100 F.S.

Size of Shot.	Range in Yards.									
	10	20	25	30	35	40	45	50	55	60
4	·0242	·0546	·0716	·0896	·1084	·1295	·1525	·1762	·2026	·2302
4½	·0241	·0546	·0717	·0898	·1090	·1305	·1540	·1782	·2055	·2341
5	·0240	·0546	·0718	·0900	·1096	·1315	·1555	·1802	·2084	·2380
5½	·0239	·0546	·0719	·0902	·1102	·1325	·1570	·1822	·2113	·2419
6	·0238	·0546	·0720	·0904	·1108	·1335	·1585	·1842	·2142	·2458
6½	·0237	·0546	·0721	·0906	·1114	·1345	·1600	·1862	·2171	·2497
7	·0236	·0546	·0722	·0908	·1120	·1355	·1615	·1882	·2200	·2536

TABLE XX

OBSERVED VELOCITY, 1,150 F.S.

Size of Shot.	Range in Yards.									
	10	20	25	30	35	40	45	50	55	60
4	·0230	·0522	·0686	·0866	·1048	·1250	·1470	·1703	·1960	·2236
4½	·0229	·0522	·0687	·0868	·1054	·1260	·1485	·1723	·1989	·2275
5	·0228	·0522	·0688	·0870	·1060	·1270	·1500	·1743	·2018	·2314
5½	·0227	·0522	·0689	·0872	·1066	·1280	·1515	·1763	·2047	·2353
6	·0226	·0522	·0690	·0874	·1072	·1290	·1530	·1783	·2076	·2392
6½	·0225	·0522	·0691	·0876	·1078	·1300	·1545	·1803	·2105	·2431
7	·0224	·0522	·0692	·0878	·1084	·1310	·1560	·1823	·2134	·2470

TABLE XXI

OBSERVED VELOCITY, 1,200 F.S.

Size of Shot.	Range in Yards.									
	10	20	25	30	35	40	45	50	55	60
4	·0222	·0500	·0672	·0837	·1032	·1238	·1429	·1660	·1914	·2164
4½	·0220	·0500	·0673	·0839	·1036	·1244	·1444	·1680	·1943	·2203
5	·0218	·0500	·0674	·0841	·1040	·1250	·1459	·1700	·1972	·2242
5½	·0216	·0500	·0675	·0843	·1044	·1256	·1474	·1720	·2001	·2281
6	·0214	·0500	·0676	·0845	·1048	·1262	·1489	·1740	·2030	·2320
6½	·0212	·0500	·0677	·0847	·1052	·1268	·1504	·1760	·2059	·2359
7	·0210	·0500	·0678	·0849	·1056	·1274	·1519	·1780	·2088	·2398

AVERAGE VELOCITIES IN FEET PER SECOND FOR DIF-
FERENT SIZES OF SHOT OVER VARIOUS RANGES FOR
DIFFERENT OBSERVED VELOCITIES

TABLE XXII

OBSERVED VELOCITY, 850 F.S.

Size of Shot.	RANGE IN YARDS.									
	10	20	30	40	50	60	70	80	90	100
A	883	850	806	768	724	685	648	613	576	538
BBB	886	850	803	763	718	677	637	599	559	520
BB	889	850	800	758	712	669	626	585	542	502

TABLE XXIII

OBSERVED VELOCITY, 900 F.S.

Size of Shot.	RANGE IN YARDS.									
	10	20	30	40	50	60	70	80	90	100
BB	938	900	841	798	753	712	669	622	584	544
B	941	900	838	793	744	700	653	604	563	518
1	944	900	836	788	735	688	638	586	540	492
2	947	900	833	783	726	676	624	568	517	468
3	950	900	831	778	717	664	610	550	491	424

TABLE XXIV

OBSERVED VELOCITY, 950 F.S.

Size of Shot.	RANGE IN YARDS.									
	10	20	25	30	35	40	45	50	55	60
BB	992	950	918	891	867	843	822	794	775	750
B	998	950	915	888	861	836	813	783	762	735
1	1,004	950	912	884	855	829	804	773	750	720
2	1,011	950	910	881	850	822	796	763	739	706
3	1,018	950	908	877	844	815	789	753	728	692
4	1,025	950	906	873	839	808	780	744	717	679
4½	1,032	950	904	870	833	802	772	735	706	667
5	1,039	950	902	867	828	796	764	726	695	655
5½	1,046	950	900	864	823	789	756	717	685	643
6	1,053	950	898	861	818	783	748	708	674	631

VELOCITY

195

TABLE XXV

OBSERVED VELOCITY, 1,000 F.S.

Size of Shot.	RANGE IN YARDS.									
	10	20	25	30	35	40	45	50	55	60
BB	1,057	1,000	965	940	910	883	863	838	814	792
B	1,061	1,000	962	937	905	876	854	827	800	776
1	1,064	1,000	959	933	900	869	845	815	787	761
2	1,068	1,000	956	929	894	862	836	804	774	746
3	1,072	1,000	954	925	888	855	827	793	761	732
4	1,076	1,000	952	921	883	848	819	783	749	718
4½	1,080	1,000	950	917	878	842	811	773	737	705
5	1,083	1,000	948	913	873	836	803	763	726	692
5½	1,087	1,000	946	909	868	830	795	753	715	679
6	1,092	1,000	944	906	863	823	787	744	704	667
6½	1,096	1,000	941	902	858	817	779	735	694	656
7	1,100	1,000	938	898	853	811	771	726	684	645
8	1,103	1,000	934	889	843	793	749	703	654	610
9	1,108	1,000	930	878	830	774	725	674	622	572

TABLE XXVI

OBSERVED VELOCITY, 1,050 F.S.

Size of Shot.	RANGE IN YARDS.									
	10	20	25	30	35	40	45	50	55	60
BB	1,128	1,050	1,010	987	954	924	902	873	851	827
B	1,132	1,050	1,008	983	950	917	892	862	837	811
1	1,136	1,050	1,006	979	944	910	883	851	824	796
2	1,141	1,050	1,004	976	939	903	874	841	812	781
3	1,145	1,050	1,003	973	934	896	865	831	800	767
4	1,150	1,050	1,002	970	929	889	856	821	788	753
4½	1,154	1,050	1,001	967	924	883	847	811	777	739
5	1,159	1,050	1,000	964	919	877	839	801	766	726
5½	1,163	1,050	999	961	914	870	831	792	755	714
6	1,168	1,050	998	958	909	863	823	783	744	702
6½	1,172	1,050	997	955	904	858	815	774	734	690
7	1,177	1,050	995	952	899	851	807	765	724	679
8	1,186	1,050	992	947	892	835	784	739	691	641
9	1,196	1,050	988	937	876	813	757	708	645	598

TABLE XXVII
OBSERVED VELOCITY, 1,100 F.S.

Size of Shots.	RANGE IN YARDS.									
	10	20	25	30	35	40	45	50	55	60
4	1,240	1,100	1,046	1,004	968	928	885	851	816	783
4½	1,245	1,100	1,045	1,002	963	921	877	842	805	770
5	1,250	1,100	1,044	1,000	958	914	868	833	794	757
5½	1,255	1,100	1,043	998	953	907	860	824	783	745
6	1,261	1,100	1,042	996	948	900	852	815	772	733
6½	1,266	1,100	1,041	994	943	893	844	806	761	721
7	1,272	1,100	1,040	992	938	886	836	797	750	710

TABLE XXVIII
OBSERVED VELOCITY, 1,150 F.S.

Size of Shot.	RANGE IN YARDS.									
	10	20	25	30	35	40	45	50	55	60
4	1,305	1,150	1,093	1,039	1,001	960	919	880	842	805
4½	1,311	1,150	1,092	1,036	995	952	910	870	830	791
5	1,317	1,150	1,091	1,034	990	945	901	860	818	778
5½	1,323	1,150	1,090	1,032	985	938	892	850	806	765
6	1,328	1,150	1,089	1,030	980	931	883	841	795	753
6½	1,334	1,150	1,087	1,028	974	924	874	832	784	741
7	1,340	1,150	1,085	1,025	968	917	865	823	773	729

TABLE XXIX
OBSERVED VELOCITY, 1,200 F.S.

Size of Shot.	RANGE IN YARDS.									
	10	20	25	30	35	40	45	50	55	60
4	1,352	1,200	1,116	1,074	1,017	970	944	903	862	832
4½	1,364	1,200	1,114	1,072	1,014	965	935	893	850	818
5	1,376	1,200	1,113	1,070	1,010	960	926	883	838	804
5½	1,389	1,200	1,112	1,068	1,006	955	917	873	826	790
6	1,402	1,200	1,111	1,066	1,002	950	908	863	814	776
6½	1,416	1,200	1,109	1,063	998	946	899	853	802	763
7	1,430	1,200	1,107	1,060	994	942	890	843	790	750

For purposes of comparison it is interesting to see how a rifle bullet behaves under similar conditions. At 300 yards the striking velocity of the ·303 Mark VI bullet happens to be 1,510 feet per second, which is a very similar velocity to that with which a charge of No. 7 shot leaves the muzzle when the Observed Velocity is 1,150 feet per second. Consequently if we take the Range Table for the ·303 Mark VI cartridge between the ranges of 300 and 360 yards we will get a very fair comparison between the behaviour of a rifle bullet of rather obsolete design and that of the pellets of an average charge of shot, particularly in regard to their respective capacities for retaining their velocity and overcoming the resistance of the air.

The particulars for the ·303 Mark VI bullet are given in the Table shown on the following page.

All the tables which have been given deserve careful study and the student of shotgun ballistics will be well repaid by such work, as the figures show more clearly and forcibly than any words what little actual effect at long range is brought about by comparatively large increases in muzzle velocity when the ordinary sizes of shot, such as No. 6, are used.

The following points in particular should be noticed.

(1) The " Observed Velocity " given by the chronograph which is usually quoted as the velocity developed by any batch of cartridges is something quite different from Muzzle Velocity. This is not nearly so generally understood as it ought to be, and there have been cases of individuals who were supposed to be authorities on the subject and who actually published statements which could only mean that they believed that Observed and Muzzle Velocities were identical. Although the difference is obvious its importance cannot be emphasised too strongly, as recoil is directly proportional to the muzzle velocity when the shot charge is the same, and for this reason a comparatively slight change in the Observed Velocity can bring about a much greater proportional change in the recoil.

Similarly, other things being equal, the muzzle velocity

TABLE XXX

RANGE TABLE FOR ·303 MARK VI CARTRIDGE FROM 300
TO 360 YARDS

Range in Yards . .	300	310	320	325	330	335
Striking Velocity in F.S.	1,510	1,494	1,478	1,470	1,462	1,454

Range in Yards	340	345	350	355	360
Striking Velocity in F.S. . .	1,446	1,438	1,430	1,422	1,415

Range in Yards.	Time of Flight in Seconds.	Average Velocity over the Range in F.S.
300 to 310	·0200	1,500
300 ,, 320	·0402	1,496
300 ,, 325	·0504	1,492
300 ,, 330	·0605	1,489
300 ,, 335	·0708	1,486
300 ,, 340	·0810	1,482
300 ,, 345	·0914	1,477
300 ,, 350	·1018	1,472
300 ,, 355	·1124	1,467
300 ,, 360	·1230	1,463

really follows the pressure ; and for this reason the pressure may have to be increased beyond the safety limit in order to bring about a seemingly small increase in Observed Velocity.

(2) The higher the velocity the more rapidly is the velocity reduced.

(3) The larger the shot the better it retains its velocity. In extreme cases this can become so marked that large shot can be propelled with a considerably lower initial velocity than small and yet have an actually higher striking velocity at long ranges.

(4) Slight variations in Observed Velocity, that is

variations of much less than 50 feet per second, can have but little practical effect.

I will not labour these points any further, but can only repeat that all these tables are well worth close study.

FACTORS AFFECTING VELOCITY

We must now consider the factors which affect the velocity of a shot charge. Once the charge has left the muzzle it has to fight its own battle against the resistance of the air, and there is little that we can do to help it. But what is possible should be done. It has been seen that the capacity for overcoming the resistance of the air which is possessed by any individual pellet is dependent on its weight, diameter and shape. Consequently it is of extreme importance that the shot should be graded as carefully as possible for size so as to ensure the weights and diameters of all the pellets in a charge being as nearly as possible constant. If, for example, a shot charge was made up of all sizes from No. 1 to No. 7 it hardly needs a study of the tables to show that the pellets will very soon string out during flight, the bigger pellets travelling much faster than the smaller ones. This is obviously undesirable, and so it is impossible to devote too great care to the proper grading of shot, and I am inclined to think that there is considerable room for improvement in this respect as I have already suggested in Chapter V.

The shape of the pellets is also of extreme importance as has already been emphasised in Chapter V. But however spherical the pellets are in the first place they are always liable to deformation during their passage up the bore, and very badly deformed pellets of one size of shot will lose velocity just as quickly as the normal pellets of even two sizes smaller.

There is no absolute remedy against deformation, and in actual practice I do not believe it has as much effect as some authorities declare. The remedies suggested to overcome this difficulty are plating the shot with some substance such as copper, nickel or tin, or else by making the shot harder.

All the metals suggested for plating shot are very nearly, if not quite, as soft as lead, and so it is difficult to see what material advantage can be gained, especially when the " plating " consists of a coating of but one-hundredth part of a thousandth of an inch, as it does in the case of one brand of shot.

Hardening the shot is an improvement to a certain extent, as experiments have shown in which the shot has been fired into water and collected.   Very soft shot was in every case found to be considerably more deformed than hard pellets.   Consequently soft shot has been discarded and at the present time there is little to choose between the hardness of the pellets of any British or foreign shot.

Many years of practical experience have shown what degree of hardness is the most satisfactory from every point of view, and this has now been generally adopted in all countries.   For this reason statements which sometimes appear in advertisements that any particular make of shot is much harder and less liable to deformation than that generally used should be regarded with caution, at the very least.

So it will be seen that the most we can do is to have our shot graded as accurately as possible for size, and if all shooters and gunmakers would constantly check the counts of the numbers of pellets to the ounce and reject any batches of cartridges or shot in which these counts varied even slightly I am sure that more would be achieved towards improvement in shot than by the adoption of any other means.

But before the shot charge leaves the muzzle of the gun there are various factors which can affect the velocity, and there are others which are commonly believed to affect it.   I propose, therefore to take these different factors in turn.

In very general terms it can be stated that anything which affects pressure will also affect velocity, as the velocity is developed by the pressure. This statement is absolutely true if we take it to mean the pressure the whole way along the barrel. It is a very common practice, however, to quote the 1-inch pressure as the pressure of a cartridge, as this is the maximum pressure developed ; and the 1-inch pressure and velocity do not necessarily vary in a manner which exactly corresponds.

The following are the factors which deserve consideration.

WEIGHT OF SHOT CHARGE. Provided the size of the bore and the weight of powder is the same a light shot charge results in a higher velocity than a heavy one. This is only to be expected as the lighter charge is more easily propelled. The increase in velocity, however, is not always so great as might be anticipated, because the light shot charge offers less resistance to the expansion of the powder gases, and so helps to lower the pressure ; and this reduced pressure cannot develop such a high velocity as the original pressure. The net result, however, is that a reduction in shot charge helps towards the attainment of a higher muzzle velocity. For example, the normal observed velocity for 26 grains of No. 60 powder and $1\frac{1}{16}$ of No. 5 or No. 6 shot is about 1,050 feet per second. If the shot charge is reduced to 1 oz. the observed velocity approaches 1,100 feet per second. But if the shot is reduced still further to $\frac{15}{16}$ oz. no further increase in observed velocity usually results unless the powder charge is also increased.

SIZE OF SHOT. We have seen how big shot retains its initial velocity much better than small. The use of small shot, however, tends to compensate for the subsequent falling-off in velocity by increasing the muzzle velocity. In Chapter VI we saw how small shot caused higher pressures, and it is the higher pressure thus produced which develops a somewhat higher muzzle velocity. The effect is that small shot is given a better start than large. But even so this compensation is not sufficient to counteract the later reduction in velocity except at very short ranges, and in actual practice it is usually noticed that the

observed velocities obtained with small shot are somewhat
lower than those given by large, even when the loading is
identical. For the normal sizes, however, that is from
Nos. 5 to 7 inclusive, the automatic compensation in
muzzle velocity does adjust matters so that the observed
velocity is practically the same.

POWDER CHARGE. The heavier the powder charge
the greater the pressure, and therefore the greater the
velocity. At the same time there is no hard and fast rule,
and it must be remembered that pressure is more affected
by tightness of loading and turnover than variations in
the powder charge. The importance of maintaining constant the resistance to the expansion of the powder gases
cannot be emphasised too strongly. If this resistance
is light the pressure and velocity resulting from the combustion of the charge will be on the low side, irrespective
of the weight of powder burned. In the case of rifles
muzzle velocity can be assumed with very fair accuracy
to vary in direct proportion to the weight of the powder
charge, provided the same bullet is used. But there is no
similar rule for shotguns ; and it is possible for a combination of 27 grains of No. 60 powder and 1 oz. of
shot to result in a lower velocity than 26 grains of the
same powder and $1\frac{1}{16}$ oz. of shot. In fact, not only is this
possible, but it is a common occurrence, and I have times
without number tested cartridges loaded with 34, 35 and
even 36 grains of a 33-grain powder and an ounce of
shot which gave no higher ballistics than the standard
33 grains and $1\frac{1}{16}$. A heavier powder charge occupies
more space in the cartridge, and this frequently results
in a shorter length of the case being left for the turnover. And a weak turnover will bring down the
ballistics to a far greater extent than they are raised
by the addition of an extra grain or two to the powder
charge.

Shooters, then, should beware of assuming that their
cartridges are developing a very high velocity just because
they happen to be loaded with an abnormally heavy
charge of powder ; for an increase in the powder is of no

avail unless the resistance to the expansion of the gases is maintained by means of a proper turnover.

DENSITY OF LOADING. The loading density, as was explained in Chapter VI, can have a very marked influence on pressure, and consequently on velocity. But even so the variations in velocity resulting from this cause will not usually be so great, especially in the case of bulk powders, as might be expected, and will not often amount to bigger differences in observed velocity than 50 feet per second.

VARIETY OF POWDER. There is a widespread and persistent belief amongst shooting-men that different kinds of powder develop very different velocities. This belief is almost certainly the result of the original advertisement of Smokeless Diamond which declared that powder to be " Marvellously Quick " ; and whenever a number of shooters are discussing loads and powders, one at least will be sure to declare that a certain brand of powder or cartridges is " very quick." Such a belief is really nothing more than a superstition, as all powders are standardised to develop the same ballistics, and the velocity of the shot charge is unaffected by the variety of powder used provided the charge, loading and ignition are correct.

The differences in the times of flight resulting from the greatest possible variations in the velocity obtainable with ordinary cartridges are so small that they cannot be detected by the human brain. I am perfectly aware that few of my readers will believe me when I make such statements ; nevertheless they are the strict truth.

Time and again have I tested particular brands of cartridges which I was assured were " extraordinarily quick," but which proved to have observed velocities of between 1,000 and 1,050 feet per second.

Similarly I have purposely given numbers of my friends samples of cartridges to try which developed observed velocities of even less than 1,000 feet per second, and yet I have been told that the cartridges were " very quick."

That cartridges can be loaded to develop higher average velocities over different ranges is an obvious truth. But that any human brain can distinguish between the different velocities at ordinary sporting ranges I cannot believe. Over 30 yards—quite an average longish shot— the difference between the time of flight of a charge of No. 6 shot which gave an observed velocity of 1,050 feet per second and one which gave an observed velocity of 1,150 feet per second is but 0·0074 of a second : that is only three-quarters of a hundredth part of a second. And this is the difference between the time of flight of the standard cartridge and that loaded to give almost the highest practical velocity. As a rule the difference in the time of flight is but little more than half the fraction of time I have given ; say at the very most one two hundredth part of a second. The man who can judge such small periods of time has yet to be born.

In an ordinary cartridge the greatest possible variations in velocity are those which have been given in the Tables, and these variations can be obtained with any variety of powder provided it is suitably loaded.

There is no greater fallacy than this " quickness " of different powders, at least when the term is applied to the average velocity of the shot charge over sporting ranges. In the case of a powder the technical interpretation of the expression " quick " is connected with the ease with which it can be ignited by a certain class of cap flame.

I can only repeat that, provided they are loaded correctly in cases which are capped with the most suitable caps, all shotgun powders develop the same velocity within certain narrow limits. These limits are dependent on the rate of combustion of the powder, which may vary with the percentage of moisture which it contains. And this, as has been explained in Chapters II and VI, can be effected by temperature.

It is possible also that different batches of the same powder may vary slightly in their combustion. But the differences in observed velocity from this cause will seldom amount to more than 10 to 20 feet per second.

The introduction of slow-burning powders such as No. 64 has provided a certain scope for increased velocities, but in actual practice this scope is too narrow for any appreciable increases in striking velocities at sporting ranges. These powders are primarily adapted for propelling heavier shot charges without increased pressures and do not give satisfactory results if the shot charges are too light. It is true that by their use heavy shot charges may be propelled with comparatively high velocities combined with normal pressures. But these velocities are no higher than those obtained with increased charges of ordinary powders and lighter shot loads. The real function of slow-burning powders is to render possible the use of increased shot charges at more or less normal velocities without raising the pressures unduly. Unless the weights of the shot charges are fully adequate the combustion is not satisfactory when the results will be poor. So the idea of employing them with light shot charges in order to obtain greatly enhanced velocities is quite unpractical.

SIZE OF BORE. It was explained in Chapter VI that a higher pressure was required to develop the same muzzle velocity in the case of bores much smaller than No. 12 owing to the fact that the relative effective area offered by the wadding against which the expanding gases exert pressure is reduced. The result is that small bores seldom give quite such high observed velocities as larger bores, although the difference is usually too little to have any practical effect. In actual practice, for instance, it is quite usual to find that 20-bore cartridges develop on an average about 25 feet per second less velocity over 20 yards than corresponding 12-bore cartridges. This difference, however, is not maintained in bores larger than No. 12 on account of the heavier shot charges which have to be propelled.

WADDING. It has been seen what an important influence the felt wadding can have on pressure : it has an exactly similar influence on velocity. This matter was dealt with at such length in Chapter VI that I will not repeat myself here, except to say that any type of wadding which causes a reduction in pressure, particularly the 6-inch pressure, will cause a big reduction in velocity. For this reason the dry felt wads which are sometimes used in hot climates often give velocities which are too low for effective results.

Cork wads reduce velocity in the same way, and if these are used with normal powder charges the observed velocities are very low indeed, frequently being but 900 feet per second and even less. By increasing the powder charge from 26 grains to 27 in the case of No. 60 powder in an ordinary 12-bore 2½-inch cartridge, normal velocities can be obtained when cork wads are used ; but even then cork wads should be employed with caution, as different types of cork wads behave in different ways, and increasing the powder charge to 27 grains will not necessarily result in normal velocities being developed, as many cartridge loaders believe. The only means of ensuring proper ballistics when cork wads are used is to test the cartridges both for pressure and velocity.

Feltine wads behave in a similar way to cork and need special loading, but these wads are so unsatisfactory and so unpleasant to use on account of the " blow back " which they give through breaking up on the discharge at the muzzle of the gun, that they are better avoided at all costs. Air-cushion wads with slightly reduced powder charges as explained on page 106 give as good results as felt.

TURNOVER. As in the case of Pressure, of all the factors which affect Velocity, Turnover is the most important, provided the loading is otherwise normal. A weak turnover offers little resistance to the initial expansion of the powder gases and so the pressure generated by the combustion of the powder charge is low, and the velocity is consequently reduced. Similarly a very hard turnover raises pressure, and therefore velocity. Variations in turnover can have far more effect on velocity than slight variations in the powder charge, and for this reason it is quite useless to split hairs over the comparative velocities developed by 33 grains of a 33-grain powder and 1 oz. of shot and by 34 grains of the same powder and the same shot charge. The turnover can have more influence on the result than an extra grain weight of powder, and if a hundred different lots of cartridges loaded with 33 grains and 1 oz. were tested for velocity against one hundred similar lots loaded with 34 grains and 1 oz., it would probably be found that there would be little, if any, practical difference in the average results obtained.

I have already laid such stress on the great importance of turnover that I fear the reader will be wearied with repetitions. But the effect of turnover can be so overwhelming that it cannot be emphasised too strongly ; for it is impossible to offer any opinion as to the likely behaviour of two different types of loads unless the turnover is carefully tested in each case.

When the full crimp turnover is used, especially with all-metal cases, variations in turnover strength are much less likely to arise.

LUBRICATION IN THE CARTRIDGE-CASE. This affects velocity in so far as it affects pressure, and for exactly the same reason. Here again, however, a very greasy cartridge-case usually means a soft paper tube which again means a weak turnover ; and so we return yet again to the factor which helps so largely to govern the ballistics developed by a cartridge.

CAP. As has already been explained the importance of matching powder and cap cannot be overestimated, and caps which do not suit the powder can lower the velocity to such an extent as to cause the cartridges to be quite ineffective.

LENGTH OF CARTRIDGE. The length of cartridge can have a very great influence on velocity, but this influence is indirect. A long case permits the use of larger charges of both powder and shot, and it is these increases in the charges which are the real cause of the higher ballistics. Consequently it is impossible to make any true comparison between cartridges of the same bore but of different lengths, as such cartridges require different guns. This is obvious ; but I am dealing with the matter because considerable misunderstandings have been caused by comparisons between American cartridges and British. Such comparisons have been invariably made by those interested in American cartridges and the British cartridges always suffer. As has already been stated, American velocities quoted are usually the observed results over 40 yards, and one sometimes sees letters in sporting papers, as well as advertisements, which declare that the velocities developed by American cartridges over 40 yards are about the same as those developed by ordinary British cartridges over 20 yards. If this statement is correct the superiority of the American cartridges would be beyond dispute. At the same time shooting men will probably wonder how it is that the Americans have been so successful in seemingly overcoming the laws of air resistance, which are the laws of Nature.

The truth is that the statement is only partly correct. The real facts are that an average velocity of about 1,040 feet per second over 40 yards is altogether exceptional and is only obtained by a combination of large shot and a very long cartridge.

The most usual American 12-bore cartridge consists of a 2¾-inch case with a fully crimped turnover and contains 1¼ oz. of shot with a corresponding powder charge. With this cartridge the average observed velocity over 40 yards is from 930 to 950 feet per second, not more, and this corresponds to an observed velocity over 20 yards of about 1,150 feet per second.

An average velocity of 1,040 feet per second over 40 yards is obtained only by the use of large shot, that is American No. 4, which corresponds very nearly to British No. 3, and by the adoption of 3-inch cases. These long cases enable heavy powder charges to be used in conjunction with 1¼ oz. of large shot with the result that a muzzle velocity approaching 1,700 feet per second is developed. Such an initial velocity gives an observed velocity over 40 yards of about 1,040 feet per second when large sizes of shot are used, and it is this combination of large shot and exceptional length of case which gives a result which is not infrequently claimed as being typical.

There can be no doubt that 12-bore 3-inch cases permit the use of very effective charges ; but partly because of the heavy recoil and partly on account of the high pressure, such cartridges require guns of 8 lb. and more in weight.

When comparisons are made between the ballistics of American and British cartridges such details as the size of shot, the length of the cartridge and the weight of the guns used should not be forgotten, or an entirely erroneous impression may be gained. For it is obviously absurd to compare the results given by guns of over 8 lb. in weight which fire 3-inch cartridges with those given by guns of but 6½ lb. or even less which take 2½-inch cartridges, quite apart from the size of shot used.

And it must be remembered that these particular results are exceptional even in America where the general length of 12-bore case is 2¾ inches and the usual weight of a 12-bore gun from 7 to 7½ lb. This combination, as has been stated, results in ballistics which are similar to those developed by the British 12-bore 2¾-inch cartridge ; and the corresponding American 12-bore load of 1⅛ ounces in the same length of cartridge gives ballistics which are the same as the British standard figures.

GUN. I have already explained that all game guns develop lower pressures than those obtained in a pressure barrel. The velocity is reduced in exactly the same way. Provided the pressures at both 1 and 6 inches are up to standard this reduction in velocity is not sufficient to make any practical difference. But if the pressures are very low the percentage loss in velocity due to the use of a game gun will be much greater than when the pressures are normal ; and for this reason cartridges which give very low pressures in a pressure barrel will very likely develop squib-like effects when fired in an ordinary gun.

There is a common belief that some guns shoot

"harder" than others, but it is quite incorrect. All game guns cause slightly lower ballistics than those developed in pressure barrels ; but the percentage reduction is, for all practical purposes, constant when any ordinary sound gun is used, and is generally between 2 and 3 per cent. Of course, if the gun was very old and worn and loose in both chamber and bore, the reduction in ballistics would be greater ; but such guns hardly deserve consideration.

STRENGTH OF STRIKER BLOW. There is also a belief that the strength of the striker blow has considerable effect on the velocity of the shot charge. But here again, the belief is erroneous. Provided the striker blow is sufficiently strong to result in a proper detonation of the cap, and not cause hang-fires, there is no proof that any extra strength of blow produces more violent combustion of the powder. Consequently an increase in the force of the striker blow will have no appreciable result on the "hard shooting" powers of a gun.

It is, however, true, as was explained on page 152, that the combination of abnormally weak cartridges and an abnormally weak striker blow will lower the ballistics, and therefore the velocity, to a greater extent than would have been the case had the striker blow been of usual strength. And similarly the combination of very violent cartridges and an extra strong striker blow will increase the velocity. But provided the cartridges develop ballistics which lie within normal limits, and the variation in the strength of the striker blow is within the limits of sound gun manufacture, there will be no practical variation in velocity.

LENGTH OF BARREL. Probably the commonest and easiest method of reducing the weight of a gun is by shortening the barrels, and since the demand for light guns is stronger than ever at the present time, many gunmakers are meeting this demand by fitting guns with barrels shorter than the more usual length. The shortest practical length seems to be 25 inches, but there are some leading gunmakers who believe that this length is too

short. Be that as it may, 25 inches is the shortest
length generally adopted, and many shooting men wonder
whether these short barrels result in sufficient loss in
velocity to cause a reduction in penetration and efficiency
against game. This is a very natural question to ask.
It is well known that the shorter the barrel in a rifle the
lower the muzzle velocity, and so it is but reasonable to
assume that a reduction in the length of shotgun barrels
has a similar effect.

The two cases, however, are not quite parallel. Rifle
powders retain their barrel pressures better than shotgun
powders so as to give enhanced velocities. In shotguns
a high barrel pressure near the muzzle causes a big
muzzle blast which tends to scatter the pattern, and so
shotgun powders are made to burn up more rapidly than
rifle powders. This being so, a reduction in barrel length
is less likely to have such a big effect on velocity in the
case of shotguns as in that of rifles.

Consequently it can be stated definitely, and with
absolute truth, that the reduction of barrel length in a
shotgun from 30 to 25 inches has no effect on velocity
as far as practical purposes of sport are concerned.
There is undoubtedly a reduction in velocity, but it is
not sufficient to cause any lack of penetration, even at
the longest sporting ranges.

It is, however, a matter of considerable importance
and interest to ascertain as nearly as we can just what
reduction in muzzle velocity does result from shortening
the barrels from 30 to 25 inches. This question is not
merely academic, as might be supposed, for it has been
suggested that it could be of the greatest help in determining the exact amount by which the weight of a gun can
be reduced when a change is made in barrel length. For
the weight of the gun determines the recoil ; and recoil
is dependent largely on the muzzle velocity as will be
seen in the next chapter. A study of the Tables of
Striking Velocities will show that a very big difference
in muzzle velocity of No. 6 shot results in comparatively
small differences in the striking velocities at sporting

ranges. This is because the resistance offered by the air is so much greater at high velocities than at lower speeds ; the effect of this difference in resistances being that velocity is reduced much more rapidly when it is high than when it is low. So whatever change in velocity is caused by shortening the barrels has little effect at sporting ranges, although the difference at the muzzle may be appreciable. And it is this difference which some gunmakers would like to ascertain in order to gain data on which to limit the weights of guns with short barrels.

In the case of rifles it has been possible to devise an empirical formula which gives an almost exact relation between muzzle velocity and length of barrel ; but in shotguns the problem is too intricate. This is not because, as is sometimes thought, we cannot calculate the muzzle velocity of the shot charge with the same degree of exactness as we can for a rifle bullet. Calculated muzzle velocities can be checked with considerable accuracy by actual measurements of recoil, and theoretical and observed results are found to agree as closely as can be expected.

The real difficulty is that there is such variation in the boring of guns that it is almost impossible to obtain actual experimental records which fit in with calculated results in the same way that can be done in the case of rifles.

The Rules of Proof lay down the dimensions for the diameter of the bore at the breech end of the barrel, but there are no such restrictions for the muzzle end. The result is that all gunmakers very wisely bore their guns so as to give the best possible patterns, and it was discovered many years ago that patterns could be improved by increasing the diameter of the bore towards the muzzle end. This widening of the bore must tend to reduce the barrel pressure in the forward part of the barrel, and this helps to reduce the muzzle blast which is a potent factor in causing irregular patterns. It is probable that no two gunmakers adopt quite the same system of boring ; and it is certainly a fact that guns built by the same maker frequently vary in their boring because the barrel regulator makes changes during the final stages of regulating the guns for pattern.

So it is really not altogether surprising that there is some discrepancy between results actually obtained in practice with game guns and those which are calculated for a pressure barrel.

Plate XI shows a calculated curve giving the development of the velocity of a shot charge of $1\frac{1}{16}$ oz. of No. 6 shot in a pressure barrel resulting from the combustion of a standard charge of smokeless powder.

According to this curve the loss in muzzle velocity due to a reduction in barrel length of from 30 to 25 inches is about 25 feet per second.

Tables IX to XI show that for ordinary observed velocities which lie between 1,000 and 1,100 feet per second any variation in the observed velocity of No. 6 shot is just about half the corresponding variation in the muzzle velocity. So it will be realised that a reduction in barrel length of from 30 to 25 inches should, in theory, only cause a reduction in observed velocity of from 12 to 13 feet per second.

In actual practice, however, the reduction is found to be considerably greater. The experiment of shooting game guns with 30- and 25-inch barrels in order to test the comparative observed velocities has been repeated again and again. The results vary, as do all experimental results ; but it seems to have been generally accepted that the loss in observed velocity when standard cartridges were used was about 40 feet per second.

In 1929 I repeated this experiment again, although I had already carried it out several times. But on this occasion I first of all fired five game guns with 30-inch barrels for velocity, and then five game guns with 25-inch barrels, and took the mean observed velocity of ten rounds from each gun. I was careful to gauge the chambers of all guns to see whether there was any marked difference in size, so as to discard any gun with an abnormally loose chamber in case this should bring about a loss in velocity which might be attributed to barrel length. The cartridge were all of the same lot and gave a standard observed velocity of about 1,050 feet per second from a pressure barrel.

The result was that in every single case the 25-inch barrels gave an appreciably lower observed velocity than the 30-inch. If the actual differences in muzzle velocities in game guns were the same as the calculated difference in a pressure barrel as shown in Plate XI, one would expect to find an occasional result in which the short barrels gave a similar, or even greater, observed velocity than the longer ones. But in every single case it was appreciably less, and the average reductions in observed velocity resulting from the 25-inch barrels was 38·6 feet per second, which would mean a corresponding reduction in muzzle velocity of about 75 feet per second.

Although this difference only confirmed previous experimental results it is no less than three times as great as that given by calculation, and so in 1930 I determined to repeat the experiment yet once more, but this time to eliminate any possible variations due to the different guns by cutting down the same barrel one inch at a time from 30 inches to 25 inches and taking the results of longer series of rounds fired with each length.

Accordingly I fired series of 20 shots from each length of the barrel and used cartridges which were loaded with accurately weighed charges of powder and shot, as well as with weighed wadding. As a further check I fired short series of shots with the same lot of cartridges through a full-choke pressure barrel between each 20-shot series in the experimental barrel in order to make sure that there was no variation in velocity during the day.

The experimental barrel which was cut down was a true cylinder, as this was the only type of boring which would remain the same on being shortened, and it is important to note that the diameter of this barrel at the forward end was 0·735 of an inch as opposed to the 0·729 of a pressure barrel.

The mean results of series of 20 shots from the different lengths of the experimental barrel as well as from the pressure barrel were as follows :

Barrel		Observed Velocity			
Pressure	30 in.	1,040 ft. per sec.			
Experimental	30 ,,	1,012	,,	,,	,,
,,	29 ,,	1,012	,,	,,	,,
,,	28 ,,	1,010	,,	,,	,,
,,	27 ,,	1,004	,,	,,	,,
,,	26 ,,	993	,,	,,	,,
,,	25 ,,	980	,,	,,	,,

These results are so regular and so confirmatory of previous experiments that myself I am inclined to accept them as being approximately correct, and think that we must recognise the fact that the actual and theoretical losses in velocity due to the variation of the length of a shotgun barrel do not agree, and that we must therefore search for an explanation.

But before we do so it will be of interest to give some details of the most exhaustive experiments in connection with this subject which have ever been carried out in this country.

The question of the recoil developed by short-barrelled guns had become so acute that Imperial Chemical Industries, Ltd., decided to investigate the problem exhaustively and the late Mr. W. D. Borland, whose name will always be associated with so much valuable work in connection with the development of E.C. powder in particular and caps and ballistic science in general, was asked to conduct the necessary experiments. This he did, and Imperial Chemical Industries, Ltd., most kindly placed the whole of the records of Mr. Borland's experiments at my disposal, and it is entirely owing to this generous act that I am able to quote these important and valuable results. Mr. Borland's experiments are so complete, and so interesting, that I have included them at length in Appendix VI, as the full details would occupy too much space in this chapter, apart from the fact that they might prove a little too technical for some readers.

I will accordingly here only describe the experiments in the briefest possible manner.

Mr. Borland used a specially constructed gun in which the length of barrel could be varied, and it was so made that the weight was always kept constant irrespective of the barrel length, extra weight being added when the barrel was shortened.

Mr. Borland spared no pains nor trouble in showing me his beautiful apparatus and in placing all his results at my disposal, and I would never have been able to epitomise them without his help.

Mr. Borland used a barrel of minimum gauge throughout, that is one of the same bore as a pressure barrel, and he found that the losses in observed velocity varied both with the type of powder and also with the amount of powder used in the charge. For instance, the greatest loss in velocity was obtained with a High Velocity load and the smallest loss with a Low Velocity load. The actual results were as follows.

Load.	Difference in Observed Velocity Developed by 30- and 25-inch Barrel.
33 grs. E.C. and $1\frac{1}{16}$ oz. No. 6	11 ft. per sec.
42 grs. Schultze and $1\frac{1}{16}$ oz. No. 6	30 ,, ,, ,,
33 grs. Smokeless Diamond and $1\frac{1}{16}$ oz. No. 6	24 ,, ,, ,,
34 grs. Smokeless Diamond and 1 oz. No. 6	42 ,, ,, ,,
30 grs. Smokeless Diamond and $1\frac{1}{4}$ oz. No. 4	7 ,, ,, ,,

It must be remembered that these differences are in observed velocity, and so the differences in muzzle velocity will be about double in each case.

Apart from the results given by E.C. powder and the Low Velocity load of 30 grains of Smokeless Diamond and $1\frac{1}{4}$ oz. of No. 4, the differences are far closer to those obtained in other experiments than to those given by calculation, and so I think they can be taken as confirming the approximate correctness of the other experimental results which have been recorded.

A reasonable explanation for the variation between theoretical and experimental results would seem to be

that in actual practice the combustion of the powder is
not quite so rapid and perfect as is assumed when making
the computations which gave the curve in Plate X. In
the case of E.C. the combustion was as rapid as was
assumed and the result was that theory and observation
agree. Similarly in the case of the Low Velocity load
there is less powder to be burnt, and so combustion was
completed more rapidly and the experimental result bore
out the theoretical. But in the other cases the combustion was very slightly slower, being slowest in the
case of the High Velocity load which contained more
powder, and in these cases the difference between theory
and practice was more pronounced.

And in an ordinary game gun, where the pressure is
lower than in a pressure barrel, combustion would tend
to become less rapid with the result that the loss in
velocity would be greater in practice than theory when
the barrel length is reduced.

So in actual practice I think that it can be assumed
that the loss in observed velocity due to a reduction in
barrel length to 25 inches will probably vary in game
guns from 10 to 50 feet per second, according to the
boring of the guns and the loads used. These differences
would mean reductions in muzzle velocity of from about
20 to 100 feet per second, and so I do not think it is
unreasonable to take the mean difference as being about
50 feet per second, especially as it fits in so well with the
results of repeated experiments.

This difference in muzzle velocity, as has been already
stated, can have no practical effect on penetration at any
sporting range : but it has long been thought possible
that it might have a certain effect on recoil. It is in this
connection, however, that Mr. Borland's experiments are
of paramount value and interest, for his researches have
shown that the recoil remained nearly constant in every
case, even though the velocity was reduced. This is a
discovery of the greatest possible importance, as it enables
us to fix the minimum permissible weight for a gun
irrespective of the length of barrel. Since, however, the

question of recoil is a subject which is being considered in the next chapter I will make no further reference to it here. I have dealt with this question of the effect of barrel length on velocity at some length because it is one about which there has been considerable misconception both in this country and abroad. It has been realised for many years that the effect on penetration was, for all practical purposes, *nil* ; but it was thought that it might affect recoil, and so the matter has been investigated exhaustively with the result that the truth has been established that reduction in barrel length from 30 to 25 inches does not help recoil, just as it does not lower penetration as far as practical purposes are concerned. It is also probable that dense double-based gelatinised powders tend to reduce the effect of barrel length of velocity.

CHOKE. The choke in a barrel, which is really a constriction in the bore near the muzzle, checks the velocity of the shot charge slightly and so the actual muzzle velocity from a choke is somewhat less than that from a true cylinder barrel, the reduction being dependent on the degree of choke.

But in spite of this reduction in muzzle velocity the actual observed velocity is slightly increased by choke.

Mr. Borland included velocity tests for a full choke and true cylinder in his experiments which have just been mentioned and found that, on an average, a full choke gave about 20 feet per second higher observed velocity than a true cylinder. This is only to be expected because the choke must keep the pellets closer together and therefore reduce air resistance during the early stages of the shot's flight ; and this reduction in air resistance enables the shot charge to retain its initial velocity better, with the result that the reduction in actual muzzle velocity is more than counterbalanced by the enhanced capacity of the shot for retaining velocity.

It is probable that the increase in observed velocity varies with the degree of choke, and so in actual practice the figure of 20 feet per second represents the maximum variation in observed velocity caused by two extreme types of boring. Game guns are seldom bored full choke and even less frequently true cylinder ; so the normal differences are less than 20 feet per second in observed velocity.

But in any case this maximum difference is too little to result in any practical effect in the shooting field.

MINIMUM EFFECTIVE VELOCITIES

I have already explained that penetration is a function of velocity, that is that penetration is dependent on velocity to a certain extent. Whatever the initial velocity of a shot charge may be there must come a range at which the striking velocity of the pellets has been reduced so much that they are no longer able to penetrate game, and it is most important to ascertain, as far as we can, what this minimum effective velocity is, as such knowledge will help us materially in any consideration of the best loads to use.

First of all it should be realised that this minimum effective velocity will vary with the size of shot used. Now there is a very general belief that small shot has a greater capacity for penetration than large when the striking velocities are the same in both cases, because the small shot is thought to " cut its way through the feathers and flesh of a bird like the sharp edge of a razor, while the large shot is like the blunt back of a razor and fails to cut in."

There can be no greater fallacy, because such a supposition completely ignores the question of the weights of the pellets. If these were the same as, for example, they might be were the small shot made of lead and the large shot made of aluminium, the small pellet would certainly penetrate farther than the large. But the weights are not the same, since all shot is made of lead, and larger shot has greater powers of penetration, velocity for velocity, just as it pushes its way more effectively through the air during flight.

Penetration is really dependent on the *energy* of the

pellet which takes into account its weight as well as its velocity, and consequently we must really study the pellet energies at different distances for various sizes of shot if we want to find out the ranges at which the pellets are likely to cease to be effective.

This is a difficult problem, and it is doubtful whether any two shooting men will agree as to the exact limits to the effective range for any particular size of shot. This is not in the least surprising because the velocities developed by shot cartridges vary ; but chiefly because individual ability for judging distance with extreme accuracy varies.

But whatever limit we impose it will always be safer to go too high rather than too low, as nothing can be worse than cartridges which are too weak to be effective.

I think that most shooting men will agree that the pellets of No. 6 from an ordinary standard cartridge will penetrate sufficiently for all ordinary purposes to ensure a kill at over 50 yards, providing only a vital spot is struck. Similarly, I think that it will generally be agreed that pellets of No. 7 shot from an ordinary standard cartridge will penetrate sufficiently at 45 yards. As a matter of fact, it is probable that the shot will penetrate sufficiently at greater ranges than these, but there is always the chance that such long shots are due to the lucky chance of some single pellet either hitting some very easily penetrable spot, or else of its having a higher velocity than usual because it happened to be rather oversized. So I think that we will be quite safe if we take 55 and 45 yards as the maximum effective ranges for No. 6 and No. 7 shot when fired with standard velocity.

If we turn to Table X and calculate the pellet energies for No. 6 at 55 yards and No. 7 at 45 yards it will be found that in each case the answer is approximately the same, namely very nearly 0·8 of a foot-pound.

Accordingly it will be perfectly safe and reasonable to take 0·8 of a foot-pound as the minimum energy necessary per pellet in order to ensure penetration on ordinary game. In doing this we will merely be following recognised custom. For instance, in artillery work it has been assumed that an energy of 40 foot-pounds is necessary to put a man out of action, and the size of the bullets for the 18-pounder and 13-pounder shrapnel shells was worked out from this assumption.

But since the energy of a pellet varies with its size as well as with a function of the velocity, the actual striking velocity necessary to result in an energy of 0·8 of a foot-pound will be different for every size of shot. So in order to simplify the consideration of this problem the following table has been compiled which gives the velocities for every size of shot which are necessary to result in a pellet energy of 0·8 of a foot-pound. These velocities have been termed the Minimum Effective Striking Velocities

TABLE XXXI

MINIMUM EFFECTIVE STRIKING VELOCITIES FOR DIFFERENT SIZES
OF SHOT

Size of Shot.	Minimum Effective Velocity in F.S.
A	215
BBB	222
BB	240
B	256
1	287
2	314
3	340
4	374
4½	406
5	426
5½	445
6	472
6½	496
7	529
8	609
9	690

Although this table gives the velocities necessary to result in a pellet energy of 0·8 foot-pound, it would be a mistake to adhere to them too rigorously. Penetration is dependent on energy, but also on the relative hardness of the pellet and the object to be penetrated. A snipe, for instance, is much more easily penetrated than a goose ; and it would be absurd to regard the same minimum pellet energy as necessary in each case. The table shows the lowest effective velocities for the average variety of game shot with a gun : pheasants, partridges, grouse, pigeon, mallard and wild duck, hares and rabbits. For birds such as wild geese the minimum pellet energy would probably have to be higher, perhaps as high as 1·5 foot-pounds ; while for woodcock, snipe and quail it can be lower ; and 0·5 foot-pound per pellet would probably be sufficient in the case of snipe, for example.

As a general guide, however, I think the table is fairly safe, especially as it does not err on the side of weakness.

The reader, however, will very likely prefer to know what the actual energies per pellet are for different sizes of shot at various ranges when propelled by different initial velocities.

The following Tables have, therefore, been included so as to enable anyone who is interested in the subject of loads and velocities to see for himself what the energy per pellet is in different circumstances, and at what ranges it drops below the limit of 0·8 of a foot-pound, as well as by how much. (See following pages, 223-225.)

STRIKING ENERGIES PER PELLET IN FOOT-POUNDS FOR DIFFERENT SIZES OF SHOT AT VARIOUS RANGES FOR DIFFERENT OBSERVED VELOCITIES

TABLE XXXII

Observed Velocity, 850 F.S.

Size of Shot.	Range in Yards.									
	10	20	30	40	50	60	70	80	90	100
A	13·90	11·60	9·60	7·88	6·42	5·16	4·12	3·28	2·53	1·98
BBB	11·57	9·54	7·58	6·33	5·08	4·03	3·17	2·43	1·88	1·42
BB	9·93	8·07	6·54	5·50	4·14	3·25	2·50	1·90	1·43	1·06

TABLE XXXIII

OBSERVED VELOCITY, 900 F.S.

Size of Shot.	RANGE IN YARDS.									
	10	20	30	40	50	60	70	80	90	100
BB	11·10	9·07	7·34	5·91	4·73	3·72	2·88	2·21	1·67	1·24
B	9·74	7·84	6·30	4·98	3·93	3·07	2·34	1·76	1·32	0·96
1	7·80	6·17	4·88	3·81	2·91	2·21	1·65	1·20	0·86	0·61
2	6·46	5·10	3·92	3·02	2·27	1·69	1·23	0·88	0·61	0·42
3	5·53	4·28	3·28	2·46	1·83	1·33	0·95	0·66	0·44	0·29

TABLE XXXIV

OBSERVED VELOCITY, 950 F.S.

Size of Shot.	RANGE IN YARDS.									
	10	20	25	30	35	40	45	50	55	60
BB	12·40	9·99	9·04	8·30	7·30	6·56	5·90	5·25	4·70	4·17
B	10·82	8·67	7·76	6·98	6·25	5·58	4·95	4·40	3·87	3·43
1	8·67	6·80	6·03	5·38	4·72	4·24	3·73	3·28	2·86	2·48
2	7·21	5·60	4·95	4·47	3·83	3·37	2·98	2·58	2·24	1·93
3	6·18	4·73	4·16	3·65	3·17	2·76	2·38	2·06	1·77	1·51
4	5·07	3·82	3·34	2·88	2·49	2·14	1·83	1·55	1·32	1·11
4½	4·30	3·20	2·77	2·38	2·03	1·73	1·47	1·24	1·05	0·88
5	3·92	2·88	2·48	2·10	1·81	1·53	1·28	1·06	0·90	0·73
5½	3·60	2·61	2·23	1·90	1·61	1·35	1·13	0·94	0·77	0·63
6	3·20	2·30	1·93	1·63	1·36	1·15	0·96	0·78	0·62	0·52

TABLE XXXV

Observed Velocity, 1,000 F.S.

Size of Shot.	RANGE IN YARDS.									
	10	20	25	30	35	40	45	50	55	60
BB	13·75	10·92	9·90	9·00	8·06	7·27	6·50	5·83	5·20	4·62
B	12·05	9·44	8·50	7·65	6·84	6·12	5·47	4·87	4·32	3·83
1	9·56	7·45	6·63	5·92	5·25	4·66	4·13	3·62	3·17	2·77
2	7·98	6·12	5·42	4·80	4·20	3·68	3·25	2·83	2·46	2·13
3	6·85	5·17	4·57	3·99	3·49	3·04	2·63	2·29	1·96	1·68
4	5·62	4·17	3·65	3·17	2·74	2·37	2·02	1·73	1·47	1·24
4½	4·78	3·49	3·02	2·60	2·23	1·91	1·62	1·37	1·15	0·96
5	4·34	3·15	2·72	2·33	1·99	1·68	1·43	1·19	1·00	0·83
5½	3·97	2·85	2·45	2·09	1·77	1·50	1·26	1·04	0·87	0·71
6	3·54	2·50	2·14	1·81	1·53	1·28	1·06	0·88	0·73	0·58
6½	3·16	2·23	1·89	1·55	1·31	1·07	0·89	0·76	0·59	0·47
7	2·80	1·95	1·63	1·36	1·13	0·93	0·76	0·61	0·49	0·39
8	2·11	1·42	1·18	0·96	0·78	0·62	0·49	0·39	0·30	0·23
9	1·64	1·06	0·86	0·69	0·54	0·43	0·33	0·25	0·19	0·14

TABLE XXXVI

Observed Velocity, 1,050 F.S.

Size of Shot.	RANGE IN YARDS.									
	10	20	25	30	35	40	45	50	55	60
BB	15·19	11·90	10·70	9·70	8·70	7·87	7·10	6·36	5·68	5·08
B	13·29	10·36	9·23	8·28	7·45	6·69	5·97	5·32	4·73	4·20
1	10·31	8·17	7·20	6·42	5·70	5·08	4·50	3·97	3·49	3·06
2	8·82	6·65	5·86	5·20	4·59	4·04	3·55	3·11	2·71	2·35
3	7·56	5·61	4·93	4·33	3·81	3·32	2·89	2·52	2·17	1·86
4	6·20	4·54	3·95	3·46	3·00	2·59	2·22	1·90	1·63	1·38
4½	5·29	3·80	3·28	2·82	2·46	2·09	1·78	1·51	1·27	1·06
5	4·79	3·42	2·94	2·53	2·16	1·85	1·56	1·32	1·10	0·91
5½	4·40	3·10	2·66	2·28	1·93	1·64	1·38	1·16	0·96	0·79
6	3·83	2·71	2·31	1·97	1·66	1·40	1·16	0·97	0·79	0·65
6½	3·50	2·43	2·04	1·73	1·45	1·21	1·00	0·83	0·70	0·54
7	3·10	2·16	1·77	1·48	1·23	1·01	0·83	0·68	0·55	0·44
8	2·33	1·53	1·26	1·03	0·84	0·68	0·54	0·43	0·34	0·26
9	1·81	1·15	0·93	0·75	0·60	0·47	0·37	0·28	0·21	0·16

TABLE XXXVII
OBSERVED VELOCITY, 1,100 F.S.

Size of Shot.	RANGE IN YARDS.									
	10	20	25	30	35	40	45	50	55	60
4	6·80	4·87	4·21	3·67	3·21	2·77	2·39	2·06	1·75	1·49
4½	5·78	4·07	3·50	3·03	2·62	2·25	1·92	1·63	1·38	1·16
5	5·25	3·67	3·13	2·70	2·32	1·98	1·68	1·42	1·19	0·99
5½	4·80	3·32	2·84	2·43	2·07	1·76	1·48	1·24	1·04	0·86
6	4·26	2·91	2·48	2·10	1·78	1·50	1·28	1·04	0·86	0·70
6½	3·83	2·58	2·18	1·85	1·55	1·31	1·04	0·89	0·73	0·59
7	3·37	2·25	1·89	1·58	1·32	1·10	0·90	0·73	0·59	0·47

TABLE XXXVIII
OBSERVED VELOCITY, 1,150 F.S.

Size of Shot.	RANGE IN YARDS.									
	10	20	25	30	35	40	45	50	55	60
4	7·38	5·14	4·43	3·87	3·38	2·93	2·53	2·18	1·86	1·59
4½	6·28	4·30	3·69	3·20	2·76	2·37	2·02	1·72	1·48	1·24
5	5·70	3·87	3·30	2·85	2·45	2·08	1·77	1·51	1·26	1·05
5½	5·22	3·51	2·98	2·57	2·18	1·86	1·57	1·32	1·10	0·91
6	4·65	3·07	2·60	2·22	1·89	1·59	1·33	1·11	0·92	0·75
6½	4·18	2·73	2·30	1·95	1·65	1·38	1·14	0·94	0·78	0·63
7	3·67	2·37	1·99	1·67	1·40	1·16	0·95	0·78	0·63	0·51

TABLE XXXIX
OBSERVED VELOCITY, 1,200 F.S.

Size of Shot.	RANGE IN YARDS.									
	10	20	25	30	35	40	45	50	55	60
4	8·00	5·40	4·63	4·03	3·47	3·03	2·61	2·24	1·92	1·64
4½	6·80	4·50	3·85	3·33	2·88	2·47	2·13	1·81	1·55	1·30
5	6·17	4·07	3·45	2·97	2·55	2·18	1·86	1·57	1·32	1·10
5½	5·65	3·67	3·11	2·68	2·28	1·94	1·65	1·38	1·16	0·96
6	5·00	3·21	2·72	2·32	1·97	1·66	1·39	1·17	0·97	0·79
6½	4·50	2·85	2·40	2·03	1·72	1·43	1·20	0·99	0·81	0·66
7	3·95	2·48	2·07	1·74	1·45	1·21	1·00	0·82	0·67	0·53

CHAPTER IX

RECOIL

O F the four Ballistics Elements Recoil is in some ways the most important, for it governs both construction of guns and the loading of cartridges. It is recoil that puts the limit to the lightness of a gun or the power of a cartridge. But in spite of its great importance the question of recoil is but little understood either by gunmakers or shooting men, while many cartridge loaders are wholly ignorant even of the elements of the problems raised by this question. There can be no doubt whatever about the existence of recoil, both because it can be felt and because it is a direct consequence of the Laws of Motion. From this it will be clear that there are two aspects of recoil : the practical aspect and the mathematical aspect.

In order to understand the question properly both aspects must be studied and the conclusions arrived at must be fitted in one with the other. In the past the practical gunmaker who built a gun and the sportsman who used it have only bothered about the practical aspect, with the result that both have been wandering in the dark and making alterations which were not based on any definite idea or principle. Similarly the ballistician who considered the mathematical aspect alone cut himself off from much valuable practical information, and fell back too much on mere theories.

In this chapter I propose to try to combine these two aspects in the hopes that the result may form a basis of useful and practical information.

Let us first consider the mathematical aspect, for when this is understood it will explain much that may have puzzled some who had only regarded the purely practical aspect.

As already stated recoil is a direct consequence of the

Laws of Motion. On the combustion of the powder charge contained in a cartridge which lies in the chamber of a gun, gases are liberated which expand immediately with great violence *and in every direction.* The walls of the chamber of the barrel are made sufficiently strong to withstand this violence, and consequently the full force of the expanding gases is directed along the line of the bore, both forwards *and backwards.* The backward force is of exactly the same degree of strength as the forward force.

Now the force developed by the expanding gases which are generated on the combustion of a powder charge is dependent on the opposition which it meets. If this opposition is light the force is very feeble, but the more this opposition is increased the greater is the force which is generated. We have already seen how in firearms this force is known as Pressure and that the greater the resistance to the immediate expansion of the powder gases the greater the pressure.

I have already dealt with this question at length in Chapter VI, but the problems of Pressure, Velocity and Recoil are so interconnected that I hope I will be forgiven for certain brief repetitions which I trust will be regarded in the light of recapitulation.

In shotgun cartridges the resistance to the expansion of the powder gases can be altered in two main ways : by changing the total weight of the shot and wads which is to be driven forwards ; or by varying the strength of the turnover.

In the first method the greater the total weight of shot charge and wads the greater the resistance ; while in the second a deep and tight turnover offers more resistance than a loose and shallow one.

Now so long as the total weights of the shot charge and wads are kept the same, and the turnover is constant in depth and tightness, the resistance to the expansion of the gases will remain the same ; and under these conditions the greater the pressure generated in the chamber the greater will be the velocity with which the shot charge leaves the muzzle of the gun. The importance of maintaining the resistance constant has purposely been emphasised because it is by no means uncommon to see comparisons drawn between the pressures and velocities generated by a certain charge of a certain powder with 1 oz. of shot and those generated with $1\frac{1}{16}$ or even $1\frac{1}{8}$ oz. of shot. Of course, the heavier shot charge will need a greater pressure to propel it with the same velocity as that given to the lighter shot charge ; and consequently comparisons such as these in no way refute the general statement that velocity is dependent on pressure.

It has already been asserted that the backward force developed by the expanding powder gases is equal in strength to the forward force. It is the latter which expels the shot charge, wads and powder gases from the muzzle of the barrel, and the former which drives the whole gun rearwards with that movement which is known as recoil or " kick." Consequently if we measure the strength of either the forward or backward force we obtain the strength of the force acting in the opposite direction. Given suitable apparatus it is equally easy to measure either the forward or backward force ; but since the measurement of the velocity of the shot charge is part of the ordinary routine of cartridge testing, both time and trouble are saved by combining the testing of cartridges with the measurement of the forward force developed by the expansion of the powder gases, for the velocity imparted to the shot charge is an indication of this force.

When any object moves it possesses what is known as momentum, and the faster it is moving the greater is its momentum. But momentum is also affected by the weight of the object as well as by its velocity : a heavy motor car running down a hill at but five miles an hour would be more difficult to stop than an empty perambulator moving at the same speed. It will be seen, therefore, that momentum depends on (1) the weight of the moving object, and (2) the velocity of the moving object. Now, like everything else, momentum can be measured, and this is done by multiplying the weight of the moving object by its velocity. For example, if a mass of 10 lb. is moving with a speed of 10 feet per second, its momentum is 10 × 10, or 100 units.

Now when a stationary object is suddenly set in motion by some force acting on it for a known short interval of time, that force can be measured by the total momentum which it imparts to the object which is set in motion. Let us assume that the object weighed 10 lb. and was given a velocity of 10 feet per second. Then the momentum imparted to that object by the force in the known time was 100 units. In other words the force acting for this time is sufficient to generate 100 units of momentum, no more and no less. So if we apply an identical force for the same short interval of time to another stationary object which weighs 20 lb. the momentum given to this second object will still be 100 units. But since this second body weighs 20 lb. the velocity which it is given cannot be so great, and it is actually obtained by dividing the 100 units of momentum by the 20 lb. weight of the body, which gives us an answer of 5 feet per second.

So we see that if we have two spherical balls on a table, one of which is just twice as heavy as the other, and a strong coiled spring is placed in a state of compression between them so that when it is released it will give each ball a straight shove off, the heavier ball will move off with just one half the velocity of the lighter one when the spring is released. If the heavy ball was four times as heavy as the light one its velocity would be but one-quarter of that of the other, and so on.

This is exactly what happens when a powder charge burns in the chamber of a gun and is converted into gas. And so it is clear that if we only measure the total forward momentum developed by the expanding gases we will also measure the total backward momentum ; and since we know the weight of the gun we will obtain the velocity with which it moves backwards by the momentum and its weight.

Let us take a concrete example. An ordinary standard 12-bore 2½-inch cartridge loaded with 26 grains of No. 60 powder, A.C. wadding and 1 1/16 oz. of No. 6 shot is fired in a gun weighing 6½ lb. The velocity of the shot charge is measured over the ordinary distance of 20 yards and proves to be 1,050 feet per second. This means that the velocity with which the shot charge actually left the muzzle was about 1,300 feet per second. So we find that the total forward momentum imparted to the shot charge by the combustion of the powder is 1 1/16 oz. multiplied by 1,300.

In order to bring this figure into the units of momentum which we quoted above the shot charge must be given in pounds ; but before we go any further we must see whether the shot charge was all that the powder gases had to eject from the muzzle. It certainly was not. In the first place there were the wads ; and then there were the actual gases themselves. On the assumption that perfect combustion took place—as it should—very nearly the whole of the powder will have been converted into gases, and so the total weight of these gases will equal the weight of the original powder charge. It is true that a certain amount of non-volatile residue will result from the combustion of the powder which is mostly blown from the muzzle of the gun. But in the case of a high-grade modern smokeless powder this proportion of non-volatile residue is small, and in any case it is quite reasonable to assume that the total weight of powder gases and non-volatile residue combined is equal to the original weight of the powder charge.

Since the shot charge and wads are expelled from the muzzle together they must leave with the same velocity. And if we assume that the average velocity of the ejection of the powder gases is the same as that of the shot and wads, we find that the shot charge, wads and powder gases were all given a velocity of 1,300 feet per second. Let us now tabulate the total weights of the ejecta. We will have

Weight of shot charge	. . 1 1/16 oz. or	464 grains.
Total weight of wadding	. . . .	45 ,,
Powder gases	. . . . . .	26 ,,
Total weight of ejecta	. . .	535 grains.

In order to bring this weight to pounds it must be divided by 7,000, since there are 7,000 grains in a pound. And to obtain the momentum it must be multiplied by 1,300, which is the velocity imparted. This is a simple sum and the answer works out almost exactly to 100 units.

So we find that the force generated by the combustion of the powder is enough to develop 100 units of momentum.

This means that the gun will also recoil backwards with 100 units of momentum ; and since its weight is 6½ lb., its velocity of total recoil is obtained by dividing 100 by 6½, which gives us 15·4 feet per second.

This velocity of recoil, together with the acceleration with which it is developed, is really the key of the problem. If these are very low the recoil is hardly felt, while if they become high the recoil in its turn becomes punishing. It is not difficult to understand this. The total momentum is a fixed quantity, and if a bullet of 1 oz. (or $\frac{1}{16}$ lb.) were given this same momentum, it would possess a velocity of 1,600 feet per second (since $\frac{1}{16} \times 1,600 = 100$) which would be more than sufficient to go right through a man, let alone kill him.

There must obviously be some limit beyond which the velocity of recoil becomes too great to be withstood, and long experience has shown that this limit is about 16 feet per second. There is nothing magical about this figure. It has simply been derived from many years of practical experience. The general consensus of opinion of shooters was taken by gunmakers who built guns to certain weights and loaded cartridges which gave certain velocities.

This is an excellent example of how the practical aspect of recoil helped the mathematical aspect. The combination of the general experience of numbers of shooters spread over a number of years provided certain data. It was but reasonable to assume that shooters did not like to use unnecessarily heavy guns, and the weights of gun in general use thus provided a very fair indication of the recoil which the normal man could withstand with comfort. And when this combination of experience and practice was analysed it was found that a velocity of recoil of about 16 feet per second was just about the limit which the ordinary man would stand when firing many shots in a day.   A velocity of 15 feet per second is comfortable : one of 10 feet per second negligible : while one of 18 feet per second is more than many men would care to tackle.

Since the total momentum of recoil is a fixed quantity when the same cartridges are used it will be obvious that the only way of reducing the velocity of recoil from the 15·4 feet per second of the 6½-lb. gun would be by increasing the weight of the gun.   Let us assume that the shooter finds from experience that he cannot stand a heavier recoil than 14·5 feet per second.   In order to determine the weight of gun he should use we must divide 100 by 14·5, when the answer is 6·9 lb., or 6 lb. 14¼ oz.   If, on the other hand, a shooter can stand a heavy recoil and wants as light a gun as possible we must divide 100 by 16, which is a high velocity of recoil, when we will get 6·25 lb., or 6 lb. 4 oz.

From this it will be clear that the combination of a light gun and a light recoil is an absolute impossibility unless we can reduce the total momentum of recoil, or in other words the total forward momentum of the ejecta.

This reduction can only be effected by reducing the weight of the ejecta or else by decreasing the muzzle velocity.   Long practical experience in the shooting field has shown that with ordinary sizes of shot a muzzle velocity of about 1,300 feet per second is necessary for a good cartridge, especially if game is to be killed clean at long sporting ranges and small sizes of shot are to be used. In the case of large shot there is no doubt that the muzzle velocity could be reduced very considerably without any loss of penetration at long range, for the simple reason that the larger sizes of shot maintain their velocity better than the small sizes.   But the smaller sizes of shot are necessary in ordinary game shooting in order to maintain pattern density.   So we find ourselves up against a limit which cannot go much below without risking loss of

PLATE XII

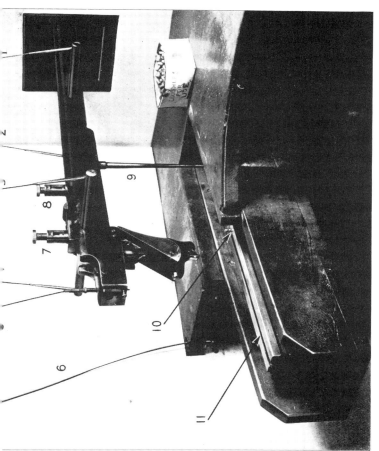

A "FIELD" PENDULUM GUN WITH WHICH SIMULTANEOUS RECORDS WERE OBTAINED FOR
VELOCITY, PRESSURE, AND RECOIL

The gun is shown with the breech open

1 2, 3, 4, Suspension wires; 5, 6, Bowden Release for firing; 7, 1-inch Piston; 8, 6-inch Piston; 9, Pointer for
operating Recoil Slide; 10, Recoil Slide; 11, Recoil Scale

power. So we must turn our attention to the weight of the ejecta.

It has already been seen that the ejecta are made up of (1) the shot charge ; (2) the wadding ; and (3) the powder gases which are equal to the weight of the powder charge.

It is now an increasingly common custom to load 12-bore cartridges with but an ounce of shot instead of the standard $1\frac{1}{16}$ oz., and this gives quite an appreciable reduction in the total weight of the ejecta.

Then the effect of the type of powder used on recoil is most interesting. The heavier the powder is bulk for bulk, the heavier will be the total weight of the gases, etc., evolved. In the case of black powder the charge corresponding to the 26 grains of No. 60 which we have taken was 3 drams, or 82 grains. This meant an increase in the total weight of the ejecta of 56 grains, and explains immediately why black powder gave a much heavier recoil than the modern smokeless powders. Similarly 42-grain bulk powders, such as Schultze and Poudre S, gave a heavier recoil than 33-grain powders, such as Smokeless Diamond or E.C., simply because the powder gases and non-volatile products together weighed 42 grains instead of 33 grains. And for the same reason 33-grain powders gave a heavier recoil than the modern dense powders.

There now only remains the wadding. The actual quantity of wadding cannot be reduced, but different types have different weights. Air Cushion wads are slightly heavier than felt while cork are much lighter. But cork wads need heavier powder charges than felt ; and A.C. wads slightly lighter charges. The net result is that the recoil developed by 33-grain powders and felt wads is similar to that given by A.C. wads and No. 60 powder. But even with extra powder the velocities developed with cork wads are frequently on the low side.

This extra powder charge adds slightly to the weight of the powder gases, but this increase in weight is more than counterbalanced by the difference between the weights of the cork and felt wads. At the same time this difference is not very large. Yet it is something ; and there is no doubt that cork wads do help to reduce recoil, although not nearly so much as is frequently claimed. It is still not altogether uncommon to find cartridges loaded with cork wads which do not contain the extra powder charge, and such cartridges usually give very feeble ballistics with low velocities. The reduction in recoil will then be very considerable, but this will be due to the lower muzzle velocity rather than to the cork wads, although it is true that the cork wads were responsible for this reduction in velocity.

In order to see exactly what difference there is in the recoil developed by the various powders, and combinations of shot and wadding which have been mentioned, I am giving the results tabulated in parallel columns. (See page 235.)

In this table the last line of all shows the increase or decrease per cent. above or below the recoil developed by a standard 12-bore 2½-inch cartridge, which is 100 units of momentum as has already been explained. These percentage differences are dependent on the weight of the ejecta which is partly made up of the wads. Now wadding varies in weight, and it is impossible to give figures which are always exact for every cartridge. I have given the actual weights of typical best quality wadding, but it is quite possible that some makes of felt wads may weigh more than those which I have taken in this table, while some makes of cork wads may weigh less. Accordingly the percentage variations can only be regarded as typical and approximate. Nevertheless it is doubtful whether the adoption of any different weights of wadding would result in a greater variation in recoil than 0·5 per cent. above those which I have given, while it would certainly be less than 1 per cent. So I think that this table can be regarded as indicating fairly correctly the average variations in recoil which are likely to result from changes in loading. The total weight of wadding when air-cushion wads are used instead of felt is practically the same as with felt.

The table shows that the two greatest advances

TABLE XL

VARIATIONS IN RECOIL RESULTING FROM DIFFERENT LOADS

LOADING.	Black Powder with Felt Wad and 1⅛-oz. Shot.	Black Powder with Felt Wad and 1 1/16-oz. Shot.	42-Grain Powder with Felt Wad and 1⅛-oz. Shot.	42-Grain Powder with Felt Wad and 1 1/16-oz. Shot.	33-Grain Powder with Felt Wad and 1 1/16-oz. Shot.	No. 60 Powder with A.C. Wad and 1 1/16-oz. Shot.	No. 60 Powder with Cork Wad and 1 1/16-oz. Shot.	No. 60 Powder with A.C. Wad and 1-oz. Shot.	No. 60 Powder with Cork Wad and 1-oz. Shot.
Weight of Shot Charge in Grains	492	464	492	464	464	464	464	437	437
Weight of Wadding in Grains	40	40	40	40	40	45	28	47	28
Weight of Powder in Grains	82	82	42	42	33	26	29	26	29
Total Weight of Ejecta in Grains	614	586	574	546	537	535	520	510	494
Momentum for M.V. of 1,300 F.S.	114	109	107	101·5	100	100	97	95	92
Percentage Difference from Standard	+ 14	+ 9	+ 7	+ 1·5	± 0	± 0	− 3	− 5	− 8

which have been made towards the reduction of recoil are due to the change from Black Powder to Smokeless and the reduction in the weight of the shot charge. The change from Black Powder to a 33-grain powder gave a reduction of 9 per cent. in recoil when $1\frac{1}{16}$ oz. of shot is used, while changes from $1\frac{1}{8}$ oz. of shot to $1\frac{1}{16}$ caused reductions of 5 and 5·5 per cent. according to whether the powder was black or a 42-grain bulk smokeless powder. And similarly the change from $1\frac{1}{16}$ oz. of shot to 1 oz. gave a reduction of 5 per cent. when a 33-grain powder was used with both charges. In all these instances felt wads have been used ; but a combination of a cork wad and an ounce of shot give an 8 per cent. reduction with No. 60 powder, which is nearly as great as that due to the change from black to smokeless.

But if the muzzle velocity of the standard cartridge were reduced by 100 feet per second the recoil momentum would be reduced from 100 to 92·3, and so we find that a reduction in muzzle velocity of but 100 feet per second actually has a greater effect on the recoil than anything that can be achieved by reducing the shot charge to an ounce or substituting cork wads for felt.

Now a reduction in muzzle velocity of 100 feet per second would mean an observed velocity of about 1,000 feet per second instead of the standard 1,050 feet per second ; and readers can see for themselves from Tables IX and X exactly what they stand to lose in striking velocity at sporting ranges by the change. A cartridge loaded with an ounce of shot and wadded with cork which develops an observed velocity of 1,000 feet per second would give a recoil momentum of 85 units, a reduction of 15 per cent. below the standard. Such a velocity is quite typical of that which is very commonly developed when cork wads are used, and this fact explains why cork wads seem to be so successful in reducing recoil. Of this reduction in recoil of 15 per cent., 7 per cent. is due to the lower velocity, 5 per cent. to the reduction of the shot charge to 1 oz., and only 3 per cent. to the cork wad. Yet the cork wad is usually given all the credit.

All sorts of statements are made to the effect that cork wads reduce recoil on account of their " cushioning " effect. Such statements merely indicate that the author is quite unacquainted with his subject. Cork wads, as has been explained, give a reduction in recoil of round about 3 per cent. because they weigh less than felt. Any further reduction in recoil beyond this 3 per cent. is invariably due either to light shot charges, or to lower muzzle velocities, or even to both.

Once this analysis or recoil is understood the reader will appreciate the enormous influence of muzzle velocity on recoil. Further, this mathematical aspect of the subject explains why it is that cartridges loaded with small shot so frequently give more recoil than those loaded with large. All the tables of Striking Velocities show that the smaller the shot the greater must be the muzzle velocity in order to attain the same observed velocity. And it has already been explained that small shot, owing to the greater resistance it offers, helps to raise the pressure and so the muzzle velocity. The net result is that the observed velocity is fairly constant for the same charges of powder and shot irrespective of the size of shot used, but that the muzzle velocity is higher in the case of small shot, and this causes a more pronounced recoil.

Another fact which will be appreciated will be the absurdity of the claims which are sometimes put forward in advertisements to the effect that certain cartridges develop " very low pressures, very high velocities and very light recoil." These three ballistic elements are intimately connected and any claim that velocity can be increased while the recoil is reduced (provided the shot charge is the same) is obviously too ridiculous to call for further comment.

It will be noticed that in this analysis of the momentum of recoil I have omitted any reference to effects which may be felt by the shooter due to differences in the rapidity with which the actual momentum is developed. Such effects are, I think, small since the rates of rise of pressure are very similar in the case of all the powders mentioned. In the case of Ballistite, however, the pressure was developed more rapidly and this steep rise of pressure resulted in a more noticeable recoil on the shoulder, although the total final momentum was slightly less than the 100 units of momentum given by the nominal load of No. 60 powder and an air-cushion wad.

At this point the practical reader may very likely say to himself : " This is all very well, but it is pure theory. How am I to know that all these statements are correct ? Nothing has been given in the way of corroboration, and I want some sort of proof before I can believe that recoil is entirely dependent on velocity and weight of the shot charge and other things."

Now this is a very proper and reasonable attitude to adopt, and so I will conclude my survey of the mathematical aspect of recoil by giving various examples of fact.

When cartridges are tested in this country a special type of pressure gun is used which is known as the " Field " Pendulum Pressure Gun. A photograph of one of these guns is given on Plate XII, and it will be seen that the gun really consists of a very heavy barrel which is sufficiently strong to be able to withstand any pressure which can possibly be generated by a shotgun cartridge. This heavy barrel is fitted with a falling block action ; the gauge is 12-bore and it is chambered and bored to minimum gauge, while the total weight of the gun is exactly 50 lb. It is suspended from the ceiling of the testing-room by two pairs of cross wires, one pair at each end, so as to permit a free recoil to take place on firing in a fixed vertical plane, after the manner of a pendulum. Hence its designation. It is fired by means of a pneumatic or bowden wire release which in no way interferes with the recoil. In order more easily to measure the rearward swing of recoil a vertical rod protrudes from underneath the gun, the lower end of which travels free in the groove of a horizontal measure which is fixed below

PLATE XIII

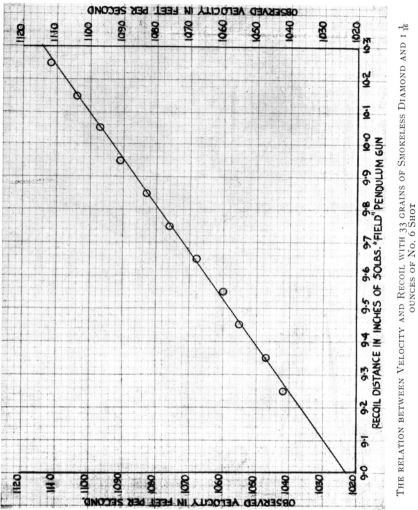

THE RELATION BETWEEN VELOCITY AND RECOIL WITH 33 GRAINS OF SMOKELESS DIAMOND AND 1 $\frac{1}{16}$ OUNCES OF NO. 6 SHOT

The graph shows the calculated relation, and the circles the results obtained by actual observation, each circle representing the mean result of ten rounds

the gun. In this groove there is placed a movable slide which is pushed back by the vertical rod when the gun recoils, and is left in the position of maximum recoil when the gun oscillates forwards once more. The total backward movement of the gun can thus be measured with great accuracy as the slide is fitted with a vernier which gives readings to one-hundredth part of an inch.

Two pistons are fitted in the barrel at distances of 1 and 6 inches from the breech face, and so pressure can be taken at these points.

Normally two chronograph circuits are used in front of the gun, and thus for every cartridge fired it is possible to obtain simultaneously values for the observed velocity of the shot charge over 20 yards, the pressure at 1 and 6 inches, and the recoil of the 50-lb. gun.

It is also possible to obtain the actual velocity of recoil of the pendulum gun by making the gun break two other chronograph circuits during its backward movement. If this velocity of recoil is measured it is a simple procedure to ascertain the velocity of recoil in the case of any other weight of gun. The product of the weight of the gun and the velocity of recoil, that is the total momentum, must be constant for each individual round ; and so the recoil velocity of a 6½-lb. gun can be obtained by taking the product of the recoil velocity of the 50-lb. pendulum gun and the weight of this gun, and dividing this total by 6½ lb., the weight of the shoulder gun.

For example, if the 50-lb. gun gave a recoil velocity of 1·965 feet per second, the total momentum of recoil would be 1·965 × 50 units, or 98·25 units. This momentum must be constant whatever the weight of the gun, so for a 6½-lb. gun the recoil velocity is given by dividing 98·25 by 6·5, which works out to 15·1 feet per second.

Accordingly, if we use two pairs of chronograph circuits, one to measure the velocity of the shot charge over 20 yards, and the other to measure the actual recoil velocity of the pendulum gun, we will obtain actual observed results of the relation between the observed velocity of the shot charge and the recoil velocity of an ordinary gun.

Then, if we take the observed velocity of the shot charge and calculate from this what the recoil velocity of the gun should be in theory, we will be able to compare the calculated relation between observed velocity and recoil with that actually given by experimental observations.

This has been done in the following table which gives a comparison between the instrumental and calculated velocities of recoil for a 6½-lb. gun for the same observed velocities.

TABLE XLI

COMPARISON BETWEEN INSTRUMENTAL AND CALCULATED
VELOCITIES OF RECOIL

Charge.		Total Weight of Ejecta including Wads in Grains.	Instrumental Results.		Calculated Results.	
Powder in Grains.	Shot in Oz.		Velocity of Shot Charge over 20 Yds.	Velocity of Recoil of 6½-lb. Gun.	Muzzle Velocity of Ejecta.	Velocity of Recoil of 6½-lb. Gun.
36 E.C. . .	1	521	1,140 f.s.	16·45 f.s.	1,458 f.s.	16·62 f.s.
33 E.C. . .	1	518	1,084 ,,	15·10 ,,	1,346 ,,	15·37 ,,
33 E.C. . .	1 1/16	543	1,062 ,,	15·73 ,,	1,300 ,,	15·54 ,,
33 E.C. . .	1⅛	568	1,034 ,,	15·85 ,,	1,237 ,,	15·50 ,,
40 Schultze .	1	525	1,076 ,,	15·80 ,,	1,330 ,,	15·30 ,,
40 Schultze .	1 1/16	550	1,060 ,,	16·12 ,,	1,296 ,,	15·67 ,,
42 Schultze .	1 1/16	552	1,094 ,,	16·62 ,,	1,366 ,,	16·57 ,,
42 Schultze .	1⅛	577	1,062 ,,	17·00 ,,	1,300 ,,	16·52 ,,

This table was originally published in the *Field* of August 6th, 1923. It should be understood that each observed result is the average obtained from a number of rounds, so as to eliminate as far as possible any chance of false results being obtained from single observations.

When the normal errors of any individual set of experiments are remembered I think it must be admitted that the observed and calculated velocities of recoil agree as nearly as can be expected.

Accordingly it should be realised that once the average observed velocity of any batch of cartridges is known it is possible to calculate with very fair accuracy the recoil velocity which will be developed in any given weight of gun.

As a corollary it is easy to see that if we measure the recoil velocity of a gun we can calculate the velocity of the shot charge with a similar degree of accuracy. In the case of a " Field " Pendulum Gun the distance through which the gun moves backward on recoil is dependent on the recoil velocity, and so it will be realised that it is not difficult to obtain a relation between this distance of recoil movement and the observed velocity of any cartridge, provided we know the weights of the powder and shot charges and wadding.

Although this problem may not have the same practical interest for sportsmen as the one which has just been examined it is of extreme importance in the testing of cartridges, because the recoil distance of the pendulum gun acts as a very excellent check on the value recorded for the observed velocity of any cartridge. And in the normal procedure of cartridge testing this system of counter checking should always be used so as to ensure the results being accurate.

Further, it must be remembered that the more evidence that can be produced in proof of the correctness of the method explained in this chapter for calculating recoil the better.

The following table was also published in the *Field* of August 6th, 1923, and gives a comparison of the actual observed velocities of different charges, and the observed velocities which were calculated from the recoil distance of the pendulum gun.

As before, every observed result is the average of a number of rounds. It will be seen that the greatest differences between the calculated and observed velocities over 20 yards is but 26 feet per second, which in the case of a velocity of 1,138 feet per second is but 2 per cent., while in the majority of cases the difference is under 1 per cent.

And some years ago I received further corroboration of the accuracy of the computed relation between

TABLE XLII

COMPARISON BETWEEN OBSERVED AND CALCULATED VELOCITIES
OVER 20 YARDS

Powder.	Load. Powder in Grains and Shot in Ounces.	Total Weight of Ejecta in Grains.	Average of Observed Results.		Calculated Velocity over 20 Yards.	Difference between Observed and Calculated Velocities.
			Recoil Distance in Inches.	Velocity over 20 Yards.		
E.C. . .	36 × 1	521	10·07	1,140	1,130	+ 10
,, . .	33 × 1	518	9·26	1,084	1,075	+ 9
,, . .	33 × 1 1⁄16	543	9·63	1,062	1,070	− 8
,, . .	33 × 1⅛	568	9·71	1,034	1,045	− 11
Schultze .	40 × 1	525	9·67	1,076	1,095	− 19
,, .	42 × 1	527	9·96	1,138	1,112	+ 26
,, .	42 × 1 1⁄16	552	10·25	1,094	1,102	− 8
,, .	42 × 1⅛	577	10·22	1,063	1,070	− 7
Black .	80 × 1⅛	655	11·35	1,042	1,055	− 13
,, .	84 × 1⅛	661	11·65	1,067	1,065	+ 2
,, .	88 × 1⅛	667	11·98	1,094	1,079	+ 15

observed velocity and recoil in the case of a pendulum gun which is really so remarkable that I feel it would be wrong not to include it in this chapter.

This corroboration was given me by the late Mr. E. F. Ashdown, who will be remembered by many as a most able ballistician, and by an even wider circle as a magnificent long-range match rifle shot, who made a record score of 223 out of 225 for 15 shots at 900, 1,000 and 1,100 yards when shooting for England in the Match for the Elcho Shield at Bisley in 1926.

Mr. Ashdown loaded up a large number of cartridges by hand with carefully weighed charges of different consignments of powder and shot, and with accurately weighed wadding. The main variation was in the consignments of powder, but there was also that inseparable from hand loaded cartridges including the tightness of the turnover. Two different powders were loaded, and in each case the shot charge was 1 1⁄16 oz. of No. 6 and the

wadding weighed 40 grains.   The powder charges were
33 grains of Smokeless Diamond and 42 grains of Schultze.

Both these lots of cartridges were then fired in a
pendulum gun and the observed velocity of the shot
charge and the recoil distance of the gun were measured
for every round.   The results were then divided into
groups of ten rounds, and the average observed velocity
and recoil distance was taken for each of these groups.

Mr. Ashdown made these tests in 1922 and was kind
enough to give me the records in 1925.

Plate XIII is a graph giving the computed relation
between the recoil distance of the pendulum gun and the
observed velocity of the shot charge when Smokeless
Diamond was the powder and which has been calculated
on the lines indicated in this chapter.   It will be seen
that within the limits of observed velocity which are
usually obtained with ordinary cartridges this graph is a
straight line.

The circles along the graph give the actual results
observed by Mr. Ashdown, and these results coincide
with the graph in a manner which can only be regarded
as remarkable.

Plate XIV shows a similar graph calculated for a 42-
grain powder, and the circles again denote Mr. Ashdown's
observed records.   In this case it will be seen that the
observed velocity as calculated for the graph is too high,
or in other words that the calculated recoil is too light.
But a second graph has been drawn in dotted lines parallel
to the calculated graph which almost exactly coincides
with the observed results.   The fact that the two graphs
are parallel shows that the difference is constant, and an
examination of the diagram shows that this difference is
exactly 15 feet per second throughout.   This means that
when a 42-grain powder was used the theoretical relation
between velocity and recoil gave an observed velocity of
15 feet per second too much, which is an error of just
about 1·5 per cent.

In itself this is a slight error, but the fact that it
existed in the case of a 42-grain powder and did not in

that of a 33-grain powder would seem to indicate that the relation between velocity and recoil is not exactly the same when a heavier type of bulk powder is used. And this is borne out by Table XLII, in which the biggest differences between calculated and observed results were those obtained with Schultze and Black Powder.

It is difficult to say definitely what is the cause for this variation of 1·5 per cent. between the results given by 33-grain and 42-grain powders. It seems not improbable that the variation was due to a difference in the velocity of efflux of the powder gases. This is admittedly pure theory, but it does not seem unreasonable.

But it is really immaterial whether the theory is correct or not. The main fact that emerges is that in the case of a 33-grain powder the calculated value of recoil corresponded as nearly as possible exactly to observed results, while in the case of a 42-grain powder it was very slightly less than that actually measured. The correctness of the general relation between velocity and recoil is beyond dispute.

Mr. Borland's experiments in connection with the effect of barrel length on velocity and recoil, which were mentioned in the last chapter and which are given in full in Appendix IV may seem, at first sight, to refute this relation between velocity and recoil. For, it will be remembered, that he found that as the barrel length was reduced from 30 to 25 inches the recoil remained practically constant even though there was a reduction in velocity.

But a closer study of Mr. Borland's work will reveal the fact that if the barrel length is reduced appreciably below 25 inches the recoil does drop as well as the velocity, and the relation is similar to that which has already been given.

Mr. Borland's explanation of this phenomenon was that in a very short barrel of 22 inches the dissipation of the powder into energy is not complete, and so the total momentum of recoil cannot be obtained with great exactness by measuring the forward momenta of the

PLATE XIV

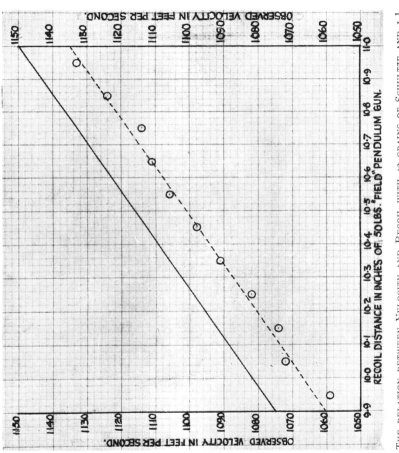

THE RELATION BETWEEN VELOCITY AND RECOIL WITH 42 GRAINS OF SCHULTZE AND $1\frac{1}{16}$ OUNCES OF No. 6 SHOT

The graph drawn with a continuous line shows the calculated relation when the same formula is used as that used for Plate XIII. The graph drawn with dotted lines shows the relation when a slightly different formula is used. The circles show the results obtained by actual observation, each circle representing the mean result of ten rounds

ejecta (shot, wads and powder gases). In a barrel of 25 inches, however, the dissipation of the powder into energy is more nearly complete and cannot be increased to any material extent by a longer barrel. The result is that the total momentum of the ejecta is to all intents the same in a 25-inch barrel as in one of 30 inches, but that the effects of the powder gases are not utilised quite so well in the shorter barrel, and do not expel the shot charge and wads from the muzzle at quite such a high velocity, and so do not utilise all their energy : this energy which is above that required for the expulsion of the shot charge and wads causes the powder gases themselves to be expelled from the muzzle of the gun with greater violence.

In other words, Mr. Borland suggested that the velocity with which the powder gases leave the muzzle is higher in comparison with the muzzle velocity of the shot charge in the case of a 25-inch barrel than one of 30 inches, while the intermediate lengths give proportional results.

This theory certainly explains all the observed facts, and seems so reasonable that personally I am inclined to regard it as being correct.

The essential point to realise is that the recoil developed in game guns fitted with barrels of from 30 to 25 inches is practically a constant quantity, even though the shorter barrels do cause a certain reduction in velocity. And it is probable that this constant recoil is due to the higher velocity with which the powder gases leave the muzzle in the case of the shorter barrels, which counteracts the lower muzzle velocity of the shot charge.

It will accordingly be realised that as far as recoil is concerned no reduction in the total weight of a gun is permissible if the barrels are shortened ; and that if any reduction is made in the weight of the gun the recoil will be increased.

Having now considered the mathematical aspect of recoil let us turn to the purely practical aspect and see how the two points of view fit in one with the other.

There can be no doubt that the study of the mathematical aspect will explain many facts which are common knowledge born of practical experience, such as the heavy recoil given by black powder in comparison to that given by a smokeless powder, and the greater recoil usually resulting from the use of small shot, points which have already been emphasised.

There are one or two points, however, which the purely mathematical aspect of recoil does not seem to take into consideration.

The first of these is the different effects on recoil given by different powders. According to the mathematical aspect the recoil was the same when any 33-grain powder was used, irrespective of the fact that it might have been Smokeless Diamond, E.C. or I.C.I. No. 51. Yet it is well known that some men found that one of these powders gave them a headache, while one of the others proved quite pleasant to use.

I think that this point should really be included in the problem of Gun Headache, which is dealt with in Vol. III. Possibly the rate of evolution of gas, which must affect the acceleration of the shot charge in the bore and therefore the acceleration of the development of momentum, is a contributory factor. This question is a very difficult one for which no satisfactory answer has yet been found ; but it is considered in Vol. III under the heading of Gun Headache.

Another point which the mathematical aspect of recoil does not seem to consider is the effect of firing very heavy charges. A 4-bore shoulder gun, for example, will always give a more punishing recoil than a smaller weapon, even if the velocity of recoil is kept down to 15 feet per second. This is partly accounted for by the increase in the total momentum of recoil due to the extra weight of the large gun. But at the same time the extra recoil seems to be greater than this increase in momentum should warrant, and I am inclined to attribute this entirely to the concussion resulting from the combustion of a very heavy charge of powder.

A further point which has very considerable effect on recoil, and which cannot be taken into account in the mathematical aspect of the subject, is the question of the proper balance of the gun itself. A well balanced gun of $6\frac{1}{2}$ lb. is altogether more pleasant to fire than a badly balanced gun of the same weight. The total momentum of recoil must be the same in each case, as is the actual recoil velocity ; yet the former gun appears to give a lighter recoil than the latter. This is simply because one holds a well balanced gun more suitably and so the recoil is taken by the arms as well as by the shoulder : and the more the force of recoil can be distributed the less severe it is on any one point. If the stock of a gun, for instance, is of such a shape that it happens to press against one small part of the shooter's face, the greater portion of the recoil will be stopped by this part of the face and a bruise will be the result. But if the stock is properly shaped to the individual shooter there will be no such concentration of pressure and the gun can then be used with comfort.

With these possible exceptions the purely mathematical aspect of recoil will help to explain all matters connected with the subject which may puzzle the practical sportsman. It will show him exactly what he stands to lose or gain as far as recoil is concerned by adopting some new load or taking to a different weight of gun : and what is more important still, it will show him *why* the loss or gain occurs.

So it now only remains to combine the mathematical aspect with practical usage and see what are the limits to the weights of guns which can normally be used by the average shooter. At the present time there is a very pronounced tendency to lighter guns : this is but natural, as the pleasure of using and handling a light gun is very real. At the same time this pleasure can be spoilt utterly if the recoil is excessive. There are some fortunate individuals who seem to be immune to recoil, but in a general consideration of the problem such should be disregarded just as we must disregard those who are hyper-sensitive and concentrate on the average type of shooter.

I have explained that long experience has proved that a velocity of recoil of about 16 feet per second seems to be the maximum which the normal man can withstand. This figure is obtained solely by an analysis of the weights of guns in general use, and so is based entirely on practice and not on theory.

But when we consider the average recoil which the normal shooter can stand with impunity we cannot adopt a figure for the recoil velocity which practical experience has proved to be the maximum. It is essential that we should adopt some value for the recoil velocity and it seems most reasonable to fix this value according to normal usage. I think that it will be generally agreed that $6\frac{1}{2}$ lb. is a very fair weight to take for an ordinary 12-bore which is used with normal cartridges firing $1\frac{1}{16}$ oz. of shot. It is perfectly true that much lighter guns are built, but either these are intended for use with light charges or else they are of a special type. The normal 12-bore game gun fitted with 28- to 30-inch barrels weighs on an average just about $6\frac{1}{2}$ lb., so we will adopt this weight as one datum point. The other is the momentum of recoil developed by an ordinary cartridge. When No. 60 powder and $1\frac{1}{16}$ oz. of shot are used this momentum has been seen to be almost exactly 100 units. This, then, is our second datum point. Working from these data the fact emerges that the average velocity of recoil of the normal gun is 15·4 feet per second. It will, accordingly, be not unreasonable to adopt this value for the recoil velocity which the average shooter can stand day in and day out.

If this is done we can determine exactly the weights of guns which will produce this velocity of recoil when different loads are used.

But there will probably be many shooters who are either less sensitive to recoil than the average, or else whose shooting consists chiefly of walking up when comparatively few shots are fired in a day. In these circumstances severity of recoil may not be so important as a light gun, for it must always be remembered that the effects of recoil can be cumulative and that many men can fire 50 cartridges in comfort who would feel the effects of recoil were they to fire 500 of the same cartridges from the same gun in a single day.

So both types of shooter must be considered. In one case the recoil velocity of 15·4 feet per second must be adopted as the maximum, but in the other case I think that we can go higher and take a recoil velocity of 16 feet per second as our limit.

Then many shooters use only an ounce of shot instead of the standard 1⅟₁₆, and this reduction in the shot charge lowers the recoil and permits the adoption of a lighter gun.

Accordingly in the following table I have given the minimum permissible weights for 12-bore guns when used with different loads if the recoil is to be kept within both normal and high limits.

TABLE XLIII

MINIMUM PERMISSIBLE WEIGHTS FOR 12-BORE GUNS WITH
DIFFERENT LOADS

Load to be Used.	Minimum Weight of Gun.	
	Normal Recoil.	Strong Recoil.
26 grs. No. 60 × 1⅟₁₆ oz.	6 lb. 8 oz.	6 lb. 4 oz.
,, ,, × 1 ,,	6 ,, 3 ,,	5 ,, 15 ,,

I am well aware that these limits are frequently exceeded, but this fact does not in any way prove that they are unnecessarily high.

Some gunmakers who build 12-bore guns which are much lighter than the limits given in the table, load special cartridges for their customers who use these guns. I have tested many of such cartridges and have invariably found them to give substantially lower velocities than the standard, which will explain at once why the resulting recoil is not severe.

Then, as has been stated, some shooters are more immune to recoil and such can use lighter guns with impunity.

But it is also a fact that in comparatively recent years the cartridge makers have received an increase in the number of complaints of excessive recoil, and in almost every case the complaint was traced to a combination of ordinary standard cartridges and very light 12-bore guns. In their desire to attract custom by building very light 12-bores some gunmakers are inclined to forget about recoil. A 12-bore which weighs but 5 lb. 12 oz. is delightful to handle in a shop and may seem quite pleasant to use when tried against clay targets with light loads at a shooting-ground. But when standard cartridges are used the recoil becomes a very different matter, and many shooters have been sadly disillusioned.

There is one outstanding fact which should never be forgotten, either by gunmaker or shooter.

A light gun needs a light load.

This is a general rule which is immutable, but it is naturally unwise to be dogmatic as to what constitutes a light gun or a light load in every possible circumstance. Allowance must always be made for individual variation. But for the average shooter the weights given in Table XLIII will prove a very useful guide.

I have considered the ordinary 12-bore at length because this is the size of gun in which greater variations are made in weight than in any other. But the weights of 16- and 20-bores are controlled in exactly the same manner. In fact, whatever the size of gun to be used the most suitable weight for the average shooter can be ascertained by taking the total momentum developed by the cartridge. This, as has been seen, is given by multiplying the total weight of the ejecta (shot charge, wadding and powder gases) by the muzzle velocity, which for general purposes can be assumed to be 1,300 feet per second. The correct weight of gun will then be given by dividing the value for the momentum by the velocity of recoil, which we have seen is best taken to be 15·4 feet per second.

There can be many slight variations to these figures, but they form an absolutely sound basis on which to work, and if due regard is paid to them the ballistic element of Recoil will prove to be of the greatest help in both the design of game guns and the loading of cartridges.

APPENDIX I

THE CALCULATION OF STRIKING VELOCITIES AND TIMES OF FLIGHT OF SHOT CHARGES

IN Chapter V it was pointed out that the actual pellets of any particular size of shot, no matter how carefully they may be sifted, will vary slightly in size, and therefore in weight. The Ballistic Coefficient of any projectile is dependent partly on the projectile's size and shape and partly on its weight. So it will be realised that the Ballistic Coefficients of the pellets which go to make up any shot charge may vary to a certain extent. For purposes of calculation we must assume some average weight to represent average behaviour. All calculated striking velocities, times of flight, etc., give the average result obtained by a pellet which is theoretically perfect : a point which must always be remembered when comparisons are pushed between individual experiments.

In order to obtain the diameter we must calculate this dimension from a truly spherical pellet of the exact theoretical size and the specific gravity of hard lead, namely 11·35.

Working on this principle, and taking d to be the diameter of any given size of pellet, and N the number of pellets of that size to the ounce, we find that

$$d = 0\cdot6628 \div \sqrt[3]{N} \text{ inches.}$$

This was the formula which was used for determining the diameters of the different sizes of pellets given in Table I.

Now the shape of individual pellets varies in exactly the same manner as does the diameter, and consequently we must adopt some value for the shape factor of the Ballistic Coefficient, or the Coefficient of Shape, which can in reality only be attributed to a perfectly spherical pellet. But here we have another difficulty, for although in theory an exact value for any Coefficient of Shape can be calculated, in actual practice really good results are only obtained with Ballistic Tables when the shape of the projectile under consideration is as nearly as possible similar to those with which the experiments were made from which the tables were calculated.

But when a great number of experiments are made with a projectile of a different shape from those used for providing the data from which the tables were computed, and when these

253

results are compared with others calculated from the tables, we are enabled, by substitution, to obtain a value for the Coefficient of Shape which can be applied with entire suitability to the differently shaped projectiles when calculating their behaviour with the tables.

Working on this principle the late Mr. F. W. Jones found that if the Coefficient of Shape was given a value of 2·3 for shot pellets it was possible to calculate striking velocities at different ranges and the times of flight over these ranges with the Shoeburyness Ballistic Tables and so obtain results which agree in a very marked manner with experimental values.

These Ballistic Tables are those which are given in the Government *Text-Books of Gunnery* and the *Text-Book of Small Arms*, 1909. The *Text-Books of Gunnery* are not available to the general public and the *Text-Book of Small Arms*, 1909, is now out of print. But these Shoeburyness Ballistic Tables were published separately before 1914 and could be obtained through any bookseller for 4s. The Ballistic Tables published in the *Text-Book of Small Arms*, 1929, were computed specially for rifle work and should not be used for shotgun calculations.

Now the Ballistic Coefficient of any projectile is denoted by C and is given by the formula,

$$C = \frac{W}{nd^2},$$

where W is the weight of the projectile in pounds, d its diameter in inches, and n a term known as the Coefficient of Reduction which in all small-arm ballistics—both rifle and shotgun—can be assumed to be synonymous with the Coefficient of Shape, which we have seen is 2·3 in the case of shot pellets.

So if we substitute with N, the number of pellets to the ounce, we obtain the formula,

$$C = 0·06186 \div \sqrt[3]{N}.$$

Working with this formula the Ballistic Coefficients of the different sizes of shot are given in the table on page 253.

The method adopted for calculating velocities at different ranges and times of flight is that universally employed when using ballistic tables, but two assumptions are made to obtain convenient starting-points.

The first, and really the most important, is the assumption that the observed velocity over 20 yards obtained with a chronograph is the actual striking velocity at 9½ yards. As was pointed out in Chapter VII, this is a perfectly reasonable assumption and one which fits in accurately with all known facts.

TABLE XLIV

BALLISTIC COEFFICIENTS OF DIFFERENT SIZES OF SHOT

Size of Shot.	Ballistic Coefficient. C
LG	0·03483
MG	·03233
SG	·03093
Special SG	·02846
SSG	·02508
SSSG	·02284
SSSSG	·02115
SSSSSG or AAAA . . .	·01991
AAA	·01890
AA	·01809
A	·01679
BBB	·01581
BB	·01501
B	·01434
1	·01332
2	·01254
3	·01191
4	·01116
4½	·01058
5	·01024
5½	·00995
6	·00955
6½	·00924
7	·00886
8	·00807
9	·00742
10	·00653

The second assumption is of a very different nature and is entirely in connection with the actual muzzle velocity of the shot charge. In practice the shooter is far more interested in the striking velocities of different shot sizes and different loads at sporting ranges than in the muzzle velocity. In fact, the only object of ascertaining the muzzle velocity is to enable calculations to be made in connection with recoil. But in any case a range table of any projectile can hardly be considered complete without the muzzle velocity, and so the muzzle velocity is calculated with the tables.

In making this calculation, however, it is assumed that the actual muzzle velocity is the same as that obtained at a range of 3 yards by means of the tables, and that for all practical purposes the velocity of the shot charge over this first 3 yards of range is constant.

This is not quite such a startling assumption as may at first sight be imagined, although the problem is admittedly difficult. The spark photographs of shot charges in flight taken by Mr. P. P. Quayle and published in the *American Rifleman* of October 15th, 1925, showed that at $3\frac{1}{2}$ feet from the muzzle the shot charge is moving as a single projectile because there was a single air-wave, while at 12 feet the pellets are giving individual air-waves. But it is both possible, and probable, that back pellets are protected from the full effects of the air resistance by the front pellets. For 3 yards, therefore, the shot charge may be moving quite independently of the size of the shot pellets of which it is composed, and in any case the air resistance must be materially less than that encountered by an independent pellet of the charge.

In the *Field* of April 1st, 1899, Mr. G. G. André published the results of his experiments with the Jervis-Smith Tram-Chronograph. These experiments showed that the velocity of the shot charge increased during the first $4\frac{1}{2}$ feet of flight from the muzzle, and then gradually decreased so that the average velocity over 10 feet was the same as that at the muzzle.

It is true that other workers with the Tram-Chronograph were doubtful whether a total time reading of but $\frac{1}{1000}$ of a second could be subdivided with sufficient accuracy to show individual variations in velocity. But the possibility of Mr. André's results being at any rate approximately correct has been emphasised in recent researches.

Consequently the assumption that the striking velocity at 3 yards as obtained with the tables is the same as the muzzle velocity cannot be regarded as being unreasonable.

So it will now be realised that the procedure adopted for the calculation of striking velocities at any range, or the time of flight over any range, is as follows :

(1) The observed velocity over 20 yards as measured by the chronograph is taken as being equal to the striking velocity at 9½ yards.

(2) With this striking velocity and the Ballistic Coefficients given in Table XLIV the velocity at 3 yards is calculated with the Shoeburyness Ballistic Tables, and this result is called the muzzle velocity. The velocity from the muzzle to 3 yards is assumed to be constant.

(3) The time of flight from the muzzle to 3 yards is obtained from the assumed constant velocity over that distance.

(4) The striking velocities, times of flight, etc., are then calculated from the muzzle velocity at 3 yards. In the case of the time of flight the actual time from 3 yards to the range required is calculated, and the constant addition of the time from the muzzle to 3 yards is added.

It should be noted that even if the assumption that the velocity is constant over the first 3 yards of ranges were subsequently proved to be incorrect, the accuracy of the range tables for shot calculated on this principle would not be impaired. For the bedrock on which the whole structure of computation is built is the observed velocity over 20 yards, which is really a definite time measurement obtained with a chronograph. The method of calculation which has just been described was evolved to fit in with this chronographic record, as it does with an error of less than 1 per cent.

But since calculated results are invariably exposed to doubt it may be as well to show how closely such results do in actual fact coincide with results obtained by instrumental measurements. For this purpose I will quote from the results obtained by various experimenters. The first of these was the late Mr. R. W. S. Griffith, who was the real pioneer of shotgun ballistics and whose results and deductions have all been confirmed rather than refuted by more recent work and experiments. Other experimenters were Mr. André, who has already been mentioned, and General Journée, the great French authority ; while numerous experiments were made by the *Field* and the results published between June and December, 1915, and on September 20th, 1919.

The comparisons between the various instrumental and calculated results are given in the following tables. In studying them it should be remembered that in every case the instrumental result is the mean obtained from a series of records.

TABLE XLV

COMPARISON BETWEEN CALCULATED AND INSTRUMENTAL VELOCITIES
OF NO. 6 SHOT

Range in Yards.	Striking Velocities in F.S.		Velocities over the Ranges in F.S.		
	Calculated.	Griffith 1888 Results.	Calculated.	Griffith 1888 Results.	André 1899 Results.
3	1,197	—	1,197	—	1,184
5	1,124	—	1,181	1,111	—
10	1,006	1,016	1,118	1,080	1,127
15	921	945	1,068	1,044	—
20	847	871	1,016	1,006	1,006
25	782	794	962	967	—
30	720	723	918	923	—
35	662	662	879	882	—
40	605	605	837	840	—
45	551	547	797	799	—
50	501	472	758	758	—
55	454	380	719	709	—
60	410	—	681	648	—

In this table the velocity at 3 yards was assumed and the remaining velocities at all the other distances were calculated from this assumed 3 yards velocity.

The instrumental results given in Table XLV were obtained by using two chronographs, one of which recorded the observed velocity over 20 yards and the other the striking velocity at 40 and 50 yards. The records were all simultaneous ; that is the same shot which gave the observed velocity on the first chronograph also gave the striking velocity at 40 or 50 yards.

TABLE XLVI

COMPARISON BETWEEN CALCULATED AND INSTRUMENTAL VELOCITIES
OF DIFFERENT SIZES OF SHOT

GRIFFITH 1888 RESULTS

Size of Shot.	Griffith Striking Velocities at		Calculated Velocities at 37½ Yards.
	12½ Yards.	37½ Yards.	
3	1,020	707	727
4	1,000	681	698
5	1,000	663	676
6	980	633	644
7	944	597	599

In this table the calculated velocities at 37½ yards were obtained by computing from Mr. Griffith's instrumental results at 12½ yards.

N.B.—In both the preceding tables it will be noticed that Mr. Griffith's results at 50 yards and over, and at 10 yards and nearer, do not agree with the calculated figures as well as those obtained at the intermediate distances. But this could quite well follow from the lack of delicacy in the instruments and appliances which were available in 1888.

The calculated results for the striking velocities at 40 and 50 yards were obtained by working from the observed velocity over 20 yards.

When considering Table XLVII it must be remembered that an exact coincidence between instrumental and calculated results cannot be expected because experimental determinations of velocities must inevitably vary between wide limits.

For example, a comparison of the two instrumental results obtained in the thirteenth and fourteenth lines of the table will show that although the observed velocities over 20 yards were, for all practical purposes, identical, yet the striking velocities as measured at 50 yards differed by 100 f.s. The first of these two results was an average of five shots, and the second an average of seven shots, and there was absolutely nothing to account for these two widely different values obtained for the striking velocity at 50 yards for one and the same velocity over 20 yards except the inherent difficulties always present in the making of experiments of this nature.

TABLE XLVII

COMPARISON BETWEEN CALCULATED AND INSTRUMENTAL VELOCITIES OF DIFFERENT SIZES OF SHOT

"FIELD" RESULTS

Size of Shot.	Observed Velocity over 20 Yards.	Instrumental Striking Velocity at		Calculated Striking Velocity at	
		40 Yards.	50 Yards.	40 Yards.	50 Yards.
4	1,012	629	—	655	—
6	857	525	—	509	—
6	1,012	598	—	608	—
6	1,032	584	—	619	—
6	1,110	623	—	656	—
8	1,021	568	—	553	—
4	1,050	—	615	—	582
4	1,051	—	544	—	583
4	1,087	—	605	—	599
4	1,097	—	589	—	603
6	1,009	—	517	—	503
6	1,014	—	505	—	505
6	1,024	—	513	—	510
6	1,025	—	615	—	511
6	1,036	—	535	—	516
6	1,052	—	491	—	524
6	1,055	—	486	—	526
6	1,064	—	544	—	529
6	1,076	—	560	—	535
6	1,085	—	583	—	538
6	1,098	—	535	—	543
6	1,107	—	583	—	547
8	991	—	472	—	426
8	1,034	—	451	—	446

But if averages are taken of very large numbers of series of results these isolated discrepancies of individual series begin to be smoothed away. This can be seen in the following table.

TABLE XLVIII

GRAND AVERAGES FROM TABLE XLVII

Size of Shot.	Striking Velocity at 40 Yards.			Striking Velocity at 50 Yards.		
	Instru-mental.	Calcu-lated.	Percentage Difference between Instru-mental and Calculated.	Instru-mental.	Calcu-lated.	Percentage Difference between Instru-mental and Calculated.
4	629	655	4·07	588	592	0·68
6	583	598	2·58	539	524	2·78
8	568	553	2·64	461	436	5·43

It will be noticed that the biggest percentage differences between instrumental and calculated results occur with No. 4 shot at 40 yards, and No. 8 at 50 yards. In these cases only one and two series respectively are used for obtaining the differences. The largest numbers of series were those taken with No. 6 at both 40 and 50 yards, and with this size of shot the total average percentage difference between the instrumental and striking velocity is but 2·68 per cent., while even the total average percentage difference for all three sizes of shot is only 3·03 per cent.

And even the French experiments endorse this method of calculating in a satisfactory manner.

From 1888 onwards General Journée made numerous experiments to ascertain the time intervals of shot charges in flight passing different targets. These targets were made so that they intercepted only a part of the charge, the remainder of the charge passing on to the next target. The time intervals were measured by chronographs, and General Journée published his results in his classic *Tir des Fusils de Chasse.*

A comparison between some typical examples of these results and calculated velocities are given in the following table.

TABLE XLIX

COMPARISON BETWEEN CALCULATED AND INSTRUMENTAL STRIKING
VELOCITIES OF DIFFERENT SIZES OF SHOT

JOURNÉE RESULTS

For Shot 315 to the Ounce.			For Shot 182 to the Ounce.		
Range in Yards.	Journée's Velocities.	Calculated Velocities.	Range in Yards.	Journée's Velocities.	Calculated Velocities.
3·0	1,181	1,181	3·0	1,181	1,181
11·2	984	971	12·8	984	984
21·0	820	816	24·3	820	837
34·7	656	642	41·3	656	667
54·4	492	432	65·3	492	468

In this table the striking velocities at the different ranges were all calculated from General Journée's velocity at 3 yards.

And in 1926 still further confirmation of the accuracy of this method of calculation was obtained in a most interesting manner with the Metford Ballistic Pendulum.

The Ballistic Pendulum is the oldest of all instruments used for measuring velocities of projectiles, being the invention of Benjamin Robins, who died in 1740. Very briefly the instrument consists of a heavy penetrable bob which is suspended so that it can swing freely in one vertical plane.

A projectile is fired into the end of the bob and stays inside the pendulum, which swings back under the force of the impact. The distance through which it swings depends on the momentum of the projectile, as the whole of this momentum is absorbed since the projectile comes to rest within the pendulum. From this it is a simple matter to calculate the striking velocity of the projectile on the pendulum bob.

The late Mr. Metford was convinced of the possibilities of the ballistic pendulum as an accurate velocimeter, and he devised an instrument which was subsequently improved by the late Colonel Henry Mellish and by Lord Cottesloe.

That the ballistic pendulum is capable of recording the actual striking velocities of rifle bullets with great accuracy is now well known, for the whole of the experimental data from which Mr. F. W. Jones computed his well-known ballistic tables for rifles were obtained with Colonel Mellish's pendulum at Hodsock. Lord Cottesloe has an exactly similar pendulum set up at Wistow, Leicestershire, and when I suggested to him in 1926 that it might be possible to use this pendulum for the measuring of shotgun velocities at very short ranges he entered into the problem with enthusiasm.

This instrument is described in full detail in the Appendix to Mr. F. W. Jones's *Hodsock Ballistic Tables for Rifles*, and so any further description here is quite superfluous. The only adaptation for shotgun use was the addition of a long box, 10 inches square, which was filled with sawdust and bolted on top of the pendulum bob. The shots were fired into this box.

Five different Lots of cartridges were loaded up with weighed charges of powder and shot, the powder and shot charges being purposely varied in the different Lots so as to develop different velocities. The size of shot was No. 6 in each case.

First of all series of observed velocities over 20 yards were obtained with a chronograph for each Lot, and then similar series were fired at the Ballistic Pendulum from a range of 3 yards. The same barrel was used for obtaining the velocities with the chronograph and pendulum in order to eliminate every possible source of error.

The striking velocity at 3 yards was also calculated from the means of the observed velocities over 20 yards.

A comparison of these striking velocities at 3 yards as calculated and measured with the Ballistic Pendulum is given in the following table.

TABLE L

COMPARISON BETWEEN STRIKING VELOCITIES AT 3 YARDS AS CALCULATED AND MEASURED WITH A BALLISTIC PENDULUM

Observed Velocity by Chronograph over 20 Yards.	Striking Velocity at 3 Yards.		Difference between Pendulum and Calculated Results.
	Pendulum.	Calculated.	
1,041	1,278	1,251	27
1,032	1,249	1,231	18
1,026	1,232	1,217	15
982	1,144	1,129	15
933	1,078	1,054	24

It will be noted that the instrumental velocities were in each case slightly higher than the calculated : it may be that this was due to the muzzle blast, the effect of which was not entirely eliminated even by firing through a hole in a screen placed 6 feet from the muzzle of the gun, as explained in Chapter V.

From the comparisons between experimental and calculated results set out in all these tables I think that it must be admitted that the method of calculation suggested certainly gives results beyond 10 yards, and possibly at shorter distances as well, which would approximate almost exactly to results which would be measured were instruments and appliances available for doing the work with the necessary exactness.

But even if this calculation of striking velocities is not regarded as being absolutely exact, the relationship between the velocities for the different sizes of shot having various velocities over 20 yards is undoubtedly quite exact. These relationships are quite true, even though the actual velocities may be doubtful. In fact, these calculated relationships are more exact than any which could be obtained except by a most extended series of experiments, because the method of computing is based on so many experimental results obtained with shot charges and also with larger projectiles of varying sizes and shapes.

It should, however, always be borne in mind that the calculations are all based on the assumption of a more or less constant proportional air resistance. This assumption is absolutely true for all velocities below 1,000 f.s., and sufficiently correct for all practical purposes for all velocities below 1,100 f.s. It was for this reason that I have emphasised the accuracy of the computed results for all observed velocities at ranges greater than 10 yards ; and, after all, these are the ranges which interest the shooter. But in the case of shot charges having observed velocities higher than 1,100 f.s. it is possible, and even probable, that a slight modification in the method of calculation could be made with advantage in order to obtain the most accurate results for muzzle velocities. But extended experiments with special apparatus would need to be completed before any justification could be obtained for adopting a modified method for calculating the muzzle velocities of shot charges having observed velocities of over 1,100 f.s.

Although I have given Range Tables for the different shot sizes in Chapter VIII which would seem to be sufficiently complete for most requirements, there may be some amateur ballisticians who are anxious to extend these tables. Such will find no difficulty in doing so for ordinary ranges if they follow the instructions given in this Appendix. It is, however, possible that they may prefer to use tables which are also suitable for calculations connected with sporting rifles. In this case they can use the *Hodsock Ballistic Tables for Rifles,* to which reference has already been made and which is published by Messrs. Edward Arnold for 10s. 6d. net.

The Hodsock tables are special rifle tables and do not give

PLATE XV

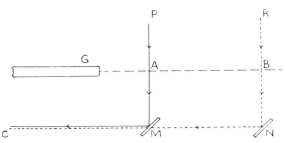

(A) Diagram showing the principle of the Interceptor Method of measuring Velocities of Shotguns and Rifles very close to the Muzzle

G is the muzzle of the gun or rifle and A, B, the path of the projectile, P, M, C, and R, N, C are two beams of light which are brought to fine foci at A and B and are reflected by the two Mirrors (M and N) so that they are collimated at C on the drum of a high-speed camera

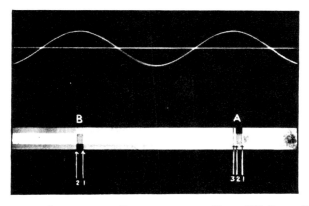

(B) An actual Interceptor Record of a .303 Mark VII Rifle Bullet

The first interception is shown at A, and the second at B. At both A and B the nose of the bullet is marked 1 and the base of the bullet 2. At A the jute wad has made a separate interception (3), but this wad has dropped out of the trajectory before it reaches the second light beam, and so has made no interception at B

The sinuoidal time marking line is seen above the ribbons made by the light beams. The distance from wave crest to wave crest represents $\frac{1}{1000}$ of a second, and so the distance between each point where the sinuoidal line crosses the straight base line represents one-half this fraction of time, or .0005 of a second

quite such good results as can be obtained with the Shoeburyness Tables, but the results are good enough for all practical purposes. In using the Hodsock Tables, however, a different value must be adopted for the Coefficient of Reduction, and Mr. F. W. Jones has found that a value of 2·6 is, on the whole, best.

This means that the Ballistic Coefficients for the various shot sizes given in Table XLIV must be multiplied by $\frac{2·3}{2·6}$ or 0·885 in order to adapt them to the Hodsock Tables.

It is, however, possible to obtain quite good calculated results without resorting to any ballistic tables at all. Such results are given by what is known as the " Quadratic Rule," which is based on Newton's deduction of the law of the square of the velocity to express the resistance offered by the air to the motion of any body travelling through it. This quadratic rule of air resistance is adopted widely for velocities below 1,000 f.s. with very good results, especially at the lower velocities. In fact at extreme ranges the Shoeburyness Tables do not go down sufficiently low and then the quadratic rule method is the best to adopt.

This method can be found in any book on Exterior Ballistics and is explained in the *Hodsock Ballistic Tables for Rifles* (pages 14 and 18), so I will make no attempt here to explain how the formulæ are derived. The two necessary formulæ are—

$$\frac{s}{C} = 40748 \ \log \ \frac{V}{v}$$

and
$$\frac{t}{C} = 17696 \left(\frac{V - v}{V \times v}\right)$$

where C is the Ballistic Coefficient of the shot pellet as given in Table XLIV ; V the higher velocity and v the lower ; s the range in feet between velocities V and v ; and t the time in seconds between these two velocities.

When working with this method *the observed velocity over 20 yards is assumed to be the striking velocity at 10 yards* and this provides a datum point. But, of course, if the striking velocity at any point is known it can be taken as the datum point instead.

As an example of the results obtained by this method it can be stated that the striking velocities for No. 6 shot at 50 yards for observed velocities of 950, 1,050 and 1,150 f.s. are 467, 516 and 565 respectively ; while with the Shoeburyness Tables these striking velocities are 465, 518 and 555 f.s.

So the difference is not great.

APPENDIX II

THE INTERCEPTOR METHOD FOR THE DETERMINA-
TION OF MUZZLE VELOCITIES

COMPARATIVELY recently an entirely new system has been devised for the determination of the velocities of both rifles and shotguns very close to the muzzle ; the results obtained by this new method must inevitably be of great interest, especially as they confirm the empirical and computed results which have hitherto been adopted for standard velocities, and while at the same time they confirm equally the doubts expressed as to the accuracy of the calculated muzzle velocities for observed velocities of 1,100 f.s. and over. Accordingly I feel that a brief description of the principles utilised in this new method should be included in this volume.

The new method is known as the "Interceptor Method." The principle was first used for the determination of the velocity of rifle bullets by Thompson, Hickman and Riffolt and published in the *Proceedings of the U.S. National Academy of Sciences* for April, 1920. The method was developed independently by the Research Department (Nobel Section) of the Imperial Chemical Industries and has been applied for the first time to shotguns with considerable success. A very brief account of the method appeared in *Nature* of December 27th, 1930, and a more detailed account which included some of the first set of results obtained was published in *Game and Gun* for April, 1931.

The principle of the method is shown diagrammatically in Plate XIVA. PM and RN are two beams of light which are projected across the line of flight of the projectile, the velocity of which it is desired to measure. These two beams are brought to a fine focus on the actual path of the projectile. In the diagram G is the muzzle end of the rifle or shotgun and the path of the bullet or shot charge is shown by the dotted line, AB, which is cut by the two beams of light at A and B.

These two beams are both reflected at right angles by two mirrors, M and N, as shown in the diagram, in such a way that they are made coincident at C. If a screen were placed at C the two beams would appear as two bright lines of light, one above the other, and slightly overlapping.

Instead of a screen a high-speed drum camera is placed at C, and when the film revolves the two beams of light make a photographic record on the film which, when printed, shows a broad, bright double ribbon.

If either of these beams of light is intercepted, or shut off, by any opaque object, the photograph will only show the single bright ribbon of the beam which is not intercepted, the extent of the break in the double ribbon being dependent on the length of the period of interception.

When a rifle bullet is fired along the path AB it first of all intercepts the beam PM and a fraction of time later it intercepts the beam RN. The effect in the resulting photograph is that there is a break in one side of the bright line caused by the interception at A, and then another break in the other line caused by the interception at B. An actual and exact photographic record is thus obtained of the bullet's flight from A to B ; and if the distance AB is known and the time interval between the occurrence of the two breaks in the line on the photograph can be measured, the velocity of the bullet over the distance AB may be derived from an elementary calculation.

The distance between A and B can be made anything that is desired, and measured with extreme precision. Dr. Taylor and Mr. Wark, the two physicists of Imperial Chemical Industries who have developed this method, use a distance of the order of 2 feet, and set the apparatus so that the first interception at A occurs at $3\frac{2}{3}$ feet and the second at $5\frac{2}{3}$ feet from the muzzle. So if the time between the two interceptions is measured, the average velocity of the bullet is obtained over a distance of 2 feet very near the muzzle, and this can be assumed to be the actual velocity at the mid-point between the two interceptions, which is $4\frac{2}{3}$ feet from the muzzle.

And it is in connection with the measurement of this very small time interval that special apparatus must be utilised. The system adopted is both simple and accurate, and is based on the fact that a tuning-fork which gives out a certain note always vibrates at the same rate.

So an instrument known as an Eccles valve-maintained tuning-fork is placed alongside the apparatus, and one prong of this tuning-fork carries a small concave mirror which deflects another beam of light on to the camera film. When the tuning-fork is at rest this beam of light appears in the resulting photograph as a thin straight streak parallel to the broad, double streak caused by the other two beams. But when the tuning-fork vibrates the concave mirror on one prong deflects the light beam backwards and forwards ; and instead of a straight line there now appears an undulating line on the photograph. This undulating line provides the actual timing marks on the photograph, because a tuning-fork is used which has a known vibration of 1,000 complete vibrations (*i.e.* the movement of each prong from one position to the other and back again constitutes one complete vibration) per second, and so the linear distance between each *wave-crest* represents $\frac{1}{1000}$ part of a second, and that between each *wave-crest* and *wave-trough* represents $\frac{1}{2000}$ part of a second.

The time marking is thus included on the same photograph which shows the two interceptions, and so enables the operator to establish the actual time interval between the first and second interceptions with great exactness.

This method has been used successfully for the determination of the velocities of rifle bullets, and Plate XVB shows the record of a ·303 Mark VII rifle bullet. The first interception is shown at A and the second at B, while the undulating time marking is very distinct. Immediately in rear of the first interception at A a thin dark line will be noticed. This is the interception of the jute wad which is always used in cartridges loaded with cordite. The wad has dropped out of the line of flight before the bullet makes the second interception, and so it does not appear at B.

Incidentally if the length of the projectile is known its actual velocity at the moment of interception can be ascertained by measuring the length of this interception.

In order to facilitate the actual measurement of the time marking a base line is put upon the sinusoidal trace of the tuning-fork. This base line is produced by the tuning-fork at rest. After the shot has been fired the interception beams are screened off from the camera which is exposed for one revolution of the drum. This puts on the base line without any further exposure of the film to the interception beams. Plate XVI shows two actual records of shots fired from a full choke barrel. If a comparison is made between the first interceptions on these records and that shown in Plate XIVB it will be seen that whereas the rifle bullet made but a single clean break in the light beam, the shot charges and wads have made a number of smaller breaks. This is merely what would be expected because the shot charge and wads begin to separate very soon after leaving the muzzle of the gun.

The first and second interceptions are marked A and B on both records on Plate XV as before. In both records the interceptions at A of the over-powder and thick felt wads, the main bulk of the shot charge, a few stray pellets, and the overshot wad, are all clearly seen. At B the overshot wads have dropped out ; the shot-charges have strung out a little more ; and the felt wads and the over-powder card wads have dropped further behind.

The actual details of the two records are slightly different,

PLATE XVI

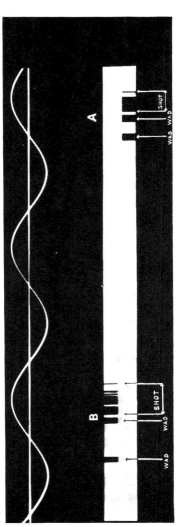

(A) AN ACTUAL INTERCEPTOR RECORD OF A SHOT CHARGE FROM A 12-BORE FULL CHOKE BARREL

The first interception is shown at A, and the second at B. The various parts of the shot column and wads are marked on the photograph in each case. The separate interception on the extreme right at A has been made by the over shot card wad, which has dropped out before B has been reached, and so there is no interruption made by this wad at B. The shot column at B has begun to string out as can be seen, by the separate interceptions made by the whole column. At both A and B the felt wad is still close behind the rear end of the shot column, but the over-powder card wad has dropped considerably further behind at B. The time marking is shown and is identical to that given in Plate XVI (B)

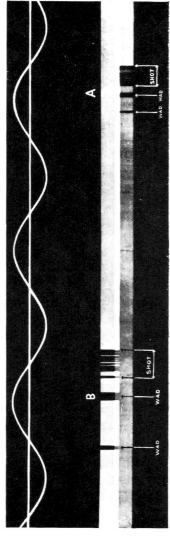

(B) ANOTHER INTERCEPTOR RECORD OF A SHOT CHARGE FROM A 12-BORE FULL CHOKE

The general nature of the record is similar to that shown in Plate XVI (A), the first and second interception being marked A and B as before. In this case the lower ribbon representing the light beam nearer to the muzzle has been partially intercepted by gas throughout the time period between the first and second interceptions of the shot charge

but their general character is the same. In Plate XVB, however, the lower ribbon is partly obscured by interceptions caused by gas.

No two records of shot charges are quite identical, as will be appreciated by examining the two shown on Plate XV.

When using this method for measuring the velocities of shot charges at 4⅔ feet from the muzzle two chronographs were also used in order to obtain a definite relation between the velocity at 4⅔ feet and the usual chronograph-observed velocity over 20 yards.

The actual procedure adopted by Dr. Taylor and Mr. Wark was to obtain the velocity at 4⅔ feet by interception and that over 30 feet by a chronograph with one and the same shot. When a series has been fired the relation between the interceptor velocity is thus obtained with a chronograph velocity over 30 feet.

Then another series is fired with cartridges from the same lot, but in this case two chronographs are used, each shot giving one record over 30 feet on the first instrument, and another record over 60 feet (20 yards) on the second intrument.

The relation between the chronograph velocity over 30 feet is thus established with the usual observed velocity over 20 yards, which equally establishes the relation between the interceptor velocity with the usual observed velocity.

So much for the principle.

But before we proceed to the results I would like to explain in parenthesis that this Appendix has been written some months after the rest of the volume, while the results were not completed until after the rest of the volume was actually in print. This point is interesting as the results confirm several theories advanced both in the text of the Volume and Appendix I.

Four series of shots were first of all fired from a full choke with No. 6 shot. Of these series, three gave rather low and standard observed velocities, while the fourth developed a high observed velocity. The first three series gave values for the velocity at 4⅔ feet which corresponded to values calculated by the method described in Appendix I in a most remarkable manner, the greatest difference being but 2 per cent.

But the fourth (high-velocity) series showed a considerable discrepancy.

Accordingly, further series of high-velocity rounds were fired, and additional series at both low and high velocities were also obtained in a true cylinder barrel. These supplementary experiments completely confirmed the agreement of the low and standard velocity results with computed values, while they also confirmed the divergence between these measured and calculated velocities very close to the muzzle for the corresponding higher observed velocities. [824]

The complete results hitherto obtained are given below. It should be mentioned, however, that every value is the mean of a series of rounds.

TABLE LI

INTERCEPTOR VELOCITIES FOR DIFFERENT OBSERVED VELOCITIES

CHOKE GUN.		CYLINDER GUN.	
Observed Velocity over 20 Yds.	Interceptor Velocity at $4\frac{2}{3}$ Ft.	Observed Velocity over 20 Yds.	Interceptor Velocity at $4\frac{2}{3}$ Ft.
f.s.	f.s.	f.s.	f.s.
941	1,066	981	1,155
952	1,086	1,128	1,396
998	1,177	1,206	1,499
1,029	1,221	—	—
1,071	1,293	—	—
1,165	1,407	—	—
1,180	1,427	—	—
1,238	1,488	—	—

If these results are considered two points will be seen to stand out.

(1) When the same cartridges are used the velocities at $4\frac{2}{3}$ feet are very nearly the same in either choke or cylinder barrels, the choke velocities being very slightly lower.

But the corresponding observed velocities are very different, those given by a choke gun being considerably higher than those given in a cylinder barrel.

The difference between the observed Velocity over 20 yards and the corresponding interceptor velocity at $4\frac{2}{3}$ feet is approximately constant for observed velocities greater than 1100 f.s. in contrast to the difference at lower velocities.

(2) There is a distinct reduction in the rate of drop of velocity between an observed velocity over 20 yards and the corresponding interceptor velocity at $4\frac{2}{3}$ feet in the case of all observed velocities of over 1,100 f.s.

In other words the method adopted for calculating the muzzle velocity has been proved to be very accurate for observed velocities of from 950 f.s. to 1,050 f.s. or 1,100 f.s., but not so accurate for the higher observed velocities as will be seen by comparing Table LI with Tables VI to XIII.

This fact merely confirms the suspicion which was advanced in Appendix I.

At present it would be useless to attempt to ascertain what alteration in the method for calculating the muzzle velocities may be necessary in the case of the higher observed velocities because the available data is too meagre.

The following Table, however, has been suggested as likely to prove of use in ascertaining the actual muzzle velocities of No. 6 shot for different observed velocities. In this Table the muzzle velocity has been obtained by increasing the interceptor velocity at $4\frac{2}{3}$ feet by 1 per cent.

A comparison of the muzzle velocities suggested in this Table with those given in Tables VI to XIII is interesting. It will be seen that it is only in the case of observed velocities of 1,150 and 1,200 f.s. that the discrepancy becomes at all marked, while the calculated muzzle velocities do not take into account the differences between choke and cylinder, although this difference was known to exist.

TABLE LII

MUZZLE VELOCITIES OF NO. 6 SHOT FOR DIFFERENT OBSERVED
VELOCITIES

Observed Velocity over 20 Yds.	Muzzle Velocity.	
	Choke.	Cylinder.
f.s.	f.s.	f.s.
950	1,086	1,101
1,000	1,186	1,203
1,050	1,271	1,291
1,100	1,343	1,367
1,150	1,407	1,436
1,200	1,465	1,500
1,250	1,519	1,561

It must, however, be remembered that the ascertainment of the exact muzzle velocity is only of importance in the consideration of recoil. The fact that the calculated muzzle velocities given in Tables VI to XIII may be erroneous in some few instances in no way alters the accuracy of the values given for the striking velocities at other distances. For, as has already been explained in Appendix I, the datum point in every case was the actual time of flight measured over 20 yards with the chronograph ; and there is no doubt as to the manner in which shot pellets travel through the air in conformity with known laws when moving individually. It is the massing together of the shot charge during the first few feet of its trajectory that comprises the difficulty in arriving at accurate computations when adopting formulæ based on the laws of movement of single projectiles.

APPENDIX III

THE PIEZOELECTRIC PRESSURE GAUGE AND ITS APPLICATION TO THE MEASUREMENT OF PRESSURE IN SHOTGUNS

By A. WATSON, B.Sc., F.Inst.P.

The lead crusher pressure gauge described in Chapter VI provides a method of measuring the maximum or peak pressure in a shotgun in terms of rather indeterminate units, and this, together with the vast amount of experience which has been accumulated in the interpretation of its results, is quite adequate for the major amount of pressure measurement required by cartridge and gunmakers. However, in research and development work it is necessary to employ a pressure measuring system which will provide a complete and continuous record of the pressure in the gun during the time between the striker hitting the cap and the shot emerging from the muzzle. Furthermore, this record must be capable of accurate interpretation in terms of time and pressure.

Several different types of gauges have been developed to meet these requirements employing such diverse physical effects as the mechanical deformation of a tubular spring, the change in electrical resistance of a graphite element or the change in electrical capacitance of a specially arranged condenser. All these gauges are, however, characterised by having a high natural frequency, that is, the responsive elements are light and rigid and thus are capable of responding faithfully to the rapid pressure rise to which they are subjected.

The most popular gauge, however, is based on the phenomenon of piezoelectricity whereby certain crystals develop electric charges when acted upon by a force. Discs of quartz, cut in a certain direction with reference to the crystallographic structure, are suitable as piezoelectric elements since their response is linear, constant and sensibly independent of temperature. The pressure to be measured is applied to a piston which thus transmits a force to the crystal, and the resulting electric charge is collected on an insulated electrode.

In order to record this small electric charge it is applied to a condenser and a proportional voltage is produced. After amplification this voltage is displayed on a cathode ray tube in such a way that the deflection of the " spot " of light in the vertical direction is proportional to the pressure applied to the gauge piston. This vertical movement of the " spot " is recorded by a drum camera, which contains photographic film or paper on a drum rotating at constant speed about a vertical axis. On the completed record the trace appears as though the spot had been travelling horizontally at constant speed and simultaneously had been deflected vertically by an amount which, at any instant, was proportional to the pressure.

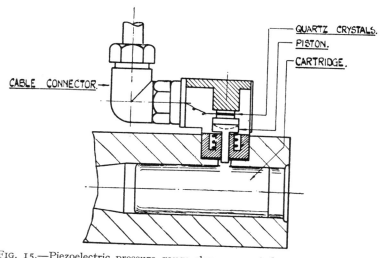

FIG. 15.—Piezoelectric pressure gauge shown mounted on a 12-bore gun.

Fig. 15 shows a piezoelectric pressure gauge mounted on a 12-bore pressure barrel. The gauge is of rectangular shape and although rigidly fixed to the barrel by two bolts can be readily removed for cleaning and calibration.

The piston diameter is 0·126 inch and it has matching concave and convex surfaces on the top to take up any lack of parallelism and to ensure that the force is applied evenly to the crystal. The two quartz crystals 0·25 inch diameter and 0·040 inch thick are held in position by the spring-loaded piston and have a thin copper foil as the central " live " electrode. By using two crystals in this fashion the sensitivity is twice that of a single crystal and it is not necessary to use any other insulating material. A thin wire connects the foil electrode to the outgoing cable.

In order to communicate with the propellant the gauge is positioned $\frac{5}{8}$ inch from the breech face and a $\frac{1}{8}$ inch diameter hole is drilled in the cartridge case. The cavity between the piston and the case is filled with sealing compound to prevent gas leakage and a piece of adhesive tape covers the hole in the case

PLATE XVII

THE DARTFORD PENDULUM GUN FITTED WITH A 22-INCH BARREL, THE BREECH BEING OPEN

Extensions, ready to be screwed on in order to give 25, 28, 30, 31, 36, and 40-inch true cylinder barrels, and also an extension to give a 30-inch full choke barrel can be seen lying under the muzzle end of the gun

to eliminate loss of powder during handling and erosion of the
sealing compound by the powder gas.

The recording apparatus, which is illustrated diagrammatically
in Fig. 16, consists of several interconnected pieces of electronic

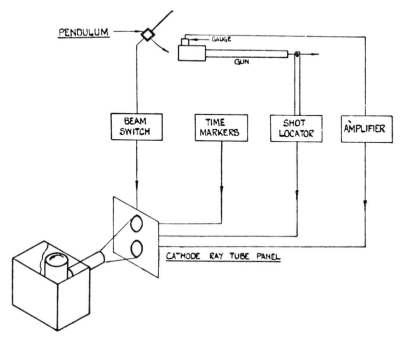

FIG. 16.—Schematic diagram of the recording apparatus.

apparatus. The cathode ray tube holds two tubes which are
photographed by the drum camera. One tube has one light
" spot " which moves vertically to indicate the pressure applied to
the gauge. The other tube has two " spots " ; one of these
moves vertically when the shot passes through a small coil placed
immediately in front of the muzzle and so indicates the instant
when the shot emerges from the barrel ; the other is caused to
move suddenly in the vertical direction at accurate intervals of
$\frac{1}{1000}$ second thus providing a time scale on the record. To
avoid the use of a synchronised shutter on the camera the light
" spots " are normally extinguished and are only brightened for
a short period when the round is fired. This brightening is
initiated by the beam switch when the striker touches the cap
and continues for about $\frac{5}{1000}$ second.

The main difficulty in the use of the piezoelectric gauge lies
in the pressure calibration. The electric charge produced by the

crystals gradually leaks away and although the rate of leakage can be made small enough to be undetectable during the firing of a round, nevertheless it precludes the use of a static pressure calibration. Accordingly, calibration must be carried out either by rapidly applying a known force or pressure to the gauge or by rapidly removing such a load. The gauge described above is calibrated on a 10/1 ratio lever press which can apply known forces to the gauge, and can rapidly remove them by means of a mechanically triggered counterbalance weight.

A .typical pressure/time record for a 12-gauge cartridge is shown in Fig. 17. The trace commences on the left when the

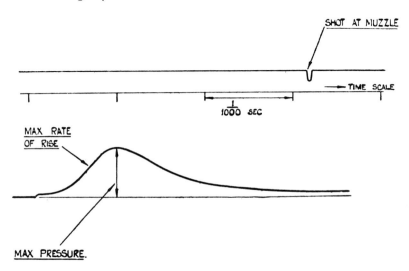

FIG. 17.—Typical pressure/time curve for 12-gauge cartridge.

firing pin strikes the cap. While the firing pin is travelling forward, deforming the cap shell and initiating the cap composition there is no pressure at all for about 0·3 milliseconds. When initiated the cap causes the pressure to rise and the rate of rise rapidly increases as the burning of the propellant progresses. The maximum rate of rise of pressure is some 10,000 tons per square inch per second. About one millisecond after the initiation of the cap the pressure reaches its maximum value when the rate of increase of pressure due to the burning of the powder is equal to the rate of pressure reduction due to the movement of the shot providing an increasing volume into which the gas can expand. After this the pressure gradually decreases as the shot travels up the bore and falls to zero after the shot leaves the muzzle.

In the development of new powders and new caps all the

features mentioned above provide important information on the functioning and design of these components.

A most interesting outcome of pressure measurements on shotgun cartridges using the piezoelectric gauge has been the comparison of the maximum pressure readings with those of the lead crusher gauge. By mounting the two gauges on opposite sides of the same gun at one inch from the breech face simultaneous readings on the same cartridge were possible. As had been known for some time, the crusher readings were less than those given by the piezoelectric gauge due to the time lag in the plastic deformation of the lead—the piezoelectric gauge piston only moves about $\frac{1}{100,000}$ inch when subjected to 2·5 tons per sq. in. and is thus free from this error. Over the range of pressures usually encountered at the one inch position in shot guns the readings given by the two gauges are related by the equation

$$P = 1 \cdot 5\ L - 0 \cdot 5 \text{ tons per sq. in.}$$

where P = the maximum pressure indicated by the piezoelectric gauge

L = the maximum pressure indicated by the lead crusher gauge.

Thus a pressure of 2·0 tons per sq. in. measured by the lead crusher gague is equivalent to 2·5 tons per sq. in. as measured by the piezoelectric gauge, 3·0 tons per sq. in. to 4·0 tons per sq. in. and 4.0 tons per sq. in. to 5·5 tons per sq. in. respectively. But a most important characteristic of the relationship between these two measurements is that it is a linear one and so for all practical purposes in comparing cartridges the mean peak pressure values indicated by lead crushers will be in reasonable relative agreement with corresponding results obtained with the piezoelectric gauge.

APPENDIX IV

AN ELECTRONIC METHOD FOR THE MEASUREMENT OF SHOT VELOCITIES NEAR THE MUZZLE

By A. Watson, B.Sc., F.Inst.P.

The Boulenge chronograph described in Chapter VIII is capable of measuring time intervals of the order of 0·050 seconds with satisfactory accuracy but cannot record smaller intervals with the necessary precision. Accordingly the range over which velocities can be measured by this instrument cannot be reduced to much less than 10 yards if accuracy is to be maintained. While measurements over this relatively long base length provide useful comparative values a more significant quantity both for control of cartridge manufacture and for theoretical work is the muzzle velocity.

Most methods of measuring projectile velocities consist of a measurement of the time of flight over a known distance, and so to approach the muzzle velocity the base length must be short and near to the muzzle. The situation is somewhat complicated in the case of shot charges because the shot emerges from the muzzle as one " bullet " and then gradually begins to spread laterally and string longitudinally. Consequently if the velocity can be measured before the stringing and spreading become appreciable then it should be possible to obtain the velocity of the bunched shot charge (actually the velocity of its centre of gravity) and to avoid complications due to stray pellets.

One excellent method of measuring the velocity near the muzzle, the light interception method, is described in Appendix II, but while an admirable technique for research purposes it is somewhat slow for routine use. More recently in the U.S.A., Bradford in 1942 and Weller in 1952, have patented a new device for detecting the passage of a metallic object in flight which can readily be used for shot velocity measurement. The method uses electrical impulses from two coils spaced a known distance apart to respectively start and stop an electronic timing device. Thus the time of flight of the shot charge over this known distance is obtained and hence the velocity can be calculated or found from tables. A typical electronic timing device can register intervals of the order of 0·001 seconds to an accuracy of 0·000001 seconds and so the coils need only be spaced a few feet apart to attain the necessary precision of timing. Thus by placing the coils within a few feet of the muzzle the velocity measurement takes place before the shot stringing and spreading have become appreciable. The overall accuracy is however not limited by that of the timing but by the ability of the coil to locate the centre of gravity of the shot charge. Bradford quotes the variation of this latter effect as $\pm$ 0·01 feet and hence over a 4 feet base length the accuracy of measurement would be $\pm \frac{1}{4}$ per cent. or, at a muzzle velocity of 1300 ft. per sec., about $\pm$ 3 ft. per sec.

Now let us see how this instrument works! The two coils referred to above each consist of four turns of thick wire, each turn being spaced about $\frac{1}{8}$ inch from the next and thus forming a coil about 1 inch long and 5 or 6 inches in diameter. These coils are each connected to an electronic oscillator which provides electrical energy of the same order of frequency as used in short wave radio. This energy produces a magnetic field in the space inside each coil and if a metallic object is placed in this space then some of the energy is absorbed by the object. This absorption of energy reacts back on the oscillator and produces a drop in voltage. If then a metallic object is projected through one coil the voltage in the oscillator is momentarily reduced and then returns to its normal level. The amount of this reduction depends on the mass of the metallic object and so the maximum voltage reduction will occur at the instant at which the greatest mass of metal is inside the coil. This is illustrated in Fig. 18 which shows the change in voltage as a shot charge passes through two coils.

Since the maximum reduction in the voltage of the oscillator occurs when the greatest mass of metal is inside the coil, with this size of coil it coincides with the centre of gravity of the shot charge passing through the central plane of the coil. Thus if we can arrange to respectively start and stop a timing device when the voltage is at its minimum value then we shall be measuring the time of flight of the centre of gravity of the shot charge between the centres of the two coils.

A special amplifier is used to modify these electrical impulses and make them suitable for starting and stopping the timing device (Fig. 19).

The timing device used is an electronic counter chronometer. This chronometer is started and stopped by the two successive impulses from the amplifier and during the time between these impulses it counts the number of electrical oscillations which are being generated by a built-in oscillator. These oscillations are produced at a constant and accurately known rate of one oscillation per millionth of a second so that the number counted during the timed period measures the interval in terms of millionths of a second. The counting is done by rather complicated electronic circuits but the result is displayed directly on a set of meter dials.

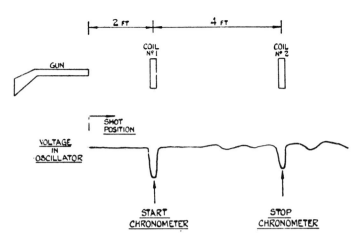

FIG. 18.—Diagram showing how the oscillator voltage changes as the shot passes through two coils.

Six dials are each scaled from o to 9 and the needles come to rest pointing to one of these numbers. The dials are arranged side by side on the front panel of the instrument and are connected in such a way that the left hand meter indicates the number of tenths of a second, the next the number of hundredths and so on until the meter on the extreme right reads the number of millionths of a second.

Operation of the instrument is extremely simple. Before

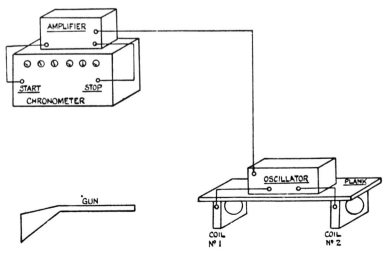

FIG. 19.—Schematic diagram of the apparatus for measuring shot velocities.

firing a button is pressed to return all the meters to zero and the round is then fired through the two coils. Within about one second the meters automatically display the time of flight and the result is noted by writing down the meter readings from left to right. Thus if the meters read 003251 from left to right then the time of flight is 0·003251 second. The velocity is obtained from this time of flight by reference to conversion tables and the instrument is then reset for the next round.

Many details have been omitted from the above description but the principles involved and the mode of operation are essentially as outlined.

The coils are mounted in frames and secured to the underside of a stout wooden plank. The distance between the centres of the coils is accurately adjusted and the plank suspended in front of the gun (Fig. 19). The oscillator supplying energy to the coils is mounted on top of the plank in a steel case on anti-vibration mountings and lined with felt to reduce the effect of mechanical shock and vibration. Cables from the oscillator carry the electrical impulses to the impulse amplifier which, together with the counter chronometer, is placed beside the gun.

An installation of this type is capable of use with all calibres between ·410 inch and 12 bore and with all velocity levels and shot loads normally produced.

APPENDIX V

THE CALCULATION OF THE RELATION BETWEEN OBSERVED VELOCITY AND RECOIL MEASUREMENTS IN A " FIELD " PENDULUM GUN

IF it is assumed that a " Field " Pendulum Gun vibrates as a simple pendulum, and a is the horizontal distance in inches through which the gun moves backwards under the influence of recoil, its maximum velocity will be

$$\frac{a}{12} \sqrt{\frac{g}{l}},$$

where l is the length of the wires by which the gun is suspended. This length is 60 inches, or 5 feet. So we find that the maximum velocity of the 50-lb. pendulum gun resulting from recoil is

$$\frac{a}{4\cdot73}.$$

It is admittedly incorrect to assume that the pendulum gun vibrates in an exactly similar manner to a simple pendulum. But the errors resulting from this assumption are so small—being but 0·4 per cent. when the recoil movement is 8 inches, and 0·6 per cent. when this movement is 12 inches—that they can be ignored.

If a curve is drawn showing the relation between the Muzzle Velocity (M.V.) and the Observed Velocity (v) over 20 yards of No. 6 shot for values of v between 950 f.s. and 1,150 f.s. it will be seen that the relation between M.V. and v will be given without material error by the equation

$$M.V. = 2v - 810.$$

On the assumption that there is an equality of momenta of the recoiling gun and the ejecta from the gun we get

$$\frac{(2v - 810)m}{7000} = \frac{M \times a}{4\cdot73},$$

where M is the weight of the gun in lb. and m that of the ejecta in grains.

In the standard "Field" Pendulum gun M is 50 lb. so we obtain the relation

$$v = 37000 \times \frac{a}{m} + 405.$$

This equation was used for the graphs given in Chapter IX.

NOTE.—The principle underlying the arrival at this equation was first suggested by the late Mr. F. W. Jones. I have, however, had the temerity to make slight modifications in Mr. Jones's original calculations, as these modifications seemed to give a result which fitted in better with actual observations.

APPENDIX VI

THE EFFECT UPON VELOCITY AND RECOIL PRO-DUCED BY VARYING THE LENGTH OF BARREL IN SPORTING SHOTGUNS

By W. D. Borland

IN considering the provision of a permanent apparatus for the determination of velocities and recoils produced by barrels of different lengths, calibres, and systems of boring, the following primary requirements were kept in view so that wider applicability than that involved in the present enquiry might be ensured :

(1) A housing capable of taking any desired heavy barrel, strong enough for use with heavy loads, designed to be suspended in a manner similar to that adopted for the Webley (" Field ") Pendulum Gun and rapidly interchangeable with that apparatus by withdrawing the swivelling ends which work in the outriggers of one and inserting them in the outriggers of the other gun, to enable the same range to be employed.

(2) The barrels must be heavy (*a*) to enable pressure gauges to be inserted and (*b*) to ensure that, when desired, extensions can be accurately and closely fitted. The extensions must be capable of being quickly screwed on or off to produce any desired length and variety of boring.

(3) The whole system of housing and barrels of the desired length for any experiment must be readily adjustable to an accurate dead weight and also balanced to bring the centre of gravity equidistant between the two outriggers, to ensure proper distribution of weight and strain upon back and front suspensions.

Some years prior to the present desire for knowledge of variations of recoil due to alterations of length of barrel, steps had been taken to study variations of velocity due to the same cause, but the apparatus in its original form was too heavy to enable it to be used as a pendulum. It was, however, found possible to remove excess of metal from the housing by cutting off a webbed stand no longer required and planing several surfaces, and it was finally found convenient to work to a total weight of 75 lb. including the heaviest barrel to be provided for, the housing, and half the weight of the suspension wires. With this weight the recoil readings in inches of backward travel have two-thirds

PLATE XVIII

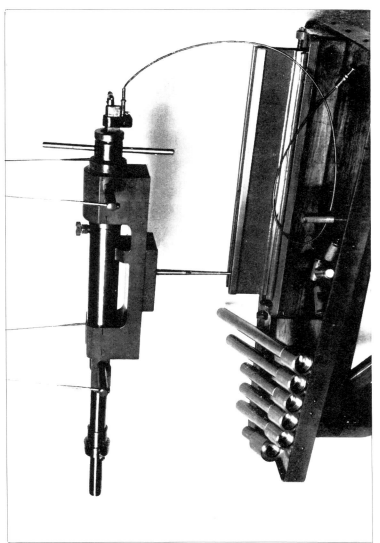

THE DARTFORD PENDULUM GUN CLOSED READY FOR FIRING
The extension in this particular case giving a 28-inch true cylinder barrel

the magnitude as compared with a pendulum of 50 lb. As a matter of interest, readings of pendulum guns of 50 and 75 lb. weight have been checked by a series of tests made with the Webley gun in its normal condition and also weighted up to 75 lb. by means of a saddle piece of lead weighing 25 lb.

The apparatus, as finally fitted up, is illustrated in the accompanying three photographs, in Plates XVI, XVII and XVIII.

Plate XVII shows a 22-inch 12-bore heavy cylinder barrel resting in the housing in position for insertion and extraction of the cartridge, together with extensions ready to be screwed on to give 25, 28, 30, 31, 36 and 40-inch true cylinder barrels, and also an extension to give a 30-inch fully choked barrel. The oblong block of metal at the top of the pointer and underneath the housing provides a means of accurate adjustment of the weight to 75 lb. without interfering with the main parts of the housing, and an additional makeweight not shown in position in this photograph is also provided for attachment at the front end of the housing. This makeweight corresponds to the difference in weight between the 22 and 30-inch complete barrels and is similar in construction to the tail weight for the 40-inch barrel shown in photograph, Plate XIX.

In the next photograph, Plate XVIII, the apparatus is shown in the firing position, the extension in this particular case giving a 28-inch cylinder barrel. It will be observed that a small adjusting collar is provided where the extension is screwed on in addition to the bottom oblong block, the reason for this being that the 30-inch extension was taken as the starting point for balancing the system and the weights of barrels of different lengths are finally adjusted by makeweights such as shown.

In Plate XIX, the expedient adopted to balance an 18-inch extension, and so produce a barrel of 40-inch, is shown. In this case it was found necessary to provide a tail weight to counter-balance the long overhang of the 18-inch extension piece, the oblong block at the top of the pointer being dispensed with.

The outriggers which carry the swivelling ends of the sus-pension system have their axial centres on the same level as the centre of the bore and a little above the centre of gravity of the whole system to ensure stable equilibrium and great steadiness of movement when the gun is fired.

The gun is fired by means of a Bowden Wire fitting specially mounted to pull the trigger backwards when the wire is trailed behind the gun.

Particular attention was paid to the boring of the barrel and extensions, and it was decided to adopt the definite 12-bore size of ·729 of an inch internal diameter with a parallel entry from chamber cone to bore without any tapered portion. The barrel is therefore of true minimum 12-bore dimensions throughout, and, with the exception of one of the 8-inch extension pieces to provide a 30-inch barrel fully choked to ·689 of an inch, all the extensions are as truly cylindrical as it was possible to bore them. As the diameter of the original barrel was rather less than ·729 of an inch, it was possible, after attaching each extension, to perform the operation of boring from end to end and so obtain the same accuracy as if barrels of various lengths had been bored from the solid.

It may be pointed out that the Webley Pendulum Gun used for comparison with the new apparatus followed the general practice of the period of its manufacture when it was customary to give a tapering entrance from chamber cone to bore, starting in this case at ·735 of an inch diameter, gradually diminishing to ·733 of an inch at 12 inches from the breech and continuing at this until the choke begins. In the records of the trials which follow, it will be seen how considerably the difference of boring of the two guns affected velocity and recoil.

In preparing the cartridges for the trials now recorded, cases, wads, and powder were conditioned separately over a 68 per cent. solution of glycerol, and the loaded cartridges were again conditioned in a similar manner for at least three weeks, kept between 65° and 70° F. before being used, only withdrawn from the conditioning vessel one by one as required, and fired immediately. Precautions were also taken to ensure even temperature of the guns and firing from each length of barrel took place at the rate of about 1 round per minute, a fouling shot being fired to remove grease and deposit normal residue for the particular powder under test after each extension was attached.

The majority of the trials consisted of 10 rounds for pressure at 1 inch and 6 inches, Recoil, and Velocity over 20 yards from the Webley Pendulum Gun of normal 50-lb. weight, 10 rounds with the same gun weighted up to 75 lb., and then 10 rounds from each length of barrel in the new apparatus, making in all 100 rounds. In a few instances, where the regularity of the first 5 rounds from each length of barrel was all that could be desired, the results of these were accepted as giving sufficient evidence of characteristic behaviour under the particular conditions.

It need hardly be remarked that, as the barrels were altered in length, the necessary precautions were taken to ensure that the distance from muzzle wire to target was correctly maintained at 20 yards.

The results of trials with eight different powders and loads are given *in extenso* and are followed by the relative graphs, together with a summary of all the averages as taken from the experimental figures as well as from the graphs. The experimental values are given on each graph to show the smallness of the amount of smoothing that has been necessary to produce comparatively simple expressions of the progressive effects upon velocity and recoil of progressive changes of length of barrel.

From the results obtained the following deductions are now made :

(1) In guns of the same weight, chamber dimensions, internal diameter and style of boring and using the same variety of cartridge, barrels of 25 inches in length have not only been found not to produce more recoil than barrels of 30 inches, but actually a little less, and this result is confirmed by comparing barrels shorter than 25 inches and longer than 30 inches.

(2) In guns of the same weight, chamber dimensions, internal diameter, and style of boring, and using the same variety of cartridge, barrels of 25 inches in length may be expected to give in round numbers an average figure of 25 f.s. lower velocity over 20 yards from the muzzle than barrels of 30 inches, with variations from this figure as shown in the detailed results.

SERIES I.

Powder: "E.C."
Cases: ⁵⁄₁₆" Brass Unlined.
Charge: 33 grains × 1¹⁄₁₆ oz. of No. 6 shot.
Wadding: ¹⁄₁₆" card; ¹⁶⁄₁₆" brown felt; ¹¹⁄₁₆" card over shot.

Webley Pendulum Gun bored with a tapered entrance from cone to bore ·735" diameter gradually reduced to ·733" at 12" from breech. Choke ·690".

Dartford Pendulum Gun with 22" barrel and extensions to give the length stated. Bore ·729". No taper lead from cone to bore. Weight 75 lb.

	Normal Weight, 50 lb.				Weighted to 75 lb.				Choke Bore. 30"		Cylinder Bore. 22"		25"		28"		30"		31"		36"		40"	
	P.1"	P.6"	R.	V.20	P.1"	P.6"	R.	V.20	R.	V.20	R.	V.20	R.	V.20	R.	V.20	R.	V.20	R.	V.20	R.	V.20	R.	V.20
	2·44	1·44	9·20	1,027	2·23	1·44	6·10	1,064	6·53	1,056	6·54	1,026	6·60	1,040	6·62	1,071	6·48	1,053	6·67	1,034	6·69	1,092	6·73	1,087
	2·52	1·52	9·31	1,052	2·75	1·46	6·36	1,064	6·66	1,096	6·77	1,066	6·46	1,040	6·54	1,071	6·71	1,037	6·53	1,037	6·63	1,044	6·58	1,100
	2·51	1·44	9·24	1,030	2·54	1·44	6·29	1,058	6·65	1,097	6·48	1,038	6·58	1,052	6·56	1,052	6·57	1,046	6·40	1,067	6·55	1,092	6·53	1,054
	2·66	1·42	9·47	1,020	2·50	1·44	6·32	1,052	6·55	1,107	6·38	1,011	6·53	1,066	6·57	1,033	6·82	1,076	6·73	1,077	6·62	1,072	6·46	1,069
	2·79	1·42	9·45	1,035	2·47	1·44	6·22	1,053	6·63	1,097	6·42	1,041	6·70	1,045	6·48	1,078	6·66	1,068	6·43	1,039	6·64	1,083	6·63	1,063
	2·65	1·46	9·38	1,056	2·34	1·48	6·14	1,062	6·57	1,110	6·61	1,049	6·49	1,022	6·51	1,033	6·56	1,047	6·45	1,023	6·50	1,053	6·73	1,063
	2·38	1·52	9·42	1,045	2·27	1·44	6·12	1,036	6·46	1,093	6·50	1,037	6·64	1,027	6·63	1,071	6·72	1,056	6·56	1,081	6·72	1,075	6·74	1,128
	2·75	1·44	9·58	1,055	2·54	1·34	6·13	1,053	6·68	1,099	6·46	1,013	6·81	1,023	6·52	1,036	6·60	1,048	6·41	1,021	6·53	1,073	6·68	1,101
	2·85	1·48	9·72	1,080	2·40	1·44	6·11	1,033	6·65	1,121	6·71	1,040	6·55	1,033	6·62	1,036	6·58	1,024	6·59	1,064	6·66	1,098	6·48	1,067
	2·65	1·46	9·55	1,042	2·62	1·52	6·40	1,052	6·73	1,098	6·79	1,023	6·58	1,056	6·62	1,043	6·45	1,053	6·81	1,107	6·71	1,084	6·77	1,079
Ave.	2·64	1·46	9·43	1,044	2·47	1·44	6·22	1,053	6·61	1,097	6·57	1,035	6·59	1,040	6·57	1,052	6·61	1,051	6·58	1,055	6·62	1,077	6·63	1,081

Velocity of Recoil of 6¼-lb. Gun.

15·40 f.s.	15·22 f.s.	16·21 f.s.	15·93 f.s.	16·14 f.s.	16·11 f.s.	16·21 f.s.	16·13 f.s.	16·23 f.s.	16·25 f.s.

SERIES II. *Powder*: Schultze. *Cases*: ⁷⁄₁₆" Brass Unlined. *Charge*: 42 grains × 1⅛ oz. of No. 6 shot. *Wadding*: ½" card; ⅜" brown felt; 1⁄16" card; 1⁄16" card over shot.

Webley Pendulum Gun bored with a tapered entrance from cone to bore ·735" diameter gradually reduced to ·733" at 12" from breech. Choke ·690".

Dartford Pendulum Gun with 22" barrel and extensions to give the length stated. Bore ·729". No taper lead from cone to bore. Weight 75 lb.

Normal Weight, 50 lb.				Weighted to 75 lb.				Choke Bore 30"		Cylinder Bore 22"		25"		28"		30"		31"		36"		40"	
P. 1"	P. 6"	R.	V. 20	P. 1"	P. 6"	R.	V. 20	R.	V. 20	R.	V. 20	R.	V. 20	R.	V. 20	R.	V. 20	R.	V. 20	R.	V. 20	R.	V. 20
2·09	1·61	10·28	1,078	2·11	1·68	6·79	1,069	7·19	1,105	7·13	1,066	7·01	1,080	6·97	1,081	7·06	1,101	7·21	1,101	7·03	1,121	7·37	1,117
2·51	1·70	10·41	1,106	2·03	1·65	6·68	1,108	7·24	1,142	6·86	1,042	6·94	1,066	7·12	1,121	7·05	1,105	7·12	1,103	7·36	1,156	7·07	1,108
2·30	1·54	10·16	1,080	1·94	1·65	6·58	1,070	6·97	1,132	6·94	1,062	6·90	1,079	7·16	1,105	7·36	1,105	7·17	1,114	7·18	1,128	7·24	1,104
2·09	1·61	9·92	1,102	2·32	1·61	6·80	1,102	7·08	1,101	7·01	1,051	7·06	1,079	6·98	1,077	7·13	1,138	7·10	1,124	7·02	1,123	7·34	1,148
2·04	1·61	9·79	1,093	2·33	1·61	6·79	1,062	7·13	1,124	7·14	1,067	7·24	1,113	7·00	1,103	7·13	1,103	7·20	1,140	7·18	1,137	7·23	1,148
2·75	1·66	10·54	1,116	2·47	1·65	6·88	1,128	7·02	1,105	6·96	1,053	7·11	1,093	7·23	1,091	7·06	1,113	7·19	1,140	7·06	1,124	7·36	1,126
2·48	1·56	10·20	1,090	2·23	1·68	6·86	1,110	7·32	1,156	6·85	1,065	6·90	1,092	7·06	1,107	7·08	1,113	7·03	1,107	7·17	1,143	7·55	1,158
2·79	1·61	10·56	1,085	2·72	1·71	7·04	1,123	7·23	1,150	6·81	1,051	6·97	1,061	7·07	1,067	7·20	1,130	7·00	1,107	7·10	1,097	7·19	1,142
2·37	1·66	10·30	1,092	2·66	1·66	6·87	1,105	7·03	1,126	7·26	1,075	6·90	1,066	7·04	1,091	6·98	1,089	7·31	1,116	7·33	1,147	7·30	1,149
2·26	1·61	10·10	1,105	2·43	1·65	6·78	1,105	7·14	1,124	6·71	1,082	6·97	1,106	7·19	1,131	7·19	1,131	7·15	1,104	7·30	1,151	7·19	1,146
Ave. 2·37	1·62	10·23	1,095	2·32	1·65	6·81	1,101	7·13	1,127	6·97	1,061	7·00	1,083	7·08	1,097	7·12	1,113	7·15	1,116	7·17	1,133	7·28	1,135
16·71 f.s.				16·68 f.s.				17·49 f.s.		17·07 f.s.		17·16 f.s.		17·36 f.s.		17·45 f.s.		17·52 f.s.		17·59 f.s.		17·84 f.s.	

Velocity of Recoil of 6¼-lb. Gun.

SERIES III.

Powder : Smokeless Diamond.
Cases : ⅞" Brass, Lined, Water-resisting.
Charge : 33 grains × 1 1/16 oz. of No. 6 shot.
Wadding : 1/16" card ; 7/16" white felt ; 1/16" card over shot.

Webley Pendulum Gun bored with a tapered entrance from cone to bore ·735" diameter gradually reduced to ·733" at 12" from breech. Choke ·690"

Dartford Pendulum Gun with 22" barre and extensions to give the length stated. Bore ·729". No taper lead from cone to bore.

Weight 75 lb.

Normal Weight, 50 lb.				Weighted to 75 lb.				Choke Bore 30"		Cylinder Bore 22"		25"		28"		30"		31"		36"		40"	
P. 1'	P. 6'	R.	V. 20	V. 20	R.	P. 6'	P. 1'	R.	V. 20	R.	V. 20	R.	V. 20	R.	V. 20	R.	V. 20	R.	V. 20	R.	V. 20	R.	V. 20
3·22	1·46	9·65	1,056	1,090	6·51	1·42	3·07	6·60	1,069	6·59	956	6·61	1,027	6·67	1,043	6·74	1,052	6·73	1,084	6·68	1,072	6·71	1,060
3·15	1·46	9·74	1,048	1,049	6·35	1·42	2·97	6·81	1,111	6·68	990	6·51	1,023	6·62	1,043	6·94	1,050	6·67	1,053	6·82	1,082	6·56	1,060
3·38	1·36	9·63	1,048	1,062	6·46	1·34	3·15	6·58	1,083	6·52	999	6·82	1,048	6·78	1,067	6·58	1,026	6·73	1,073	6·79	1,073	6·88	1,093
2·51	1·52	9·41	1,056	1,035	6·32	1·42	2·78	6·57	1,052	6·66	1,010	6·48	1,007	6·53	1,047	7·08	1,097	6·64	1,047	6·79	1,083	6·70	1,093
2·55	1·36	9·18	1,030	1,064	6·36	1·42	3·13	6·80	1,081	6·66	993	6·48	997	6·69	1,059	6·44	1,019	6·59	1,037	6·89	1,061	6·76	1,093
2·64	1·46	9·38	1,046	1,060	6·32	1·40	3·07	6·55	1,072	—	—	6·43	1,038	6·82	1,034	6·86	1,077	6·57	1,033	—	—	—	—
3·22	1·40	9·93	1,058	1,067	6·44	1·48	2·87	6·79	1,061	—	—	6·57	1,016	6·91	1,061	6·82	1,072	6·76	1,078	—	—	—	—
3·18	1·36	9·55	1,057	1,091	6·41	1·52	2·40	6·73	1,073	—	—	6·78	1,066	6·59	1,074	6·48	1,073	6·77	1,072	—	—	—	—
2·86	1·46	9·50	1,057	1,059	6·26	1·38	2·89	6·80	1,053	—	—	6·53	1,032	6·59	1,051	6·89	1,061	6·65	1,026	—	—	—	—
2·71	1·50	9·54	1,035	1,059	6·42	1·44	2·86	6·76	1,061	—	—	6·55	1,032	6·74	1,072	6·79	1,091	6·70	1,047	—	—	—	—
Ave. 2·94	1·43	9·55	1,049	1,064	6·38	1·42	2·92	6·70	1,071	6·62	990	6·58	1,028	6·69	1,055	6·76	1,062	6·68	1,055	6·79	1,074	6·72	1,080
15·60 f.s.				15·63 f.s.				16·42 f.s.		16·23 f.s.		16·12 f.s.		16·40 f.s.		16·57 f.s.		16·37 f.s.		16·63 f.s.		16·47 f.s.	

Velocity of Recoil of 6¼-lb. Gun.

SERIES IV. Powder: Smokeless Diamond.
Cases: ⅞" Brass, Lined, Water-resisting.
Charge: 33 grains × 1⅛ oz. of No. 6 shot.
Wadding: 1/16" card; 7/16" brown felt; 1/16" card; 1/16" card over shot.

Webley Pendulum Gun bored with a tapered entrance from cone to bore ·735" diameter gradually reduced to ·733" at 12" from breech. Choke ·690".

Dartford Pendulum Gun with 22" barrel and extensions to give the length stated. Bore ·729". No taper lead from cone to bore.

Normal Weight, 50 lb.				Weighted to 75 lb.				Choke Bore 30"		Cylinder Bore 22"		25"		28"		30"		31"		36"		40"	
P. 1"	P. 6"	R.	V. 20	P. 1"	P. 6"	R.	V. 20	R.	V. 20	R.	V. 20	R.	V. 20	R.	V. 20	R.	V. 20	R.	V. 20	R.	V. 20	R.	V. 20
3·25	1·44	9·79	1,046	3·21	1·50	6·39	1,072	6·68	1,071	6·60	1,001	6·80	1,051	6·86	1,052	6·80	1,061	6·86	1,071	6·61	1,067	6·81	1,087
3·28	1·42	9·79	1,082	2·97	1·48	6·49	1,072	6·77	1,101	6·74	1,006	6·73	1,032	6·63	1,081	6·77	1,061	6·72	1,084	6·92	1,098	6·83	1,067
2·82	1·46	9·47	1,035	3·46	1·68	6·67	1,132	6·75	1,111	6·60	1,021	6·61	1,032	6·70	1,051	6·86	1,071	6·96	1,072	6·57	1,072	6·71	1,083
3·38	1·44	9·66	1,081	3·07	1·42	6·37	1,058	6·73	1,053	6·78	1,049	6·77	1,062	6·76	1,047	6·73	1,061	6·57	1,040	6·88	1,098	6·86	1,083
3·00	1·46	9·61	1,081	3·06	1·46	6·34	1,071	6·64	1,091	6·94	1,070	6·64	1,037	6·69	1,053	6·85	1,081	6·90	1,102	6·81	1,054	6·91	1,067
Ave. 3·15	1·44	9·66	1,065	3·15	1·51	6·45	1,081	6·71	1,085	6·73	1,029	6·71	1,043	6·73	1,057	6·80	1,067	6·80	1,074	6·76	1,078	6·82	1,077

Velocity of Recoil of 6¼-lb. Gun.

15·78 f.s.	15·80 f.s.	16·44 f.s.	16·48 f.s.	16·44 f.s.	16·48 f.s.	16·67 f.s.	16·68 f.s.	16·57 f.s.	16·71 f.s.

Series V. Powder: Smokeless Diamond.
Cases: ⅞" Brass, Lined, Water-resisting.
Charge: 34 grains × 1 oz. of No. 6 shot (High Velocity Load).
Wadding: 1/16" card; ⅜" white felt; 1/16" card; 1/16" card over shot.

Webley Pendulum Gun bored with a tapered entrance from cone to bore ·735" diameter gradually reduced to ·733" at 12" from breech. Choke ·690".

Dartford Pendulum Gun with 22" barrel and extensions to give the length stated. Bore ·729". No taper lead from cone to bore.

| | Normal Weight, 50 lb. | | | | Weighted to 75 lb. | | | | Choke Bore. | | Cylinder Bore. | | | | | | | | | | | | | | | | | |
| | | | | | | | | | 30" | | 22" | | 25" | | 28" | | 30" | | 31" | | 36" | | 40" | | | | | |
	P. 1"	P. 6"	R.	V. 20	P. 1"	P. 6"	R.	V. 20	R.	V. 20	R.	V. 20	R.	V. 20	R.	V. 20	R.	V. 20	R.	V. 20	R.	V. 20	R.	V. 20
	3·04	1·54	9·47	1,082	2·69	1·61	6·39	1,076	6·79	1,156	6·52	1,035	6·61	1,082	6·60	1,089	6·74	1,101	6·74	1,097	6·65	1,114	6·56	1,087
	2·61	1·52	9·30	1,090	2·66	1·54	6·29	1,135	6·49	1,116	6·43	1,052	6·58	1,080	6·66	1,103	6·73	1,124	6·61	1,081	6·86	1,132	6·74	1,111
	2·57	1·46	9·10	1,072	2·86	1·54	6·34	1,082	6·67	1,124	6·52	1,067	6·54	1,052	6·63	1,061	6·64	1,124	6·90	1,124	6·90	1,113	6·55	1,111
	3·00	1·60	9·55	1,082	3·06	1·46	6·37	1,076	6·76	1,081	6·63	1,062	6·79	1,090	6·68	1,088	6·63	1,067	6·71	1,083	6·67	1,088	6·90	1,142
	2·87	1·54	9·69	1,120	2·82	1·52	6·25	1,082	6·70	1,118	6·80	1,056	6·49	1,061	6·65	1,073	6·89	1,103	6·93	1,111	6·52	1,088	6·66	1,084
	—	—	—	—	—	—	—	—	6·85	1,158	6·70	1,056	6·58	1,051	6·61	1,089	6·62	1,074	6·80	1,116	6·66	1,116	6·69	1,091
	—	—	—	—	—	—	—	—	6·77	1,122	6·36	1,047	6·55	1,063	6·62	1,093	6·63	1,061	6·81	1,102	6·88	1,102	6·78	1,109
	—	—	—	—	—	—	—	—	6·66	1,103	6·46	1,035	6·64	1,081	6·53	1,075	6·68	1,116	6·82	1,093	6·79	1,082	6·78	1,142
	—	—	—	—	—	—	—	—	6·84	1,142	6·60	1,029	6·66	1,056	6·81	1,096	6·80	1,089	6·59	1,089	6·58	1,092	6·62	1,077
	—	—	—	—	—	—	—	—	6·87	1,156	6·64	1,079	6·68	1,064	6·50	1,077	6·69	1,132	6·84	1,123	6·63	1,080	6·52	1,067
Ave.	2·82	1·53	9·42	1,089	2·82	1·53	6·33	1,090	6·73	1,128	6·57	1,055	6·57	1,068	6·63	1,084	6·70	1,098	6·77	1,102	6·71	1,102	6·68	1,101
Velocity of Recoil of 6¼-lb. Gun.	15·38 f.s.				15·50 f.s.				16·50 f.s.		16·09 f.s.		16·12 f.s.		16·24 f.s.		16·44 f.s.		16·60 f.s		16·46 f.s.		16·37 f.s.	

Weight 75 lb.

SERIES VI.

Powder: Smokeless Diamond.
Cases: ⅝" Brass, Unlined.
Charge: 30 grains × 1¼ oz. of No. 4 shot (Low Velocity Load).
Wadding: 1/16" card; ⅝" brown felt; 1/16" card; 1/16" card over shot.

Webley Pendulum Gun bored with a tapered entrance from cone to bore ·735" diameter gradually reduced to ·733" at 12" from breech. Choke ·690".

Dartford Pendulum Gun with 22" barrel and extensions to give the length stated. Bore ·729". No taper lead from cone to bore. Weight 75 lb.

Normal Weight, 50 lb.				Weighted to 75 lb.				Choke Bore. 30"		22"		25"		28"		Cylinder Bore. 30"		31"		36"		40"	
P. 1"	P. 6"	R.	V. 20	P. 1"	P. 6"	R.	V. 20	R.	V. 20	R.	V. 20	R.	V. 20	R.	V. 20	R.	V. 20	R.	V. 20	R.	V. 20	R.	V. 20
3·08	1·56	9·73	983	2·93	1·56	6·11	933	6·58	982	6·66	973	6·72	983	6·71	965	6·66	989	6·72	978	6·68	999	6·76	1,024
2·94	1·38	9·51	957	2·65	1·25	6·15	933	6·50	959	6·67	943	6·65	983	6·71	1,019	6·73	1,002	6·81	989	6·87	1,031	6·61	976
2·93	1·30	9·47	963	2·65	1·34	6·20	966	6·58	994	6·66	973	6·60	983	6·67	989	6·58	955	6·78	1,033	6·68	992	6·72	986
2·99	1·30	9·45	966	2·75	1·38	6·35	993	6·54	1,012	6·62	983	6·70	998	6·72	999	6·80	1,014	6·79	1,012	6·82	1,013	6·90	1,002
3·25	1·30	9·58	979	2·90	1·40	6·40	990	6·60	970	6·72	956	6·64	963	6·69	999	6·77	1,014	6·73	1,008	6·86	1,031	6·88	1,048
2·82	1·34	9·32	940	2·75	1·32	6·18	966	6·63	989	6·69	946	6·69	1,014	6·72	989	6·66	978	6·77	998	6·64	1,002	6·90	1,011
2·68	1·27	9·05	933	2·62	1·36	6·17	966	6·72	993	6·62	946	6·52	946	6·68	982	6·51	968	6·62	980	6·82	1,031	6·71	1,011
2·72	1·30	9·15	933	2·61	1·20	6·11	960	6·78	1,025	6·61	958	6·70	998	6·55	948	6·52	958	6·60	989	6·72	1,034	6·80	960
2·82	1·32	9·65	990	2·61	1·34	6·24	966	6·78	1,008	6·45	933	6·78	1,002	6·80	1,018	6·73	985	6·73	988	6·59	980	6·72	1,010
2·86	1·32	9·38	973	2·34	1·27	6·15	946	6·69	1,021	6·83	986	6·50	953	6·71	985	6·65	968	6·69	988	6·66	990	6·86	969
Ave. 2·91	1·34	9·43	961	2·62	1·34	6·21	962	6·64	995	6·64	959	6·65	982	6·70	989	6·66	989	6·72	996	6·73	1,010	6·77	1,000

Velocity of Recoil of 6¾-lb. Gun.

Normal Weight, 50 lb.	Weighted to 75 lb.	Choke Bore 30"	22"	25"	28"	Cylinder 30"	31"	36"	40"
15·40 f.s.	15·20 f.s.	16·27 f.s.	16·27 f.s.	16·29 f.s.	16·42 f.s.	16·34 f.s.	16·47 f.s.	16·49 f.s.	16·59 f.s.

SERIES VII.

Powder : Smokeless Diamond.
Cases : 8/16″ Brass, Unlined.
Charge : 28 grains × 1⅛ oz. of No. 4 shot (Very Low Velocity Load).
Wadding : 11/16″ card ; 3/16″ brown felt ; 11/16″ card over shot.

Webley Pendulum Gun bored with a tapered entrance from cone to bore ·735″ diameter gradually reduced to ·733″ at 12″ from breech. Choke ·690″.

Dartford Pendulum Gun with 22″ barrel and extensions to give the length stated. Bore ·729″. No taper lead from cone to bore.

Weight 75 lb.

Velocity of Recoil of 6¼-lb. Gun.

	Normal Weight, 50 lb.			Weighted to 75 lb.			Choke Bore. 30″		Cylinder Bore.														
										22″		25″		28″		30″		31″		36″		40″	
	P. 1″	P. 6″	R.	V. 20	P. 1″	P. 6″	R.	V. 20	R.	V. 20	R.	V. 20	R.	V. 20	R.	V. 20	R.	V. 20	R.	V. 20	R.	V. 20	R.	V. 20
	2·75	1·36	9·74	927	2·76	1·38	6·50	953	6·91	964	6·80	927	6·84	918	6·69	942	6·92	970	7·06	954	7·07	966	6·98	972
	2·71	1·34	9·78	934	2·83	1·30	6·51	953	6·90	964	6·71	908	6·64	923	6·90	931	6·90	937	6·72	925	6·95	957	6·78	962
	2·59	1·30	9·59	934	2·76	1·34	6·51	927	6·80	964	6·68	920	6·65	913	6·73	924	6·88	963	6·70	934	6·84	935	6·97	945
	2·78	1·42	9·70	951	2·52	1·30	6·42	934	6·72	964	6·71	913	6·61	923	6·93	965	7·09	954	7·10	968	6·88	976	7·08	952
	2·48	1·32	9·65	923	2·89	1·30	6·53	945	6·87	970	6·81	913	6·85	941	6·94	934	6·86	944	6·93	946	7·05	966	6·94	976
Ave.	2·68	1·35	9·69	934	2·75	1·32	6·49	942	6·84	965	6·74	916	6·72	924	6·84	939	6·93	954	6·90	945	6·94	954	6·95	961
	15·82 f.s.				15·92 f.s.				16·76 f.s.		16·52 f.s.		16·47 f.s.		16·76 f.s.		16·99 f.s.		16·93 f.s.		17·01 f.s.		17·03 f.s.	

PLATE XIX

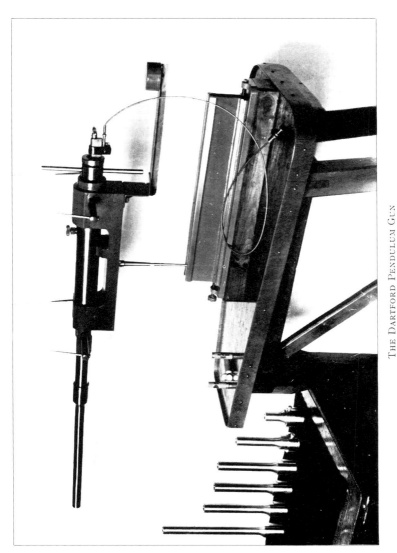

THE DARTFORD PENDULUM GUN

Showing the expedient adopted to balance an 18-inch extension and so produce a barrel of 40 inches

SERIES VIII.   *Powder*: Improved Sporting Ballistite.
Cases: 2¼" Special Ballistite Cone Base Water-resisting.
Charge: 25 grains × 1⅛ oz. of No. 6 shot.
Wadding: ¹⁄₁₆" card; ⁷⁄₁₆" No. 30 white felt; ⅛" B.E.; ¹⁄₁₆" card over shot.

Webley Pendulum Gun bored with a tapered entrance from cone to bore ·735" diameter gradually reduced to ·733" at 12" from breech.   Choke ·690".

Dartford Pendulum Gun with 22" barrel and extensions to give the length stated. Bore ·729". No taper lead from cone to bore.

	Normal Weight, 50 lb.				Weighted to 75 lb.				Choke Bore. 30"		22"		25"		28"		Cylinder Bore. 30"		31"		36"		40"	
	P. 1"	P. 6"	R.	V. 20	P. 1"	P. 6"	R.	V. 20	R.	V. 20	R.	V. 20	R.	V. 20	R.	V. 20	R.	V. 20	R.	V. 20	R.	V. 20	R.	V. 20
	3·14	1·48	10·20	1,097	3·07	1·48	6·61	1,102	7·10	1,146	6·98	1,090	7·04	1,108	7·14	1,103	7·33	1,091	7·34	1,163	7·23	1,132	7·12	1,154
	3·31	1·56	10·19	1,090	3·39	1·58	6·89	1,125	7·27	1,211	6·97	1,101	7·23	1,093	7·17	1,121	7·18	1,126	7·20	1,133	7·32	1,147	7·24	1,165
	3·31	1·54	10·16	1,114	3·41	1·48	6·78	1,101	7·16	1,189	7·08	1,047	7·06	1,071	7·17	1,126	7·15	1,133	7·10	1,118	7·14	1,133	7·15	1,148
	3·31	1·56	10·32	1,115	3·10	1·60	6·72	1,133	7·09	1,168	6·88	1,081	7·21	1,120	7·12	1,093	7·16	1,143	7·09	1,138	7·20	1,148	7·30	1,135
	3·32	1·61	10·40	1,125	3·35	1·50	6·76	1,122	7·37	1,192	7·01	1,056	7·07	1,093	7·26	1,124	7·27	1,148	7·17	1,118	7·10	1,140	7·11	1,153
Ave.	3·28	1·55	10·25	1,108	3·26	1·53	6·75	1,117	7·20	1,181	6·98	1,075	7·12	1,097	7·17	1,113	7·22	1,128	7·18	1,134	7·20	1,140	7·18	1,152
Velocity of Recoil of 6¼-lb. Gun.			16·75 f.s.				16·50 f.s.			17·65 f.s.		17·13 f.s.		17·45 f.s.		17·62 f.s.		17·70 f.s.		17·60 f.s.		17·65 f.s.		17·62 f.s.

SUMMARY OF AVERAGE RESULTS TAKEN FROM SERIES I TO V, TOGETHER WITH FIGURES AS CORRECTED FROM THE RELATIVE GRAPHS.

Load.	Webley Pendulum Gun bored with a tapered entrance from cone to bore ·735″ diameter gradually reduced to ·733″ at 12″ from breech. Choke ·690″.								Velocities of Shot over 20 yards in feet per second, and Velocities of Recoil of a 6½-lb. gun, as obtained from trials with the Dartford Pendulum Gun with 22″ barrel and extensions to give the length stated. Bore ·729″. No taper lead from cone to bore. Weight 75 lb.							
	Normal Weight 50 lb.				Weighted to 75 lb.				Choke Bore.	ylinder Bore.						
	P. 1″	P. 6″	R.	V. 20	P. 1″	P. 6″	R.	V. 20	30″	22″	25″	28″	30″	31″	36″	40″
"E.C." Powder. 33 × 1 1/16 × 6 · 5/16″ Brass, Unlined Cases.	2·64	1·46	9·55	1,044	2·47	1·44	6·22	1,053	1,097	1,035	1,040	1,052	1,051	1,055	1,077	1,081
Recoil in f.s. of 6½-lb. gun			15·40				15·22		16·21	15·93	16·14	16·11	16·21	16·13	16·23	16·25
Figures corrected by Graph I { Velocity over 20 yards										1,035	1,043	1,052	1,057	1,060	1,074	1,082
{ Recoil in f.s. of 6½-lb. gun										15·95	16·12	16·15	16·16	16·16	16·20	16·25
Schultze Powder. 42 × 1 1/16 × 6 · 5/16″ Brass, Unlined Cases.	2·37	1·62	10·23	1,095	2·32	1·65	6·81	1,101	1,127	1,061	1,083	1,097	1,113	1,116	1,133	1,135
Recoil in f.s. of 6½-lb. gun			16·71				16·68		17·49	17·07	17·16	17·36	17·45	17·52	17·59	17·84
Figures corrected by Graph II { Velocity over 20 yards										1,061	1,079	1,097	1,110	1,116	1,133	1,135
{ Recoil in f.s. of 6½-lb. gun										17·05	17·20	17·35	17·48	17·55	17·65	17·75
Smokeless Diamond Powder 33 × 1 1/16 × 6. 5/8″ Brass Lined Cases. White Felt.	2·94	1·43	9·55	1,049	2·92	1·42	6·38	1,064	1,071	990	1,028	1,055	1,062	1,055	1,074	1,080
Recoil in f.s. of 6½-lb. gun			15·60				15·63		16·42	16·23	16·12	16·40	16·57	16·37	16·63	16·47
Figures corrected by Graph III { Velocity over 20 yards										990	1,026	1,056	1,061	1,064	1,074	1,080
{ Recoil in f.s. of 6½-lb. gun										16·10	16·27	16·45	16·55	16·58	16·64	16·45
Smokeless Diamond Powder 23 × 1 1/16 × 6. 5/8″ Brass, Lined Cases. Brown Felt	3·15	1·44	9·66	1,065	3·15	1·51	6·45	1,081	1,085	1,029	1,043	1,057	1,067	1,074	1,078	1,077
Recoil in f.s. of 6½-lb. gun			15·78				15·80		16·44	16·48	16·44	16·48	16·67	16·68	16·57	16·71
Figures corrected by Graph IV { Velocity over 20 yards										1,028	1,043	1,058	1,068	1,074	1,078	1,077
{ Recoil in f.s. of 6½-lb. gun										16·45	16·51	16·60	16·64	16·65	16·65	16·65
High Velocity Load. 34 × 1 × 6 Smokeless Diamond Powder. 5/8″ Brass, Lined Cases.	2·82	1·53	9·42	1,089	2·82	1·53	6·33	1,090	1,128	1,055	1,068	1,084	1,098	1,102	1,102	1,101
Recoil in f.s. of 6½-lb. gun			15·38				15·50		16·50	16·09	16·12	16·24	16·44	16·60	16·46	16·37
Figures corrected by Graph V { Velocity over 20 yards										1,055	1,066	1,084	1,096	1,102	1,102	1,100
{ Recoil in f.s. of 6½-lb. gun										16·05	16·10	16·15	16·45	16·60	16·45	16·35

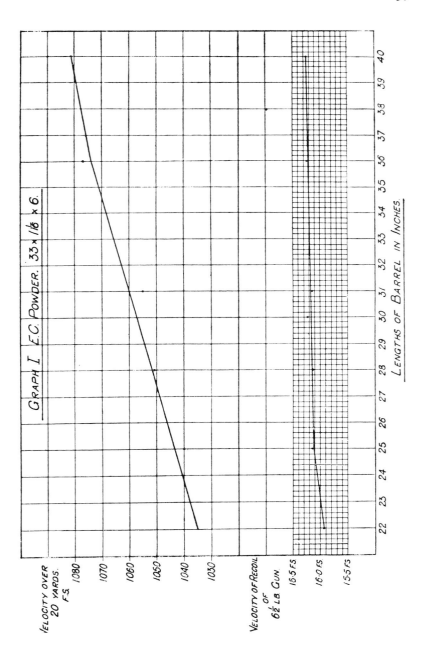

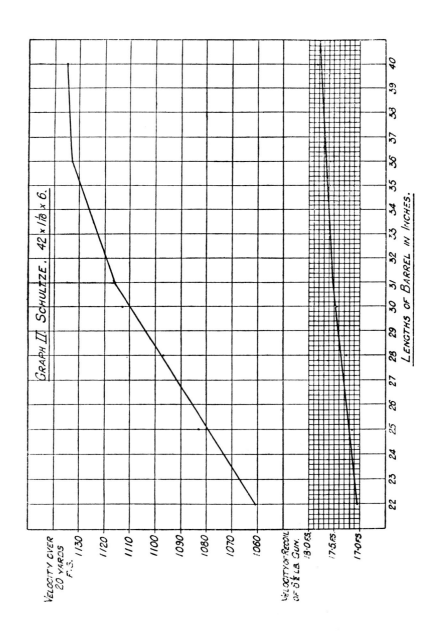

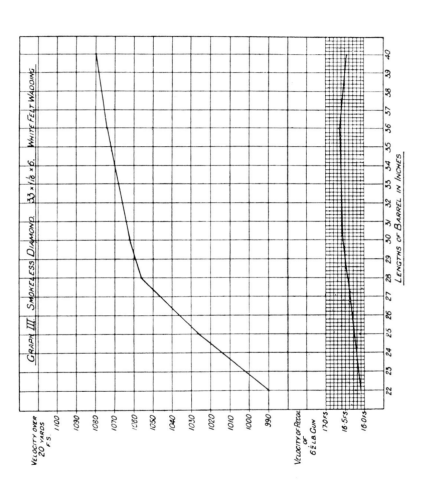

GRAPH III. SMOKELESS DIAMOND 33 x 1/16 x 6. WHITE FELT WADDING

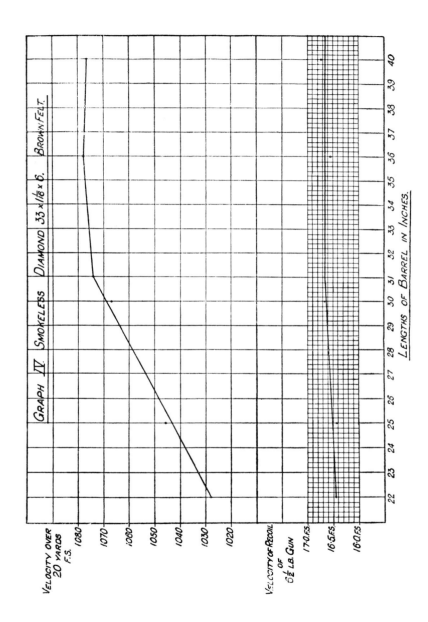

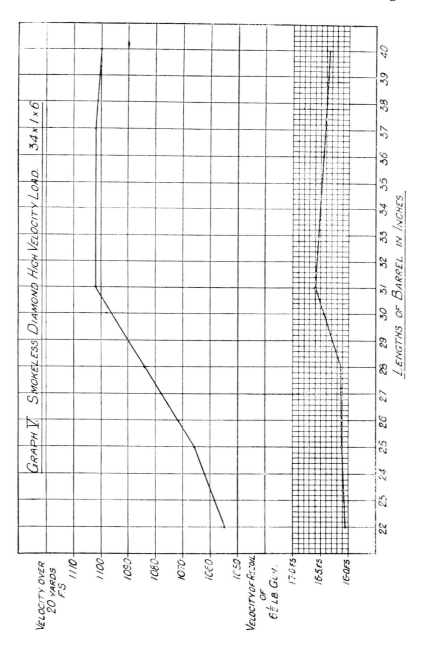

GRAPH V. SMOKELESS DIAMOND HIGH VELOCITY LOAD. 34 x 1 x 6

LENGTHS OF BARREL IN INCHES

SUMMARY OF AVERAGE RESULTS TAKEN FROM SERIES VI TO VIII, TOGETHER WITH FIGURES AS CORRECTED FROM THE RELATIVE GRAPHS.

Load.	Webley Pendulum Gun bored with a tapered entrance from cone to bore ·735″ diameter gradually reduced to ·733″ at 12″ from breech. Choke ·690″.								Velocities of Shot over 20 yards in feet per second, and Velocities of Recoil of a 6½-lb. gun, as obtained from trials with the Dartford Pendulum Gun with 22″ barrel and extensions to give the length stated. Bore ·729″. No taper lead from cone to bore. Weight 75 lb.								
	Normal Weight 50 lb.				Weighted to 75 lb.				Choke Bore.	Cylinder Bore.						
	P. 1″	P. 6″	R.	V. 20	P. 1″	P. 6″	R.	V. 20	30″	22″	25″	28″	30″	31″	36″	40″
Low Velocity Load. 30 × 1¼ × 4. Smokeless Diamond Powder. 5/16″ Brass, Unlined Cases.	2·91	1·34	9·43	961	2·62	1·34	6·21	962	995	959	982	989	989	996	1,010	1,000
Recoil in f.s. of 6½-lb. gun			15·40				15·20		16·27	16·27	16·29	16·42	16·34	16·47	16·49	16·59
Figures corrected by Graph VI { Velocity over 20 yards										959	982	898	995	997	1,010	1,000
Figures corrected by Graph VI { Recoil in f.s. of 6½-lb. gun										16·25	16·30	16·35	16·39	16·40	16·50	16·56
Very Low Velocity Load. 28 × 1⅜ × 6. Smokeless Diamond Powder. 5/16″ Brass, Unlined Cases.	2·66	1·35	9·69	934	2·75	1·32	6·49	942	965	916	924	939	954	945	954	961
Recoil in f.s. of 6½-lb. gun			15·82				15·92		16·76	16·52	16·47	16·76	16·99	16·93	17·01	17·03
Figures corrected by Graph VII { Velocity over 20 yards										912	912	941	950	951	955	958
Figures corrected by Graph VII { Recoil in f.s. of 6½-lb. gun										16·50	16·70	16·85	16·95	16·96	17·00	17·05
Improved Ballistite Powder. 25 × 1 1/16 × 6. Ballistite Cone Base Water-resisting Cases.	3·28	1·55	10·25	1,108	3·26	1·53	6·75	1,117	1,181	1,075	1,097	1,113	1,128	1,134	1,140	1,152
Recoil in f.s. of 6½-lb. gun			16·75				16·50		17·65	17·13	17·45	17·62	17·70	17·60	17·65	17·62
Figures corrected by Graph VIII { Velocity over 20 yards										1,075	1,096	1,115	1,129	1,135	1,143	1,150
Figures corrected by Graph VIII { Recoil in f.s. of 6½-lb. gun										17·14	17·45	17·62	17·62	17·62	17·62	17·62

	Velocity f.s.	Recoil f.s.
Average decrease of velocity over 20 yards and velocity of recoil of 6½-lb. gun by reducing cylinder barrel from 30″ to 25″	26	0·29 (Experimental)
Average decrease of velocity over 20 yards and velocity of recoil of 6½-lb. gun by reducing cylinder barrel from 30″ to 25″	25·4	0·22 (From Graphs)
Increase of velocity over 20 yards and velocity of recoil of 6½-lb. gun produced by new gun of ·729″ diameter as compared with that yielded by Webley gun of ·733″ diameter, both 30″ Choke	35	0·87
Increase of velocity over 20 yards and velocity of recoil of 6½-lb. gun produced by 30″ Choke barrel of new gun compared with that yielded by cylinder barrel of same gun	22 but	recoil reduced 0·12 f.s.

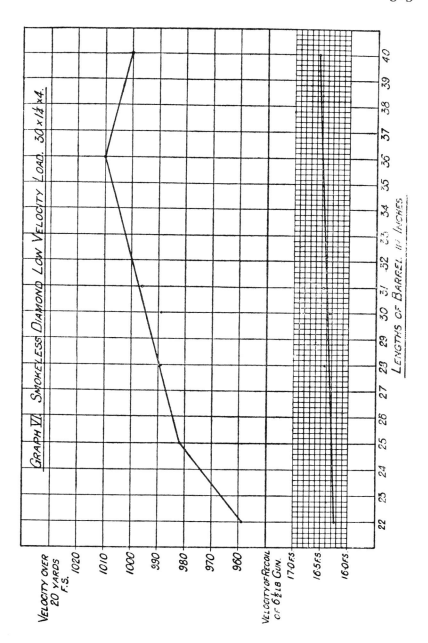

Graph VI. Smokeless Diamond Low Velocity Load. 30×1¼×4.

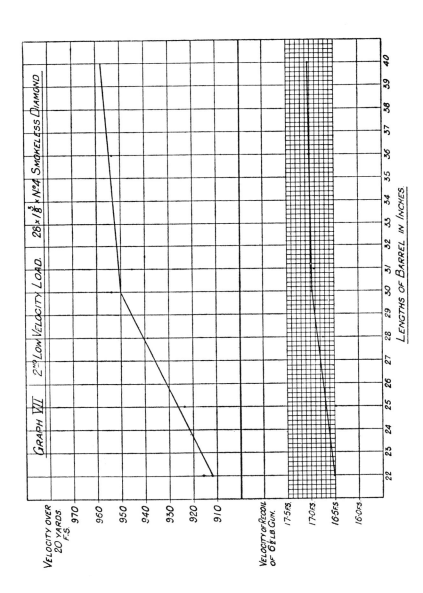

GRAPH VII   2ᴺᴰ LOW VELOCITY LOAD.   28×1⅛×Nº4 SMOKELESS DIAMOND

PLATE XX

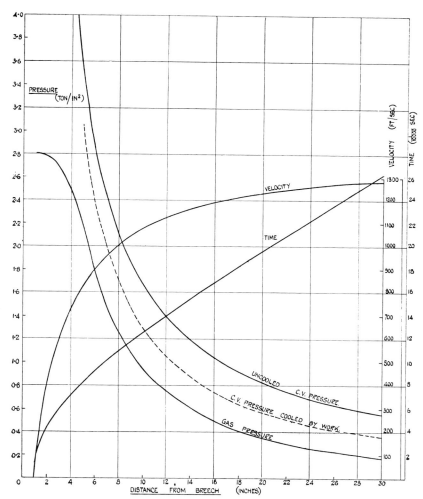

GRAPHS SHOWING THE DEVELOPMENT OF GAS PRESSURE, VELOCITY, AND TIME
OF MOVEMENT OF THE SHOT CHARGE FOR A STANDARD 2½-INCH 12-BORE CARTRIDGE
LOADED WITH 33 GRAINS OF SMOKELESS DIAMOND POWDER AND 1 1/16 OUNCES
OF No. 6 SHOT

The graphs of the closed vessel pressures (both uncooled and cooled by work) are also given. The closed
vessel pressure at any distance is the maximum pressure which can possibly be generated by the powder
charge specified within that volume of the bore

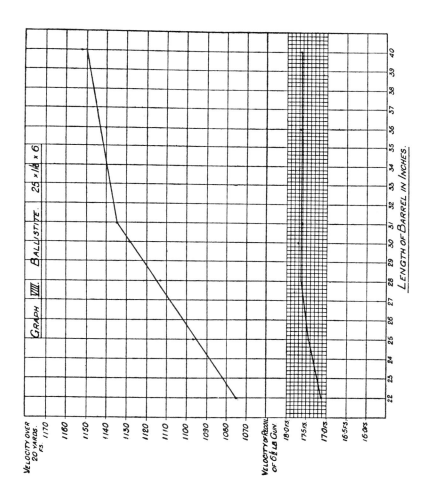

APPENDIX VII

THE INTERPRETATION OF INSTRUMENTAL BALLISTICS

IN order to ascertain the reliability and effectiveness of shotgun cartridges samples are submitted for ballistic tests, and if these tests prove satisfactory it can be assumed with absolute confidence that the cartridges will prove effective against game in the field. The conducting of such tests necessitates the use of a chronograph and a pressure barrel, and it is certainly advisable that the latter should be mounted as a pendulum gun in order to enable readings of Recoil to be obtained as well as those of Velocity and Pressure. The actual taking and recording of the results obtained is simple, but the interpretation of these readings is a different matter and needs a proper understanding of the subject as well as a realisation of the difficulties which are inseparable from the measurement of shotgun velocities. It is probable that in the majority of cases when a lot of cartridges is submitted to the usual routine tests a rule of thumb interpretation is sufficiently accurate for normal practice. But every now and then results are obtained which may depart sufficiently from the normal to puzzle an inexperienced observer or even to tempt him to draw a wrong conclusion.

I propose, therefore, to give a few records of series which I have taken myself in the hopes that a brief discussion of these results may suggest to the unwary some of the pitfalls which can be encountered in the somewhat tortuous path of cartridge-testing.

First I would warn the rifle ballistician, who may be new to shotgun work, that he must not expect to find shotgun velocities nearly as regular as those recorded from rifles, as I hope those who have had the fortitude to read through the chapters on Pressure and Velocity will realise. But I will give some examples of the variations which can occur in rifle and shotgun observed velocities, the first lot being regular and the second irregular.

REGULAR VELOCITIES

RIFLE f.s.	SHOTGUN f.s.
2,879	1,095
2,882	1,053
2,882	1,069
2,878	1,051
2,881	1,076

Mean :   2,880   1,069

Greatest variation from mean :

0·069 per cent.   2·18 per cent.

IRREGULAR VELOCITIES

f.s.	f.s.
3,030	959
3,120	1,098
3,020	1,008
3,005	1,044
3,060	1,062

Mean :   3,047   1,034

Greatest variation from mean :

2·40 per cent.   7·26 per cent.

There is nothing extraordinary about any of these four series, but they do suggest the type of regularity which can be expected both from rifles and shotguns.

In the case of shotguns the mean result of a series undoubtedly gives a reasonably close approximation to the velocity of the main bulk of the shot charge, and it is this velocity which counts in actual sport. So the mean of a series should always be considered when assessing the potential killing power of any lot of cartridges.

But velocities should never be considered by themselves if any records of pressure and recoil are also available, for frequently —and more so in the case of wire screens than the later copper rod type—an abnormal instrumental velocity is obtained which is merely the result of the circuit being broken by a front or back pellet in the charge. This fact will be immediately apparent if recoil readings are taken in conjunction with those of velocity, as they always should be whenever it is possible to do so. And the following series gives an example of such an abnormally low instrumental velocity. The cartridges were 2½-inch 12-bore loaded with 33 grains of Nobel Smokeless Powder (since been replaced by I.C.I. No. 51) and a full $1\frac{1}{16}$ ounce of No. 6 shot.

Pressure at 1 inch in Tons.	Recoil of Pendulum Gun in Inches.	Observed Velocity in F.S.
2·61	9·9	1,056
2·68	9·6	1,074
2·47	9·8	978
2·82	9·8	1,046
2·82	9·7	1,091

The velocity of the third round appears very low, and some observers might be led into regarding it as a weak round. But if the recoil reading is taken into consideration it will immediately be seen that there cannot possibly be any appreciable difference between the combined forward momenta of the ejecta of this round and those of the others in the series. It might be suggested that the result was produced by an abnormally heavy shot charge which caused a big fall in velocity while maintaining the recoil at the normal level. But this explanation is contradicted by the pressure, which is similar to the others. Had there been an exceptionally heavy shot charge in this round the pressure would have been distinctly higher.

There is only one true explanation, and that is that the circuit was broken by a back pellet in the shot column which gave an abnormally low record. Consequently, in assessing the mean value for the observed velocity of the series the velocity of the third round should be ignored. To condemn this lot of cartridges as being irregular or " weak " would be quite wrong.

In support of this interpretation a further series of five rounds is given below which were fired with the same lot of cartridges immediately after the series just quoted as a check. This series of instrumental pressures, recoils and velocities is as follows :

2·33	9·9	1,065
2·40	9·8	1,055
2·75	9·8	1,078
2·73	10·0	1,082
2·61	9·7	1,042

It should, therefore, be realised that no lot of cartridges should ever be condemned on account of low instrumental velocities unless the recoil readings confirm such velocities and the pressures also show a tendency to fall.

For the three Ballistic Elements of Pressure, Recoil and Velocity are all interpendent and should never be considered separately from one another.

It may happen, however, that low instrumental velocities are confirmed by low recoil readings, and in such circumstances it is important to understand how low the mean velocity can be before the efficiency of the cartridges is likely to be insufficient for ordinary sport.

The generally accepted " Standard " instrumental velocity is from 1,050 f.s. to 1,070 f.s., but this allows a large margin of power, and with all shot sizes a mean observed velocity of 1,000 f.s. is ample to ensure efficiency against game in ordinary circumstances and up to the longest sporting ranges. Naturally this generalisation must be accepted reasonably for it does not mean that cartridges loaded with No. 8 shot which develop this 1,000 f.s. observed velocity will be effective against geese at 60 yards although such cartridges would be perfectly effective for snipe at 45 yards. In the case of large shot an appreciably lower instrumental velocity is sufficient, 950 f.s. being ample for No. 4, or even No. 5, and 900 f.s. for No. 1 and larger.

The pressures, however, must be satisfactory, and unless these average over 2 tons at least in the case of 2½-inch 12-bore, or similar, cartridges, any lot giving instrumental results appreciably below the standard should be regarded with suspicion.

The following two series indicate the importance of pressure in the general assessing of results. In both cases the shot size was No. 5.

LOT 1

	PRESSURE	RECOIL	VELOCITY
	2·75	9·4	1,002
	2·33	9·2	1,011
	2·03	9·1	950
	2·47	9·5	993
	2·68	9·6	1,016
Mean :	2·45	9·36	994

LOT 2

	1·36	8·6	972
	1·65	9·1	1,037
	1·46	8·9	1,025
	1·25	8·5	979
	1·34	8·5	998
Mean :	1·41	8·7	1,002

The difference in the mean recoils was due partly to the fact that the shot charge in Lot 1 was a full 1$\frac{1}{16}$ ounce and that of Lot 2 a bare 1$\frac{1}{16}$ but chiefly to the fact that less and lighter wadding was used in Lot 2 than in Lot 1.

Lot 1 was reported on as being satisfactory and "should prove effective against game"; Lot 2 was reported on as being weak and unreliable. Both these reports were fully and completely substantiated in the actual shooting field.

Just by way of comparison I will give a series of cartridges loaded with a full 31 grains of Smokeless Diamond Powder, Air-Cushion Wads and a bare 1$\frac{1}{16}$ ounce of No. 6 shot about which there can be no possible doubt, and as a matter of interest I am including the 6-inch pressures as well.

PRESSURES		RECOIL	VELOCITY
1-in.	6-in.		
2·44	1·50	9·6	1,057
2·40	1·56	9·6	1,064
2·55	1·54	9·8	1,073
2·38	1·48	9·5	1,055
2·48	1·50	9·6	1,067
2·55	1·52	9·6	1,066
Mean : 2·47	1·53	9·6	1,064

I need hardly say that such a series can be regarded as ideal.

Sometimes, however, a series is obtained in which the velocities are comparatively constant but considerable variations occur in the pressures and recoils. An example of this type is the following :

PRESSURE	RECOIL	VELOCITY
3·79	10·7	988
2·96	9·6	979
3·38	10·5	1,014
3·45	10·1	968
3·07	10·0	991

When such a series is recorded it can only mean that the loading must be irregular, and that probably the shot charge will be found to vary considerably, as were the powder charges to be markedly irregular the velocities would also show big variations.

In this example enough cartridges remained to make a thorough check of the loading. The cartridge which had been opened in the first place contained a bare 30 grains of Smokeless Diamond and 1$\frac{5}{16}$ ounces of No. 4$\frac{1}{2}$ shot. But after firing the series eight more cartridges were opened. The powder charges in these were : 30, bare 30, 30, 30, full 30, 30, 30 and bare 30 grains, which is regular loading. But the corresponding shot charges proved to be : $1\frac{3}{8}$, $1\frac{5}{16}$, bare $1\frac{3}{8}$, full $1\frac{5}{16}$, $1\frac{5}{16}$, bare $1\frac{1}{4}$, bare $1\frac{3}{8}$, full $1\frac{5}{16}$ ounces. Such variations are inexcusable and explain completely, for example, the great difference in the pressures and recoils of the first two shots of the series. The first shot must have been a very heavy shot charge and the second a light one. In each case the velocity was similar, as would be expected in such a low-velocity load. It may be added that the specified load was 30 grains of powder and $1\frac{1}{4}$ ounces of shot.

But just as an example of what *can* sometimes occur I may mention that in January, 1948, I tested some cartridges in which the powder charges varied from 31·1 to 34·2 grains and the shot charges from a full ounce to $1\frac{1}{4}$ ounces. The pressures ranged from 2·03 to 3·87 tons, which was not surprising.

I will give one final example of two lots of cartridges which were loaded with great care with weighed charges of powder and shot for experimental purposes, these charges being the same in both lots.

LOT 1

PRESSURE	RECOIL	VELOCITY
3·52	10·1	1,097
3·03	10·1	1,127
3·46	10·0	1,136
2·11	9·7	1,071
1·81	9·3	1,037

LOT 2

PRESSURE	RECOIL	VELOCITY
3·45	10·3	1,122
3·38	10·5	1,124
3·24	10·1	1,093
3·45	10·1	1,093
3·38	10·2	1,095

All the results in Lot 2 were very regular, but those in Lot 1 showed extraordinary variations in pressure with more or less corresponding variations in velocity and recoil. There could be no question of irregular loading and so the only possible explanation was that for some reason the combustion of the powder in Lot 1 was irregular and not always complete, a fact which was confirmed by the abnormal amount of smoke which accompanied the fourth and fifth shots of this series. But when the same powder gives very regular combustion and ballistics in another lot of cartridges the cause of the faulty combustion must lie in the ignition. In other words the caps used in Lot 1 differed from those used in Lot 2 and did not suit the powder. This explanation, I may say, proved to be correct, although there was no visible difference in the caps when seen in the loaded cartridges.

Incidentally the powder charge was excessive in both Lots, as is shown by the high pressures, but a reduction would certainly have produced excellent results with the caps used in Lot 2.

APPENDIX VIII

AN ANALYSIS OF THE INTERIOR BALLISTICS OF A 12-BORE SHOTGUN

BY F. W. JONES, O.B.E.

IT is possible to make an analysis of the interior ballistics of a shotgun which will supply answers to some questions which are undoubtedly correct ; while to many other questions the answers provided must be in the correct order of magnitude, even though they may not be quite exact. This means that such answers will state quite definitely whether one thing is greater than another, even though the values given may not be exactly true. Some of these answers are admittedly at variance with actual measurements : and the truth of others is not generally accepted. Nevertheless, an analysis of interior ballistics is the only reliable source of evidence for some factors, and so a study of such an analysis is to be recommended.

Experiments with propellants in closed vessels have established certain relations between the pressures developed by explosive charges and their temperatures on combustion, together with the volumes of gases evolved per unit weight.

In a shotgun the muzzle velocity is known with accuracy sufficient for the purpose, as are the pressures near the breech end of the barrel. The muzzle velocity fixes what the pressures must be between 6 or 9 inches of the breech and the muzzle, for there is no absolutely reliable instrumental information in regard to the gas pressure and the velocity of the shot charge for the final 18 inches of the barrel. Interior ballistics can supply this important information.

As an example, Smokeless Diamond powder will be taken with its standard charge of 33 grains and $1\frac{1}{16}$ oz. of shot in a $2\frac{1}{2}$-inch 12-bore case.

The chemical composition adopted for the powder will not be quoted in order to avoid the raising of minor points on the composition which are immaterial to the problems under investigation, but the raising of which can confuse the real issues. Further, the charcoal ingredient will be taken as only half burnt, a provision considered necessary in view of the residues left in the barrel after firing.

For the purposes of this analysis the composition of Smokeless Diamond adopted is one which, with 100 grammes, gives the products stated ; and in which the ingredients had the heats of formation which, in the sum, amounted to 55,763 calories. For the calculation of the temperature of combustion reliable specific heats must be adopted, and for this analysis the specific heats published by Nernst and Wohl in 1929 will be adopted, which in linear form can be placed with sufficient accuracy, for average molecular specific heats, as follows :

Hydrogen : Mean specific heat, $4·7 + 0·0004\,t$ above $500°$ C.
Nitrogen and
carbon monoxide : ,, ,, $4·96 + 0·0005\,t$,, $300°$ C.
Carbon dioxide : ,, ,, $9·2 + 0·0009\,t$,, $1300°$ C.
,, ,, ,, ,, $8·0 + 0·0018\,t$ below ,,
Water : ,, ,, $6·3 + 0·0010\,t$ above $1000°$ C.
,, ,, ,, $6·0 + 0·0012\,t$ below ,,

For barium oxide and potassium monoxide the following mean specific heat has been adopted :
$$11·7 + 0·00045\,t.$$
The products on combustion of 100 grammes of powder are :
$$0·392CO_2 + 1·578CO + 0·832H_2O + 0·463H_2 + 0·415N_2$$
$$+ 0·047BaO + 0·009K_2O + 0·236C.$$

Specific Volume, $V_0 = \dfrac{3·68 \times 22,320}{100} = 821$ c.c.

Heat Evolved.
(CO$_2$) . . . . $0·392 \times 94,550 = 37,063·6$ calories.
(CO) . . . . $1·578 \times 26,330 = 41,548·7$,,
(H$_2$O) . . . . $0·832 \times 57,830 = 48,114·6$,,
(CO$_2$, CO, H$_2$O, H, N) . $3·680 \times 542·4 = 1,996·1$,,
　　　　　　　　　Total　128,723 ,,
Less heat of formation of the ingredients　55,763 ,,
Total heat per 100 grms. . . . 72,960 ,,
∴ Heat per grm. = 729·6.

Temperature.
(H)　　　$0·463 \times 4·7 = 2·1761$　$0·463 \times 0·0004 = 0·0001852$
(CO, N)　$1·993 \times 4·96 = 9·8853$　$1·993 \times 0·0005 = 0·0009965$
(H$_2$O)　$0·832 \times 6·3 = 5·2416$　$0·832 \times 0·0010 = 0·0008320$
(CO$_2$)　$0·392 \times 9·2 = 3·6064$　$0·392 \times 0·0009 = 0·0003528$
(BaO, K$_2$O)$0·056 \times 11·7 = 0·6550$　$0·056 \times 0·00045 = 0·0000252$
(C)　　　$0·236 \times 1·8 = 0·4248$　　　　　　　　$\overline{0·0023917}$
　　　　　　　　$\overline{21·9992}$
　　say　　$22·0$　　　　　　　　　　$0·00239$

$$t = \frac{(22 \times 22 + 0·00956 \times 72,960) - 22}{0·00478} = 2,596°\text{ C.}$$
$$T = \text{temp. absolute} = 2,869°\text{ abs.}$$

Closed Vessel (C.V.) pressures in tons, p.

$$p = K \div \left(\frac{1}{d} - \text{co-vol.}\right)$$

where d = loading density.

This C.V. pressure formula has been developed on sound views from the kinetic theory of gases. The co-vol. is the volume occupied by the products. The rule proposed by Sarrau more than forty years ago is adopted, namely, that the volume of the gases is $1/1000$ the specific volume, therefore

co-vol. $= \dfrac{821}{1,000}$ + vol. solids = 0·821 + 0·035 = 0·856.

The constant K by the kinetic theory of gases is equal to $TV_0 \div 273 \times 152\cdot38$, where $152\cdot38$ is the number of atmospheres pressure in one ton. Therefore

$$K = \frac{2,869 \times 821}{41,500} = 51\cdot36.$$

Density in Shotgun. Zero position of wads is 1 inch from breech face. Let x = distance in inches from zero position. Volume of powder chamber is 84 grs. water. Volume of barrel = $0\cdot41854 \times 252\cdot84x = 106x$ grs. water. At any point

$$d = \frac{33}{84 + 106x}, \text{ therefore } \frac{1}{d} = 2\cdot55 + 3\cdot21x.$$

Consequently

$$p = 51\cdot36 \div (3\cdot21x + 1\cdot694) = 16 \div (x + 0\cdot528).$$

This formula gives the uncooled C.V. pressures at any point in the barrel. These are shown in Table LIII and also on Plate XX.

The muzzle velocity is known, and this fixes the gas pressures in the barrel. For $1\frac{1}{16}$ oz. shot the muzzle velocity is near 1,300 f.s. With Smokeless Diamond the 1-inch and 6-inch pressures are known, and from other experiments the pressures at 9 inches and 12 inches can be fixed with little doubt. Beyond 12 inches experimental results are of little use, for these distances the calculated velocity and the shape of the cooled C.V. pressures curve are the best guide. The gas pressures adopted are given in Table LIII, and also on Plate XX. The effective accelerating pressure is less than the gas pressure by the amount of friction in the bore. The maximum for friction is fixed by the knowledge that a 30-inch barrel gives higher velocity than a 25-inch barrel. By statical measurement friction is low. Friction in the cartridge-case must be greater than in the barrel proper. Considering all these things the following values have been adopted. Friction in barrel 0·05 ton or 47 lb. Friction in cartridge-case 0·50 ton initially and dropping linearly to 0·05 ton at 3 inches.

Calculation of velocity and time in barrel. Weight moved 1 $\frac{1}{16}$ oz. shot and 46 grs. wads. Total, ·073 lb.

$$V^2 = 2a.s. \quad a = \frac{V^2}{2s} \text{ or } = 6\frac{V^2}{s} \text{ when } s \text{ is in inches}$$

$$F = mf = \frac{W}{g} 6 \frac{V^2}{s} = 937\cdot5\, p. \quad \text{Therefore } V^2 = 68,920\, ps,$$

where p is the pressure in tons per square inch and 937·5 equals the product of 2,240 and the area of the bore in square inches.

If U is the velocity at the beginning of an interval and V at the end of the interval, then $V^2 = U^2 + 68,920\, ps$. Intervals s 1 inch up to 12 inches and then 2 inches. The time over an interval is obtained from the mean velocity over the interval. The velocity and time curves are shown on the diagram, and the particulars are in Table LIII.

The amount by which the powder gases are cooled in foot pounds is given to the shot and wads and also absorbed by friction, and is definitely fixed by the velocity curve. Call these C.V. pressures cooled by work. The calories in the powder must be converted into ft.-lbs. The calories per gramme divided by 5 gives the ft.-lb. per grain.

Therefore for Smokeless Diamond a charge of 33 grs. contains

$$\frac{729\cdot6}{5} \times 33 = 4,815 \text{ ft.-lb.}$$

The work given out in ft.-lb., multiplied by 100 and divided by 4,815, will give the percentage drop of work or calories in the powder gases. These percentages are not appropriate for reducing the uncooled C.V. pressures, because pressures are proportionate to T and not calories. However, calculations proved with this Smokeless Diamond that the relations of percentage drops in calories and absolute temperatures lie practically on a straight line, and to convert the percentage drops in calories to approximate percentage drops in absolute temperatures the former must be divided by 1·27. The C.V. pressures cooled by work are given in Table LIII, and also on Plate XX. The difference between the gas pressures and the C.V. pressures cooled by work take on a constant value from 20 inches to 30 inches, namely about 0·20 ton. Clearly, if barrel friction were raised and the same increase given to the gas pressures then the velocity curve would not be altered, but the gas pressures would approach nearer the work cooled C.V. pressures.

Assuming all the powder is burnt by the time the shot arrives at the muzzle, then 1,560 calories should have been developed, and of this amount $33·8 \times 1·27 = 437$ has been expended in work. If the actual gas pressure at the muzzle is only 0·17 ton, the total loss of calories would be $\dfrac{0·54 - 0·17}{0·54} \times 1·27 = 87$ per cent. This means $1,560 \times 44$ per cent. $= 686$ calories have been used up in warming the barrel. These numbers of calories would raise the temperature of a $1\frac{1}{4}$ lb. barrel about $10°$ C., an amount that appears excessive.

It is quite clear several alternate reasonable assumptions could be made other than those adopted, and, further, if some additional factors were ascertained experimentally, the analysis could be made more definite.

TABLE LIII

INTERNAL BALLISTICS OF A 12-BORE SHOTGUN

Inches.	Pressures in tons per sq. in.		Velocity in F.S.	Time in $\frac{1}{10,000}$ of a Sec.	Percentage Drop of T.	C.V. Pressures.		Difference Gas and Cooled C.V. Pressures.
	Gas.	Effective.				Uncooled.	Cooled by work.	
1	2·80	2·30						
2	2·80	2·50	407	4·100	3·4			
3	2·69	2·64	586	5·779	7·1			
4	2·50	2·45	720	7·055	10·6	4·53	4·05	1·55
5	2·19	2·14	822	8·136	13·6	3·54	3·06	0·87
6	1·78	1·73	901	9·103	16·2	2·89	2·42	0·64
7	1·49	1·44	953	10·002	18·1	2·46	2·01	0·52
8	1·26	1·21	1,005	10·853	20·1	2·13	1·70	0·44
9	1·08	1·03	1,043	11·667	21·6	1·88	1·47	0·39
10	0·95	0·90	1,074	12·455	23·0	1·68	1·29	0·34
11	0·83	0·78	1,100	13·222	24·1	1·52	1·15	0·32
12	0·75	0·70	1,124	13·970	25·1	1·39	1·04	0·29
13	0·61	0·56	1,162	15·428	27·0	1·19	0·87	0·26
16	0·49	0·44	1,190	16·845	28·4	1·03	0·74	0·25
18	0·41	0·36	1,213	18·234	29·6	0·91	0·64	0·23
20	0·35	0·30	1,231	19·598	30·5	0·82	0·57	0·22
22	0·30	0·25	1,248	20·943	31·4	0·74	0·51	0·21
24	0·26	0·21	1,260	22·273	32·1	0·68	0·46	0·20
26	0·23	0·18	1,271	23·590	32·7	0·62	0·42	0·19
28	0·20	0·15	1,280	24·895	33·5	0·58	0·39	0·19
30	0·17	0·12	1,287	26·193	33·8	0·54	0·36	0·19

INDEX